This 2010 edition is guar
unique selection of Eur
and luxury guest house

Listen to the waves fror
sand between your toes, marvel at the colourful souks, inhale the citrus aroma in the "patios" and "piazzas," and savour fresh produce from local vineyards and markets.

Book your next holiday, relaxing spa, weekend getaway or romantic sojourn at one of our fabulous Recommendations; each approved by one of our experienced Inspectors.

Our Gift Vouchers make ideal presents for all special occasions. For these and the latest hotel "Special Offers" go online at www.condenastjohansens.com.

Lastly, don't forget to sign up to our e-newsletter for all our monthly hotel updates and travel tips.

Cette edition 2010 vous promet d'accroître vos sens en vous proposant une sélection unique d'hôtels, villas, resorts, maisons d'hôtes de luxe et spas parmi les plus exclusifs en Europe dans destinations uniques.

Ecoutez le bruit des vagues depuis votre chambre, sentez le sable chaud sous vos pieds, émerveillez-vous devant les souks colorés, respirez les arômes fruitiers dans les "patios" et "piazzas" et dégustez les produits frais des marchés et vignobles locaux.

Réservez vos prochaines vacances, un spa relaxant, une escapade de week-end ou un séjour romantique dans l'une de nos magnifiques recommandations, toutes visitées et approuvées par nos Inspecteurs expérimentés.

Nos Chèques Cadeaux sont parfaits pour les occasions spéciales. Pour les acheter ou pour consulter les dernières "Offres Spéciales" des hôtels, connectez-vous sur www.condenastjohansens.com.

Enfin, n'hésitez surtout pas à vous inscrire à notre newsletter pour recevoir mensuellement les news, nouveautés et conseils de voyage.

Le aseguro que esta edición 2010 agudizara todos sus sentidos, pues ofrece una selección única de los más exclusivos hoteles, resorts, villas, spas y lujosas casas de huéspedes de Europa en lugares apasionantes.

Escuche el ir y venir de las olas desde el confort de su habitación, sienta la calida arena bajo sus pies, admire el maravilloso colorido de los "souks", aspire el aroma de naranjos y limoneros en patios y "piazzas" y saboree los productos frescos provenientes de viñedos y mercados locales.

Reserve ahora sus próximas vacaciones, una estancia en un relajante spa, un de fin de semana fuera de casa o una escapada romántica en uno de los fabulosos hoteles que recomendamos, cada uno de ellos acreditado por nuestros expertos Inspectores.

Nuestros Cheques Regalo son el obsequio ideal para todo tipo de acontecimiento. Para adquirirlos, y también para ver las "Ofertas Especiales" que ofrecen actualmente nuestros hoteles, vaya a www.condenastjohansens.com.

Por ultimo, no se olvide de inscribirse para recibir nuestro boletin mensual que le mantendra al dia con noticias sobre nuestros hoteles asi como consejos para sus viajes.

Happy Travelling, Bon Voyage ¡Buen Viaje!

Andrew Warren
Managing Director

Hospes Maricel, Mallorca, Spain – p277

Vitalie Taittinger, who works for the family Champagne house

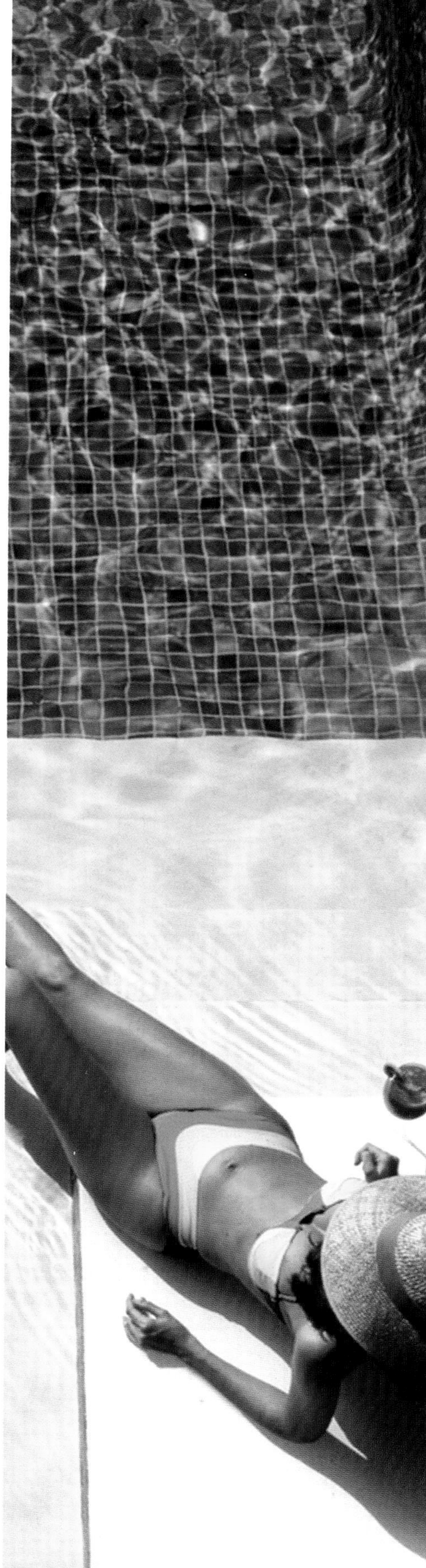

Hotel San Roque, Tenerife, Spain – p287

Contents

Sommaire / Contenido

Our Recommendations are allocated into 3 categories:

- **Hotel:** properties providing a high standard and wide range of services and facilities.
- **Charming Hotel**: properties with a more homely and intimate atmosphere.
- **Luxury Guest House:** properties that are usually owner managed and only serve breakfast.

Nos Recommandations se divisent en 3 catégories:

- **Hotel:** établissements offrant une prestation haut de gamme ainsi qu'un vaste choix de services.
- **Charming Hotel:** établissements à l'atmosphère plus intime et chaleureuse.
- **Luxury Guest House:** établissements généralement gérés par les propriétaires et ne servant que le petit-déjeuner.

Nuestros Hoteles Recomendados se dividen en 3 categorías:

- **Hotel:** establecimientos que ofrecen un alto nivel de comodidad y una variedad amplia de servicios y de instalaciones.
- **Charming Hotel:** establecimientos con una atmósfera más íntima y acogedora.
- **Luxury Guest House:** establecimientos que son dirigidos generalmente por los propietarios y sirven solamente el desayuno.

No
North
Sea
Ireland
Great Britain
p88
The Netherlands
p231
Belgium p20
Channel Islands
p24
Luxembourg
p223
Atlantic
Ocean
France p31
Andorra p14
Madeira
Portugal
p233
Spain p259
Atlantic
Ocean
Canary Islands
Balearic Islands
Mediterranean Sea
Morocco p228

Estonia
Russia p255
Sweden p325
Latvia
Lithuania
Belarus
Poland
Ukraine
ermany
Czech Republic p27
Slovakia
Moldova
Austria p17
Hungary p113
Romania
Slovenia p257
Croatia
BLACK SEA
Serbia
Bosnia i Herzegovina
Bulgaria
Montenegro
Italy p115
FYR Macedonia
Corsica
Albania
Turkey p331
Greece p99
Sardinia
Sicily
Crete
Malta p225

Keys to Symbols

Signification des Symboles / Símbolos

23 Total number of rooms / Nombre de chambres / Numero de habitaciones

The property participates in a minimum of 3 environmentally-friendly practices specified by Condé Nast Johansens / L'hôtel participe à un minimum de 3 actions favorables à l'environnement spécifiées par Condé Nast Johansens / El hotel participa en un mínimo de 3 de las practicas ecológicas especificadas por Condé Nast Johansens

Exclusive use available / Utilisation exclusive possible / Uso exclusivo disponible

Wheelchair access - we recommend that you contact the hotel / Accès pour fauteuils roulants - nous vous recommendons de contacter l'hôtel / Acceso para sillas de ruedas - recomendamos que se pongan en contacto con el hotel.

Gastronomic restaurant (holds at least 1 Michelin Star or mark above 14/20 GaultMillau) / Restaurant gastronomique (au moins 1 étoile Michelin ou note supérieure à 14/20 au GaultMillau) / Restaurante gastronómico (por lo menos 1 estrella Michelin o superior a 14/20 GaultMillau)

Restaurant / Restaurante

24-hour room service / Service en chambre à toutes heures / Room-Service 24 horas

23 Meeting/conference facilities with maximum number of delegates / Salle(s) de conférences – capacité maximale / Salon(es) de reunion(es) – capacidad maxima

Dogs accommodated in rooms or kennels / Chiens autorisés / Se admiten perros

Family friendly, crêche facilities available / Excellente pour les familles, service crêche / Excelente para familias, servicio de guardería

At least 1 room has a four-poster bed / Lit à baldaquin dans au moins 1 chambre / Camas con dosel disponibles

CD player in all bedrooms / Lecteur CD dans toutes les chambres / Lector de CD en todas las habitaciones

DVD DVD player in all bedrooms / Lecteur DVD dans toutes les chambres / DVD en todas las habitaciones

WiFi Wireless internet connection available in part or all rooms / Connection Internet sans-fil disponible dans certaines ou toutes les chambres / Conexión a Internet sin cable en algunas o todas las habitaciones

Smoking is allowed in some bedrooms / Il est permis de fumer dans quelques chambres / Se permite fumar en algunas habitaciones

Lift available for guests' use / Ascenseur / Ascensor

Hotel the Crystal, Tirol, Austria – p18

Hotel the Crystal, Tirol, Austria – p18

Air conditioning in all bedrooms / Climatisation dans toutes les chambres / Aire acondicionado en todas las habitaciones

Gym / Salle de gym / Gimnasio

SPA Dedicated spa with an on-site qualified staff and indoor pool - offering extensive body, massage, beauty and water treatments / Spa dans l'hôtel avec personnel qualifié sur place et une piscine intérieure - offre une variété de massages, soins de beauté et traitements thermaux / Zona dedicada a spa, con personal cualificado permanente y piscina interior, donde se ofrecen extensivos tratamientos de agua, corporales, de belleza y masajes

Wellness centre – offering body, massage and beauty treatments / Centre Wellness - offre une variété de massages, soins de beauté et traitements thermaux / Zona Wellness - se ofrecen tratamientos corporales, de belleza y masajes

Indoor swimming pool / Piscine couverte / Piscina interior

Outdoor swimming pool / Piscine en plein air / Piscina exterior

Fishing on-site / Pêche sur place / Pesca in situ

Fishing can be arranged / Pêche peut être organisé / Se puede organizar pesca

Golf course on-site / Terrain de golf sur site / Campo de golf in situ

Golf course nearby, which has a green fee arrangement with the hotel / Terrain de golf à proximité, qui a un arrangement avec l'hôtel / Campo del golf cerca con acuerdo de green fee

Horse riding can be arranged / Équitation possible / Equitación posible

Located in a ski resort / Situé dans une station de ski / Situado en una estación de esquí

Skiing nearby / Ski à proximité / Esquí cerca

Some rooms have lake views / Certaines chambres ont vue sur lac / Algunas habitaciones con vistas al lago

Some rooms have sea views / Certaines chambres ont vue sur mer / Algunas habitaciones con vistas al mar

The hotel has direct access to a beach / L'hôtel a un accès direct à la plage / Acceso directo a la playa

Property has a helicopter landing pad / Hélipad / Helipuerto

Licensed for wedding ceremonies / Licencé pour cérémonies de mariage / Licencia para celebrar bodas

Condé Nast Johansens

Condé Nast Johansens Ltd, 6-8 Old Bond Street, London W1S 4PH
Tel: +44 (0)20 7499 9080 Fax: +44 (0)20 7152 3565
E-mail: info@johansens.com
www.condenastjohansens.com

Publishing Director:	Charlotte Evans
Assistant to Publishing Director:	Nicola Brooke
Hotel Inspectors:	Sharla Ault
	Rosemary Bailey
	Ana María Brebner
	Joe Cawley
	Michèle Cooren-Lahaye
	Stéphanie Court
	Agnes Exton
	Gianna Illari
	Tunde Longmore
	Barbara Marcotulli
	Murat Özgüç
	Olga Papadaki
	Maureen Scrutton
	Seamus Shortt
	Danielle Taljaardt
	Christopher Terleski
Production Manager:	Kevin Bradbrook
Production Editor:	Laura Kerry
Senior Designer:	Rory Little
Copywriters:	Sasha Creed
	Norman Flack
	Debra O'Sullivan
	Rozanne Paragon
Translators:	Ana María Brebner
	Caroline Caron
	Stéphanie Court
	Eroulla Demetriou
Client Services Director:	Fiona Patrick
PA to Managing Director:	Lucy Mankaryous
Managing Director:	Andrew Warren

Condé Nast Johansens Ltd. is part of The Condé Nast Publications Ltd.
ISBN 978-1-903665-47-3
Printed in England by St Ives plc
Distributed in the UK and Europe by Portfolio, Brentford (bookstores).
In North America by Casemate Publishing, Pennsylvania (bookstores).
Front cover picture: St Nicolas Bay Resort Hotel & Villas, Crete, Greece, p104
Back cover picture: Kempinski Hotel Barbaros Bay, Bodrum, Turkey, p334

Tharroe of Mykonos, Greece – p109

Awards for Excellence

The winners of the Condé Nast Johansens 2009 Awards for Excellence

The Condé Nast Johansens 2009 Awards for Excellence were presented at the Condé Nast Johansens Annual Dinner held at the Jumeirah Carlton Tower on 11th November, 2008. Awards were given to properties from all over the world that represent the finest standards and best value for money in luxury independent travel. An important source of information for these awards was the feedback provided by guests who completed Condé Nast Johansens Guest Survey Reports. Guest Survey Reports can be found on page 374.

Les vainqueurs des Condé Nast Johansens 2009 Awards for Excellence

Les Condé Nast Johansens 2009 Awards for Excellence ont été remis lors du dîner de gala annuel de Condé Nast Johansens à l'hôtel Jumeirah Carlton Tower, à Londres, le 11 novembre 2008. Ces prix ont été décernés aux établissements qui, à travers le monde, offrent les meilleurs standards et rapport qualité-prix dans l'hôtellerie de luxe indépendante. Une source d'information importante pour ces prix provient des Questionnaires de Satisfaction renvoyés par les clients. Les Questionnaires de Satisfaction sont disponibles à la page 374.

Los ganadores de los Condé Nast Johansens 2009 Awards for Excellence

Los Condé Nast Johansens Awards for Excellence del 2009 fueron presentados durante la cena anual de Condé Nast Johansens en el hotel Jumeirah Carlton Tower de Londres, el 11 de noviembre del 2008. Han sido premiados aquellos establecimientos de todas partes del mundo que ofrecen el más alto estándar y la mejor relación calidad-precio dentro del sector de turismo de lujo independiente. Una fuente de información importante para la adjudicación de estos premios proviene de los Cuestionarios de Calidad que nos envían los clientes. Estos cuestionarios se pueden encontrar en la página 374 de esta guía.

Domes of Elounda, All Suites and Villas Spa Resort, Crete, Greece – p101

Domes of Elounda, All Suites and Villas Spa Resort, Crete, Greece - p101

Awards for Excellence

2009 Winners appearing in this Guide:

Readers' Award

- CASA HOWARD GUEST HOUSES - ROME AND FLORENCE
  - Tuscany, Italy, p178

Most Excellent Hotel for Service

- L'ALBERETA - Lombardy, Italy, p138

Most Excellent Hotel

- RELAIS LA SUVERA (DIMORA STORICA)
  - Tuscany, Italy, p195

Most Excellent Luxury Guest House

- ABBADIA SAN GIORGIO - HISTORICAL RESIDENCE
  - Liguria, Italy, p132

Most Excellent Charming Hotel

- A'JIA HOTEL - Istanbul, Turkey, p335

Most Excellent Spa Hotel

- PETRIOLO SPA & RESORT - Tuscany, Italy, p196

Most Romantic Hotel

- BARCELÓ LA BOBADILLA - Andalucía, Spain, p263

Most Excellent Value for Money Hotel

- ROMANTIK HOTEL JOLANDA SPORT- Valle d'Aosta, Italy, p207

Most Excellent Hotel for Design & Innovation

- HOSPES PALACIO DEL BAILÍO - Andalucía, Spain, p260

The Perfect Combination...

Condé Nast Johansens Gift Vouchers

Condé Nast Johansens Gift Vouchers make a unique and much valued present for birthdays, weddings, anniversaries, special occasions and as a corporate incentive.

Vouchers are available in denominations of €140, €70, £100, £50, $150, $75 and may be used as payment or part payment for your stay or a meal at any Condé Nast Johansens 2010 recommended property.

To order Gift Vouchers call +44 (0)207 152 3558 or purchase direct at www.condenastjohansens.com

Other Condé Nast Johansens Guides

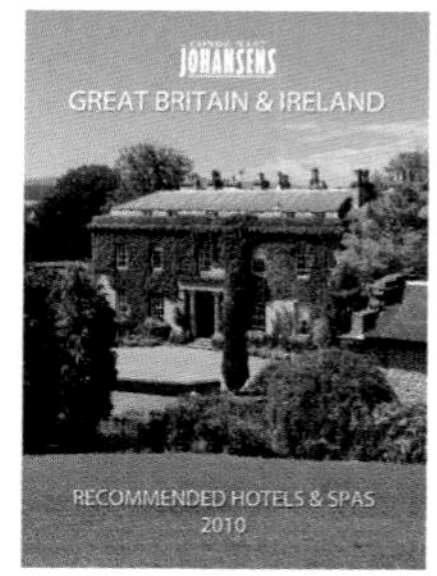

As well as this Guide, Condé Nast Johansens also publish the following titles:

- Recommended Hotels & Spas, Great Britain & Ireland 2010
- Recommended Small Hotels, Inns & Restaurants, Great Britain 2010
- Recommended Hotels & Spas, The Americas, Atlantic, Caribbean & Pacific 2010
- Luxury Spas Worldwide 2010
- Recommended Venues for Meetings & Special Events 2010

To purchase Guides please call +44 (0)208 955 7067 or visit our Bookshop at www.condenastjohansens.com

Andorra

Mérens-les-Vals

El Serrat

Llorts

L'Aldosa

Soldeu

16

Arinsal

La Cortinada

Canillo

Odino

B. d'Envalira

Pal

La Massana

Pas de la Casa

15

Encamp

Port d'Envalira

Anyos

ANDORRA-LA-VELLA

Les Escaldes

Santa Coloma

Bixesarri

Sant-Julià de Lória

Juberri

Lles de Cerdanya

SPAIN

La Seu d'Urgell

Hotel Grau Roig

GRANDVALIRA SKI RESORT, AD 200 GRAU ROIG, ANDORRA
Tel: +376 75 55 56 **Fax:** +376 75 55 57
Web: www.johansens.com/hotelgrauroig **E-mail:** info@hotelgrauroig.com

Our inspector loved: *The location right by the ski lifts in winter and pretty walks in the summer.*

Price Guide: (half board)
double €160-380
junior suite €270-500
suite de luxe €360-650

Attractions: Trekking in Summer, on the doorstep; Skiing, 1-min walk; Duty Free Shopping, 25km

Nearby Towns: Pas de la Casa, 6km; Andorra, 25km
Airports: Toulouse Airport, 180km; Barcelona Airport, 200km

Category: Hotel
Closed: Mid-April - mid-June and mid-October - 1st December 2010

If you enjoy the freshest of air, silence, peace and luxurious comfort this could be your dream mountain paradise. Located on cloud-topped slopes where incomparable views encompass colourful, weaving skiers in winter and grazing cows in summer, this intimate retreat boasts traditional, modernised rooms, delicious cuisine and spa facilities you'll dream over.

Si vous aimez l'air frais, le silence, le calme et le grand confort, ceci pourrait être votre rêve des montagnes du paradis. Situé sur les pentes de sommets entourés de nuages, d'où les vues incomparables englobent les skieurs colorés durant l'hiver et les vaches dans leurs pâturages durant l'été, cet endroit retiré possède des chambres traditionnelles modernisées, une cuisine délicieuse et un spa dont les équipements vous feront rêver.

Si le gusta disfrutar del aire más refrescante, el silencio, la tranquilidad y el lujo en el confort, éste podría ser su paraíso de montaña soñado. Su situación de ladera con las nubes por montera con inigualables vistas en las que se pueden ver vistosos y zigzagueantes esquiadores en invierno y vacas pastando en verano le permitirá disfrutar de un íntimo lugar de descanso provisto de habitaciones tradicionales y modernas, una deliciosa carta e instalaciones de spa de ensueño.

ANDORRA (SOLDEU)

Sport Hotel Hermitage & Spa

CTRA. GENERAL S/N, AD100 SOLDEU, ANDORRA
Tel: +376 87 06 70 **Fax:** +376 87 06 71
Web: www.johansens.com/sporthotelhermitage **E-mail:** hotel.hermitage@sporthotels.ad

Our inspector loved: *The fabulous bathrooms in the suites.*

Price Guide:
double €210-550

Take in the mountain fresh air from this exclusive retreat where outdoor activities abound. Enveloped by and directly located on ski slopes, this is a sport enthusiast's paradise with year-round facilities, and those in need of an indulgent spa break need look no further. Dominated by wooden furnishings, the interior is modern and bedroom balconies overlook the gorgeous landscape.

Prenez l'air frais de la montagne depuis ce refuge sélect où les activités extérieures abondent. Situé au pied pistes de ski, c'est un paradis pour les amoureux du sport, avec des équipements pour chaque saison. Ceux qui ont besoin d'une pause au spa n'ont pas besoin d'aller loin. Meublés en bois, cet hôtel a un intérieur moderne et les balcons des chambres surplombent un paysage extraordinaire.

Inspire el aire fresco de la montaña desde este exclusivo refugio donde abundan las actividades al aire libre. En plena pista de ski, este hotel es un verdadero paraíso para amantes de los deportes, pues esta provisto de instalaciones durante todo el año. Aquellos que necesiten un complaciente descanso en un spa no tienen que buscar más. Con el pino como elemento dominante, su interior es moderno y los balcones de las habitaciones disponen de vistas a su espléndido paisaje.

Attractions: Sport Wellness Mountain Spa, Gondola to Grandvalira Ski Station, Skiing with Ski Guide and Snowmobiling, on-site; During the Summer: Walking with Mountain Guide, Horse Riding and Quad Biking, on-site; 2,000m-High Golf Course, 10-min gondola ride

Nearby Towns: Andorra la Vella, 20-min drive
Airports: Carcassonne, France, 150km; Toulouse, France, 180km; Barcelona, Spain, 220km

Category: Hotel

Austria

Leipzig
Wroclaw
Erfut
Dresden
POLAND
Frankfurt am Main
Hof
Prague
Plzen
CZECH REPUBLIC
GERMANY
Nürenberg
Brno
Ceske Budejovice
Gmünd
Horn
Poysdorf
Passau
SLOVAKIA
Ulm
Augsburg
Linz
Vienna (Wien)
Bratislava
München
Ried
Wels
Amstetten
19
Baden
Eisenstadt
Ebensee
Wiener Neustadt
Salzburg
Gyor
Bad Ischl
Bregenz
Liezen
Kitzbühel
Reutte
Bischofshofen
Bruck an der Mur
Feldkirch
Innsbruck
Pinkafeld
Blundenz
Judenburg
HUNGARY
Bad Gastein
Landeck
Graz
Vaduz
18
Zalaegerszeg
Wolfsberg
SWITZERLAND
Lienz
Sillian
Leibnitz
Spittal
Bolzano
St Moritz
Klagenfurt
Villach
Maribor
Traviso
SLOVENIA
Trento
ITALY
Udine
CROATIA
Ljubljana
Zagreb
Verona
Venice
Milan
Rijeka
Prijedor
Parma
Gospic
BOSNIA &
HERZEGOVINA
Bologna
ADRIATIC
SEA
Sarajevo
Florence
Split
Mostar

AUSTRIA (TIROL - OBERGURGL/SÖLDEN)

HOTEL THE CRYSTAL

GURGLERSTRASSE 90, OBERGURGL/SÖLDEN, TIROL, AUSTRIA

Tel: +43 5 256 6454 **Fax:** +43 5 256 6369

Web: www.johansens.com/thecrystal **E-mail:** info@thecrystal.at

Obergurgl-Hochgurgl is Austria's highest ski village and is guaranteed snow from November to May. You don't even have to leave the hotel to access the slopes thanks to a connecting passageway to a cable car depot! Extremely chic and comfortable, and contemporary in style, the hotel offers several dining options, a Wine Lounge, relaxing bar and large modern spa.

Obergurgl-Hochgurgl est le village de ski le plus haut d'Autriche et la neige y est garantie de novembre à mai. Vous n'avez même pas à sortir de votre hôtel pour accéder aux pistes grâce à un passage vers la gare du téléphérique! Extrêmement chic et confortable, d'un style contemporain, l'hôtel propose plusieurs options pour les repas, un salon de dégustations de vins, un bar accueillant et un vaste spa moderne.

Obergurgl-Hochgurgl es el pueblo más alto de Austria para la práctica del ski y donde la nieve está garantizada desde noviembre hasta mayo. Ni siquiera tendrá que dejar el hotel para acceder a las pistas gracias a que hay un corredor que le llevará a una estación de teleférico. Enormemente elegante y confortable, de estilo contemporaneo, el hotel ofrece varias opciones a la hora de cenar, un Wine Lounge, un bar tranquilo y un gratificante spa.

Our inspector loved: *The cool spa. There is no better way to relax after a day on the slopes!*

Price Guide: (half board)
double €180-448
suite €288-1,436

Nearby Towns: Innsbruck, 100km; Munich, Germany, 225km
Airports: Innsbruck, 100km; München, 300km; Verona, Italy, 360km

Category: Hotel
Closed: 2nd May - 12th November

AUSTRIA (VIENNA) 

Palais Coburg Residenz

COBURGBASTEI 4, 1010 VIENNA, AUSTRIA
Tel: +43 1 518 180 **Fax:** +43 1 518 18 100
Web: www.johansens.com/palaiscoburg **E-mail:** hotel.residenz@palais-coburg.com

Our inspector loved: *The superb service.*

Price Guide:
suite €590-2,670

Awards: Wine Spectator Grand Award 2009

Attractions: Musikverein, 1km; Hundertwasser House, 2km; Schönbrunn Palace, 7km; Lake Neusiedl, 75km

Nearby Towns: Bratislava, Slovakia, 66km; Sopron, 75km; Linz, 193km; Budapest, Hungary, 244km
Airports: Vienna, 18km; Bratislava, Slovakia, 70km

Category: Hotel

In the heart of Vienna, the Palais Coburg is a fascinating treat where you can experience 6 centuries of architectural splendour in one building. Enjoy the luxurious comforts, gourmet restaurant, a preponderance of excellent wines in 6 cellars and service that will make you want to return time and again.

Situé au cœur de Vienne, le Palais de Coburg est un endroit captivant où l'on se confronte à 6 siècles de splendeur architecturale en un seul bâtiment. Vous apprécierez les luxueux aménagements, le restaurant gastronomique, une prépondérance d'excellents vins dans les 6 caves et un service qui vous donnera envie de revenir encore et toujours.

En pleno corazón de Viena, el Palais Coburg constituye una fascinante delicia en la que podrá revivir 6 siglos de esplendor arquitectónico en un solo edificio. Disfrutará de sus comodidades de lujo, su restaurante gourmet, un auténtico despliegue de excelentes vinos en sus 6 bodegas y un servicio que le hará querer regresar una y otra vez.

Belgium

Zwolle
Amsterdam
Apeldoorn
NORTH SEA
The Hague
Utrecht
THE NETHERLANDS
Arnhem
Rotterdam
Breda
Tilburg
Duisbur
Eindhoven
Knokke-Heist
21
23
Mönchengladbach
Oostende
Brugge
Antwerpen
St-Niklaas
Gent
Dunkerque
Mechelen
GERMANY
Hasselt
Genk
Roeselare
Aalst
Leuven
Maastricht
Kortrijk
22
Bruxelles
Aachen
Mouscron
Lille
Wavre
Liège
Tournai
Seraing
Verviers
Arras
La Louvière
Mons
Namur
Charleroi
Bitburg
FRANCE
Bastogne
St-Quentin
Charleville-Mézières
LUXEMBOURG
Arlon
Trier
Luxembourg
Aubange
Reims
Paris
Metz

Hotel Manoir du Dragon

ALBERTLAAN 73, 8300 KNOKKE~HEIST, BELGIUM
Tel: +32 50 63 05 80 **Fax:** +32 50 63 05 90
Web: www.johansens.com/dudragon **E-mail:** info@manoirdudragon.be

Our inspector loved: *The wonderful ambience at this small luxury property with new de luxe suites and ideal location, near the beach, shops and golf clubs!*

Price Guide:
room €235-285
suite €345-500

Attractions: Beaches and Water Sports, 10-min walk; Art Galleries, Boutiques, Fish Restaurants, 10-min walk; Zwin Nature Reserve, 3km

Nearby Towns: Bruges, 18km; Ostend, 35km; Ghent, 50km; Antwerp, 60km
Airports: Zeebrugge Ferry Port, 10-min drive; Brussels, 1-hour drive; Calais Eurotunnel Train Station, France, 1.5-hour drive

Category: Charming Hotel

Dating back to 1927, this romantic manor house has a particularly special ambience and overlooks the Royal Zoute Golf Club. Most of the exquisitely decorated rooms and suites offer a private terrace and a relaxing Jacuzzi bath. Delicious buffet breakfasts are served in the garden during summer and the central location is ideal for exploring the area on foot or by bicycle.

Datant de 1927, ce manoir romantique surplombe le Golf Royal du Zoute et vous accueille dans une atmosphère tout à fait particulière. La plupart des chambres et suites, délicatement décorées, possède une terrasse privée et une relaxante baignoire Jacuzzi. Le délicieux buffet du petit-déjeuner est servi dans le jardin en été. Profitez de l'emplacement idéal pour visiter le centre ville à pied ou en vélo.

Este romántico hotel con vistas al campo de golf Royal Zoute se remonta al 1927 y tiene un ambiente verdaderamente especial. La mayoria de las habitaciónes y suites, exquisitamente decoradas, tienen terrazas y relajantes bañeras con jacuzzi. En verano, los deliciosos desayunos buffet se sirven en el jardin. Puede aprovechar la ideal posicion del hotel para visitar la zona a pie o en bicicleta.

GRAND HOTEL DAMIER

GROTE MARKT 41, 8500 KORTRIJK, BELGIUM

Tel: +32 56 22 15 47 **Fax:** +32 56 22 86 31

Web: www.johansens.com/damier **E-mail:** info@hoteldamier.be

One of the oldest hotels in Belgium, the façade of this city centre hotel has remained unchanged since it was built in 1769. Its art deco interior is enhanced with an ever-changing collection of artworks by local contemporary artists throughout the year. Previous celebrity guests include Margaret Thatcher, George Bush and various eminent sportsmen who no doubt loved the ambience, elegant rooms and plush Daemberd Barlounge.

Cet hôtel de centre ville, l'un des plus vieux hôtels de Belgique, a gardé sa façade depuis sa construction en 1769. Sa décoration intérieure dans le style art déco est mise en avant par le changement régulier, tout au long de l'année, de collections d'arts par des artistes contemporains locaux. Parmi les anciens clients on trouve Margaret Thatcher, le Président George Bush et de nombreux sportifs connus qui ont sans aucun doute apprécié l'ambiance, les chambres élégantes et le luxueux Daemberd Barlounge.

La fachada de este céntrico hotel de ciudad, uno de los mas antiguos de Bélgica, sigue intacta desde su construcción en 1769. El bello interior de estilo art deco se realza con una serie de colecciones de arte, ejecutadas por artistas contemporáneos del lugar, que van cambiando durante el año. Su clientela a incluido a Margaret Thatcher, George Bush y varios eminentes deportistas a quienes sin duda les encantó el ambiente, las elegantes habitaciones y el suntuoso Daemberd Barlounge.

Our inspector loved: *The authentic art-nouveau décor, and the kindness of the staff.*

Price Guide:
single from €119
double from €139
suite from €199

 49    150 

Attractions: Market Square Dining, Shopping and Night-life, 2-min walk; Museums and Begijnhof, 4-min walk; Xpo Exhibition Centre, 4km

Nearby Towns: Lille, France, 23km; Ghent, 34km; Bruges, 30km; Brussels, 1-hour drive
Airports: Lille Eurostar Terminal, 20-min train ride; Lille Lesquin, 25km; Brussels,1-hour train ride

Category: Hotel

Hostellerie Ter Driezen

18 HERENTALSSTRAAT, 2300 TURNHOUT, BELGIUM
Tel: +32 14 41 87 57 **Fax:** +32 14 42 03 10
Web: www.johansens.com/terdriezen **E-mail:** terdriezen@yahoo.com

Our inspector loved: *The newly decorated rooms, and the warm welcome.*

Price Guide:
single €116
double €144-158

 15    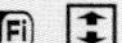

Attractions: The Old Convent, 300 metres; The Dukes of Brabant Castle, 300 metres; Breda City Centre, 29km; Lower Kempen Park, 29km

Nearby Towns: Eindhoven, 46km; Antwerp, 50km; Rotterdam, 92km; Brussels, 96km
Airports: Eindhoven, 46km; Antwerp, 50km; Rotterdam, 90km

Category: Luxury Guest House
Closed: During the Christmas period and New Year, and 1 week in July

Once the Mayor's official residence, the Keersmaekers have owned this 18th-century house for 28 years. Love and care show in the classic furnishings, crystal chandeliers, Oriental rugs and wooden floors. Enjoy pre-dinner drinks by the fireplace, and in summertime, feel the sun on your face as breakfast is served in the garden.

Autrefois la résidence officielle du Maire, les Keersmaekers possèdent cette maison du XVIIIe siècle depuis 28 ans. La passion et l'attention se retrouvent dans le mobilier classique, les chandeliers en cristal, les tapis d'orient et les parquets en bois. Profitez d'un apéritif près de la cheminée, et en été laissez le soleil vous caresser le visage en prenant le petit-déjeuner dans le jardin.

Esta casa del siglo XVIII fue residencia oficial del alcalde pero desde hace 28 años los Keersmaekers han sido sus dueños. El cariño y el cuidado se muestran en el mobiliario clásico, arañas de cristal, alfombras orientales y suelos de madera. Disfrute de los aperitivos junto a la chimenea y en verano sienta el sol en su cara mientras desayuna en el jardín.

Channel Islands

THE ATLANTIC HOTEL AND OCEAN RESTAURANT

LE MONT DE LA PULENTE, ST BRELADE, JERSEY JE3 8HE, CHANNEL ISLANDS
Tel: +44 1534 744101 **Fax:** +44 1534 744102
Web: www.johansens.com/atlanticeuro **E-mail:** info@theatlantichotel.com

Our inspector loved: *The location with its breathtaking views, and the comfortable, relaxed atmosphere.*

Price Guide: (excluding VAT)
single £100-150
double £150-350
suite £350-550

Awards: 3 AA Rosettes 2009-2010; 1 Star Michelin 2009; Condé Nast Johansens Most Excellent Service 2007

Attractions: La Mare Vineyards, 4 miles; Jersey War Tunnels, 5 miles; Eric Young Orchid Foundation, 8 miles; Durrell Wildlife Conservation Trust, 9 miles

Nearby Towns: St Helier, 5 miles
Airports: Jersey, 3 miles

Category: Hotel

Uninterrupted views of the ocean, acres of grounds alongside La Moye Golf Course, stylish interiors adorned with vibrant island art, exceptional service and a Michelin-starred restaurant, are just some of the stunning attributes of The Atlantic. The object of continuous and thoughtful investment by its owner, the running of this hotel is a labour of love, and it shows.

L'océan à perte de vue, des hectares de terrain le long du parcours de golf de La Moye, des intérieurs chics ornés d'oeuvres d'art local plein de vie, un service exceptionnel et un restaurant étoilé Michelin sont quelques uns des sublimes attributs de l'Atlantic. Source d'investissements continus et attentionnés par son propriétaire, cet hôtel est géré avec amour et ça se voit.

Sus ininterrumpidas vistas al océano, sus hectáreas de zona verde a lo largo de La Moye Golf Course, sus elegantes interiores adornados con su dinámico arte isleño, su excepcional servicio y su restaurante galardonado por Michelín son algunas de las deslumbrantes características del Atlantic. Fruto del continuo y meticuloso esfuerzo inversor de su propietario, la gestión de este hotel es una labor de cariño y entrega, lo cual resulta perceptible.

Longueville Manor

ST SAVIOUR, JERSEY JE2 7WF, CHANNEL ISLANDS
Tel: +44 1534 725501 **Fax:** +44 1534 731613
Web: www.johansens.com/longuevilleeuro **E-mail:** info@longuevillemanor.com

This hotel is a fine example of sumptuous luxury and is deserving of its much admired reputation for excellence. Beautiful bedrooms are adorned with freshly picked flowers from the kitchen gardens, the quality of the food is consistently excellent, and the gardens, set in a private wooded valley, have an enchanting lake on which elegant black swans effortlessly glide.

Cet hôtel est l'exemple parfait d'un luxe somptueux et mérite son immense réputation de perfection. Les magnifiques chambres sont ornées de fleurs fraîches cueillies dans le potager, la qualité de la nourriture est constamment excellente, et les jardins, situés dans une vallée arborée privée, possèdent un lac enchanteur sur lequel d'élégants cygnes noirs glissent sans effort.

Este hotel es un gran ejemplo de lujo suntuoso y merecedor de la alta reputación que goza por su excelencia. Las bellas habitaciones están adornadas con flores recién cogidas de los jardines de la cocina, la calidad de la comida es excelente por costumbre y los jardines, situados en un valle arbolado privado, tienen un lago encantador en el que elegantes cisnes negros se deslizan suavemente.

Our inspector loved: *The unique ambience of this superb hotel with its exemplary standards throughout.*

Price Guide: (room only, excluding VAT)
single from £175
double/twin £230-480
suite £500-800

Awards: AA 5 Red Stars

Attractions: Jersey Pottery, 5km; Durrell Wildlife Conservation Trust, 10km; Jersey War Tunnels, 15km; La Mare Vineyards, 17km

Airports: Jersey, 11km

Category: Hotel

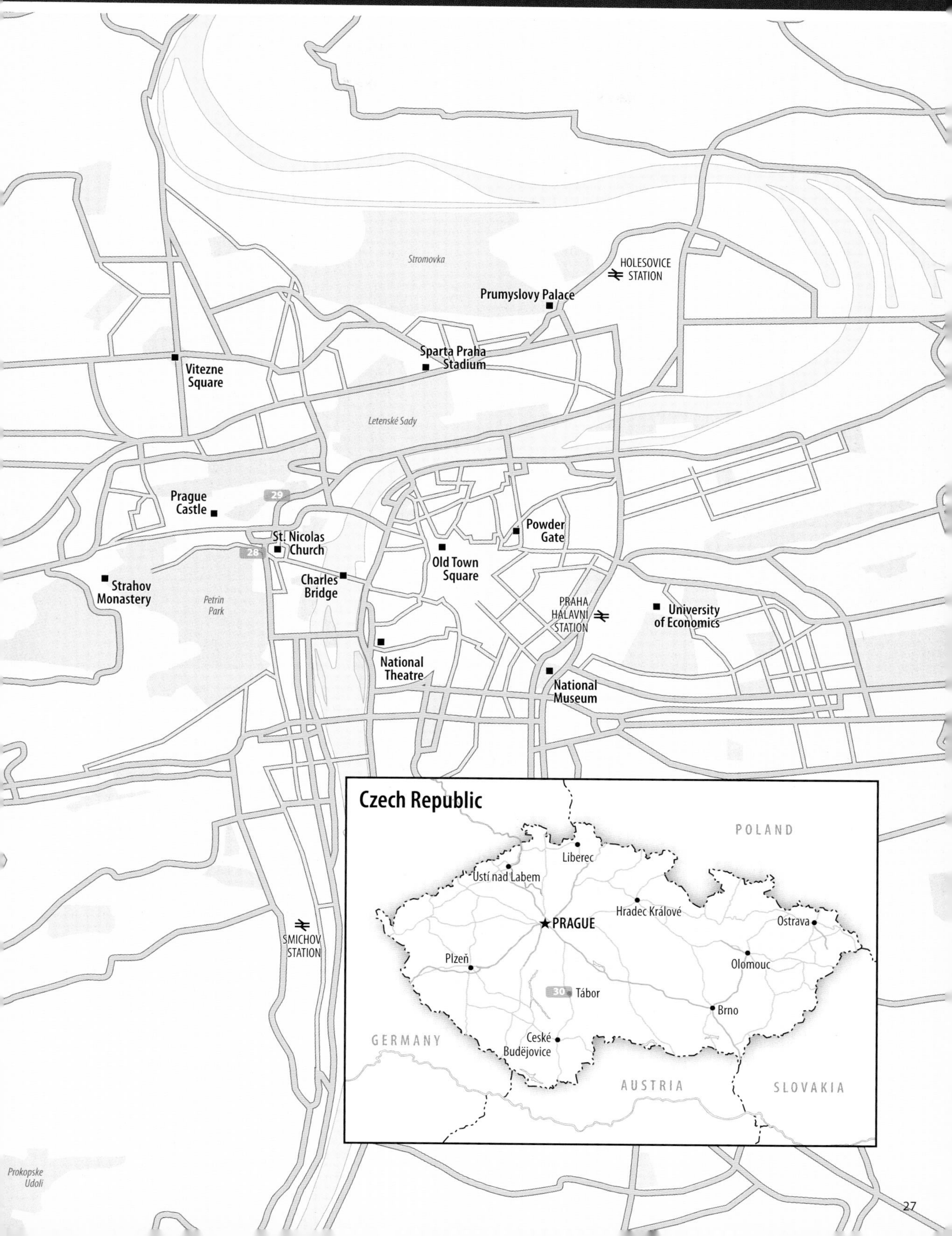

Czech Republic (Prague) 

Stromovka
HOLESOVICE STATION
Prumyslovy Palace
Sparta Praha Stadium
Vitezne Square
Letenské Sady
Prague Castle
29
St. Nicolas Church
28
Powder Gate
Old Town Square
Strahov Monastery
Petrin Park
Charles Bridge
PRAHA HALAVNI STATION
University of Economics
National Theatre
National Museum
SMICHOV STATION
Prokopske Udoli

Czech Republic

POLAND
Liberec
Ústí nad Labem
Hradec Králové
PRAGUE
Ostrava
Plzeň
Olomouc
30
Tábor
Brno
GERMANY
Ceské Budějovice
AUSTRIA
SLOVAKIA

CZECH REPUBLIC (PRAGUE)

Aria Hotel Prague

TRZISTE 9, 118 00 PRAGUE 1, CZECH REPUBLIC
Tel: +420 225 334 111 **Fax:** +420 225 334 666
Web: www.johansens.com/aria **E-mail:** stay@aria.cz

Space, tranquillity and Italian designer interiors are the unique selling points of this hotel, minutes from Prague Castle. Bedrooms pay tribute to musicians and composers, and the Winter Garden, where you can relax by the fire, boasts a grand piano. You will appreciate the bird's-eye city views from the rooftop terrace. A fully-equipped business centre is available.

Espace, tranquillité et intérieurs de designers italiens sont les points forts de cet hôtel situé à quelques minutes du Château de Prague. Les chambres rendent hommage à des musiciens et compositeurs et le Jardin d'Hiver, où vous pouvez vous relaxer près du feu, possède un magnifique piano. Vous apprécierez les vues panoramiques sur la ville depuis la terrasse panoramique. Un centre d'affaires bien équipé est disponible.

Espacio, tranquilidad e interiores de diseño italiano son los singulares puntos fuertes de este hotel, a minutos del Castillo de Praga. Las habitaciones prestan tributo a músicos y compositores, y el Jardín Invernal, donde puede relajarse a la vera del fuego, presume de su grandioso piano. Podrá apreciar el paisaje urbano a vista de pájaro desde la terraza en lo alto del edificio. Hay a su disposición un centro de negocios totalmente equipado.

Our inspector loved: *The delightful meals created by David Sasek, served on the roof garden terrace, weather permitting!*

Price Guide: (excluding VAT)
de luxe €205-310
junior suite €245-370
luxury suite €475-1,200

Awards: Best Luxury Hotel - Travelers' Choice, Trip Advisor 2009

Attractions: Charles Bridge, 5-min walk; Shopping, 5-min walk; Prague Castle, 10-min walk

Nearby Towns: UNESCO Cesky Krumlov, 3-hour drive
Airports: Prague, 20km

Category: Hotel

CZECH REPUBLIC (PRAGUE) 

GOLDEN WELL HOTEL

U ZLATÉ STUDNE 166/4, 118 01 PRAGUE 1, CZECH REPUBLIC
Tel: +420 257 011 213 **Fax:** +420 257 533 320
Web: www.johansens.com/goldenwell **E-mail:** hotel@goldenwell.cz

Our inspector loved: *The excellent comfort and service, which makes you feel like a king or queen.*

Price Guide: (excluding VAT)
single €172-274
double €187-289
suite €500-700

Awards: Best for Romance, Best In Service and Best in Top 25 Cities, Trip Advisor 2009; Best Hidden Gem in the World, Trip Advisor 2008

Attractions: Prague Castle, 2-min walk; Charles Bridge, 5-min walk

Nearby Towns: UNESCO Cesky Krumlov, 3-hour drive
Airports: Prague, 20km

Category: Charming Hotel

This 16th-century Renaissance building's views speak volumes, with spacious rooms looking out to the Ledeburg gardens filled with Baroque fountains and the rooftops of the city. Previous owner Emperor Rudolph II gave this romantic bolthole as a gift to the famous astonomer Tycho de Brahe. Today, it is an exclusive retreat complete with rooftop restaurant serving delicious international food to a backdrop of panoramic vistas.

Cet impressionnant et volumineux bâtiment renaissance du XVIe siècle a des chambres spacieuses qui donnent sur les jardins de Ledeburg, remplis de fontaines baroques, et sur les toits de la ville. L'ancien propriétaire, l'Empereur Rudolph II a donné en cadeau ce refuge romantique au fameux astronome Tycho de Brahe. Celui-ci est devenu aujourd'hui ce lieu unique où le restaurant sur le toit sert une délicieuse cuisine internationale, avec en arrière plan des vues panoramiques.

Las vistas desde este edificio renacentista del siglo XVI hablan por sí solas y sus espaciosas habitaciones dan a los jardines Ledeburg repletos de fuentes barrocas y a los techos de la ciudad. Su antiguo propietario, el Emperador Rodolfo II, regaló al famoso astrónomo Tycho de Brahe el romántico refugio. Actualmente, es un refugio exclusivo lugar que incluye un restaurante en el ultimo piso donde se sirve una deliciosa cocina internacional con vistas panorámicas como telón de fondo.

CZECH REPUBLIC (TÁBOR)

Hotel Nautilus

ŽIŽKOVO NÁMESTÍ 20, 39002 TÁBOR, CZECH REPUBLIC
Tel: +420 380 900 900 **Fax:** +420 380 900 999
Web: www.johansens.com/nautilus **E-mail:** info@hotelnautilus.cz

Our inspector loved: *The original architectural design, and the delicious lunches served in the contemporary restaurant.*

Price Guide:
single €96
double €112-129
suite €156-312

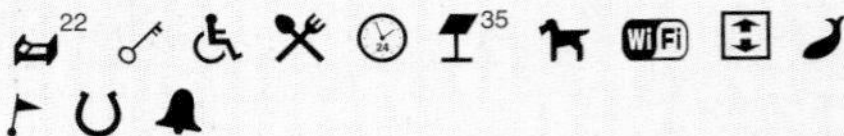

With the aid of local craftsmen and artisans, British couple Angie and Neil Harbury have created this truly chic boutique hotel, painstakingly designed with no attention to detail spared. Dine at Restaurant Goldie, drink at the Wine Bar, relax in the Gallery and explore the 13th-century cellar and tunnels under the old town.

Avec l'aide des artisans et des artistes locaux, Angie et Neil Harbury, couple de britanniques, ont créé ce ravissant boutique hôtel, décoré avec un grand soin et une attention aux détails toute particulière. Dînez au Restaurant Goldie, prenez un verre au bar à vins, relaxez-vous dans la galerie et explorez les caves et tunnels du XIIIe siècle sous la vieille ville.

Con ayuda de maestros y artesanos de la zona, la pareja británica Angie y Neil Harbury han creado este elegante hotel boutique de elaborado diseño sin escatimar un ápice su esmero por el detalle. Cene en el Restaurante Goldie, pruebe los vinos del Wine Bar, relájese en la Galería y no deje de visitar la bodega del siglo XIII y los túneles que se encuentran bajo el casco antiguo.

Attractions: Cervena Lhota, 25km; Orlik Castle, 40km; Hluboka Castle, 50km; Konopiste Castle, 50km

Nearby Towns: Ceské Budejovice, 65km; Cesky Krumlov, 90km; Prague, 95km; Plzen, 115km
Airports: Prague, 95km

Category: Charming Hotel

GREAT BRITAIN
Birmingham
Cardiff
Bristol
London
Southampton
Brighton
Dover
Plymouth
NORTH SEA
ENGLISH CHANNEL
The Hague
Amsterdam
NETHERLANDS
Rotterdam
Oostende
Dunkerque
Calais
Antwerp
Brussels
BELGIUM
Liege
Charleroi
Dusseldorf
GERMANY
Bonn
LUX.
Luxembourg
Mannheim
Saarbrucken
Stuttgart
Lille
Valenciennes
Amiens
North ~ Picardy
Cherbourg
Le Havre
Rouen
Caen
Normandy
Reims
Metz
Châlon-sur-Marne
Paris
Paris Region
Strasbourg
Nancy
Brest
Brittany
Saint-Malo
Rennes
Troyes
Champagne~Ardennes
Alsace~Lorraine
Freiburg
Mulhouse
Basel
Lorient
Le Mans
Orléans
Auxerre
Loire Valley
Angers
Saumur
Tours
Saint-Nazaire
Nantes
Dijon
Besançon
Bourges
Bern
Zuric
SWITZERLAND
Poitiers
Burgundy ~ Franche~Comté
LAKE GENEVA
La Rochelle
Poitou~Charentes
Geneva
BAY OF BISCAY
Clermont-Ferrand
Limoges
Lyon
Cognac
Auvergne~Limousin
Chambéry
ITALY
Saint-Etienne
Rhône~Alpes
Grenoble
Turin
Alessandria
Valence
Bordeaux
Bergerac
South West
Languedoc~Roussillon
Côte d'Azur
Avignon
Midi~Pyrénées
Nîmes
MONACO
Nice
Cannes
Santander
San Sebastian
Biarritz
Toulouse
Provence
Montpellier
Bilbao
Pau
Marseille
Carcassonne
Toulon
GULF OF LION
Pamplona
Perpignan
Burgos
ANDORRA
Andorra la Vella
Port-Bou
Bastia
Corsica
SPAIN
Gerona
Zaragoza
Ajaccio
Barcelona
Calatayud
MEDITERRANEAN SEA
Bonifacio
61
60
58
57
44
59
43
39
38
42
62
36
35
33
32
34
54
56
37
52
53
40
41
55
74
83
81
85
82
84
86
75
76
77
48
46
50
87
78
80
79
45
49
51
47

FRANCE / ALSACE~LORRAINE (COLMAR)

Hôtel Les Têtes

19 RUE DES TÊTES, BP 69, 68000 COLMAR, FRANCE
Tel: +33 3 89 24 43 43 **Fax:** +33 3 89 24 58 34
Web: www.johansens.com/lestetes **E-mail:** les-tetes@calixo.net

Our inspector loved: *The carefully prepared food and the spacious, well decorated bedrooms in this charming, picturesque Alsatian house.*

Price Guide: (breakfast €14)
single €95-239
double/twin €95-239
suite €255

Welcoming host Marc Rohfritsch beckons you to his beautiful Renaissance hotel, covered with 105 grotesque masks, at the heart of this labyrinthine cathedral town. Highly atmospheric, Baroque features flow through the interior, with ancient beams, attractive stonework and an intimate courtyard where you can relax with coffee or a cool drink.

L'hôte des lieux, Marc Rohfritsch, vous invite dans son magnifique hôtel de la Renaissance, dont la façade est couverte de 105 masques grotesques, au coeur du dédale de ruelles de cette ville épiscopale. Dans cette maison de caractère, l'atmosphère baroque est retentie à l'intérieur grâce à des poutres anciennes, de ravissants travaux de maçonnerie et une cour intérieure qui vous acceuille pour vous relaxer ou boire un verre.

Su amable anfitrión y propietario Marc Rohfritsch les da la bienvenida a su bello hotel renacentista, recubierto de 105 grotescas máscaras, en pleno corazón del laberinto de esta ciudad catedralicia. Su encantador ambiente se saborea gracias a los detalles barrocos que fluyen por sus interiores repletos de antiguas vigas, atractivas obras de arte en piedra y un intimista patio donde podrá relajarse con un café o un refresco.

Attractions: Colmar Old Town and Little Venice, on the doorstep; Alsace Vineyards, 10km; Ecomusée d'Alsace, 25km

Nearby Towns: Mulhouse, 43km; Strasbourg, 74km
Airports: Basel - Mulhouse, 40km

Category: Hotel
Closed: During February

Romantik Hôtel le Maréchal

4 PLACE SIX MONTAGNES NOIRES, PETITE VENISE, 68000 COLMAR, FRANCE
Tel: +33 3 89 41 60 32 **Fax:** +33 3 89 24 59 40
Web: www.johansens.com/marechal **E-mail:** info@le-marechal.com

Our inspector loved: *The friendly owners, and new bedroom, Schütz.*

Price Guide: (breakfast €15)
single €85-95
double €105-225
suite €255

Attractions: Ancient and Traditional Alsace Villages, 5km; Alsace Wine Route, 5km

Nearby Towns: Colmar, on the doorstep
Airports: Mulhouse, 40km; Strasbourg Entzheim, 60km

Category: Hotel

For the perfect romantic weekend break, look no further. Set beside a canal in Colmar's most beautiful quarter, "Little Venice," this charming house has delightful bedrooms, all named after famous musicians, and offers warm hospitality. To complete the picture, L'Echevin restaurant serves Alsatian delicacies and superb wines by candlelight and accompanying classical music.

Ne cherchez pas plus loin l'emplacement idéal de votre week-end romantique. Situé le long d'un canal dans l'un des plus beau quartier de Colmar "La Petite Venise", cette maison de charme offre des chambres ravissantes, toutes nommées après un compositeur de renom, ainsi qu'un accueil chaleureux. Pour compléter cette image parfaite, le restaurant L'Echevin propose des spécialités alsaciennes et de délicieux vins autour de chandelles et de musique classique.

Lugar ideal para pasar un perfecto romántico fin de semana. Esta encantadora casa ubicada junto a un canal en el barrio más bonito de Colmar, "Little Venice", posee hermosas habitaciones todas ellas con nombres de músicos famosos y rebosa cálida hospitalidad. Para completar el conjunto, el restaurante L'Echevin sirve delicadezas alsacianas acompañadas de grandes vinos y todo ello a la luz de las velas y con música clásica.

DOMAINE DE LA GRANGE DE CONDÉ

41 RUE DES DEUX NIEDS, 57220 CONDÉ NORTHEN, FRANCE
Tel: +33 3 87 79 30 50 **Fax:** +33 3 87 79 30 51
Web: www.johansens.com/grangedeconde **E-mail:** lagrangedeconde@wanadoo.fr

Our inspector loved: *The high standard of cuisine.*

Price Guide: (room only)
single €105
double €105
suite €230-250

Attractions: Alsace-Lorraine Countryside, on-site; Metz, 20km; Luxembourg, 50km

Nearby Towns: Nancy, 90km
Airports: Metz, 20km; TVG Connection, 20-min drive; Luxembourg, 40-min drive

Category: Charming Hotel

No stone has been left unturned in designing this lovely hotel with spacious rooms, luxurious carpets and solid wood furniture. Some have terraces overlooking the grounds. Pool-side barbecues are popular, and with 6 dining rooms on offer you know you won't go hungry! A charming little spa offers a sauna, hammam and massages.

Tout a été mis en oeuvre lors de la rénovation de ce ravissant hôtel avec ses chambres spacieuses, dont certaines avec terrasses surplombant les jardins, ses moquettes luxueuses et son mobilier en bois. Les barbecues au bord de la piscine sont un succès et avec ses 6 salles à manger vous ne serez jamais affamé ! Un petit spa charmant propose sauna, hammam et massages.

No ha quedado piedra sin levantar para diseñar este encantador hotel de amplias habitaciones, lujosas alfombras y mobiliario de madera maciza. Algunas disponen de terrazas con vistas a sus terrenos. Las barbacoas a la vera de la piscina son de lo más populares y con 6 comedores a su disposición, ¡seguro que no se quedará con hambre! Su pequeño y encantador spa cuenta con sauna, hammam y masajes.

HOSTELLERIE LES BAS RUPTS LE CHALET FLEURI

181 ROUTE DE LA BRESSE, 88400 GÉRARDMER, VOSGES, FRANCE
Tel: +33 3 29 63 09 25 **Fax:** +33 3 29 63 00 40
Web: www.johansens.com/basrupts **E-mail:** basrupts@relaischateaux.com

Our inspector loved: *The fantastic chef.*

Price Guide: (breakfast €22)
single €160-210
double/twin €160-210
suite €280-500

Awards: 1 Star Michelin

Attractions: Mountain Walks, on-site; Mountain Biking, on-site; Lake Gérardmer, 2km; Ski Slopes, 3km

Nearby Towns: Gérardmer, 2km; Colmar, 50km
Airports: Basel - Mulhouse, 80km

Category: Hotel

In the heart of Les Vosges mountain region, the Hostellerie and adjoining Chalet Fleuri are a magical treat all year round. Inspired interpretations of local specialities are served in the panoramic restaurant. Lovely bedrooms with hand-painted flowers on the walls and doors, and the welcoming ambience, envelope you in warmth.

Au cœur de la région montagneuse des Vosges, l'Hostellerie et son Chalet Fleuri voisin sont un plaisir tout au long de l'année. Des interprétations inspirées de spécialités locales sont servies dans le restaurant panoramique. Les chambres confortables, avec leurs fleurs peintes à la main sur les murs et portes, ainsi que l'ambiance accueillante vous envelopperont de chaleur.

En el corazón de la región Los Vosgos, la Hostellerie y el Chalet Fleuri adjunto son un placer durante todo el año. Sus platos inspirados en especialidades locales se acompañan con excelentes vinos en el restaurante panorámico. Las cómodas habitaciones con flores pintadas a mano en paredes y puertas, junto con el ambiente acogedor le envuelven con su calidez.

Hôtel à la Cour d'Alsace

3 RUE DE GAIL, 67210 OBERNAI, FRANCE
Tel: +33 3 88 95 07 00 **Fax:** +33 3 88 95 19 21
Web: www.johansens.com/couralsace **E-mail:** info@cour-alsace.com

This unique medieval hotel is utterly captivating. Its 23 carefully restored houses surround a central courtyard with light and airy guest rooms, including 12 new, spacious and luxury bedrooms that combine Alsatian tradition with European living. Visit the new indoor pool and wellness centre that have been carefully built into this historic property before taking a summer evening's dinner in the garden.

Cet hôtel médiéval unique est véritablement captivant. Ses 23 maisons rénovées avec soin entourent une cour centrale et possèdent des chambres claires et aérées, dont 12 nouvelles et spacieuses chambres de luxes qui allient tradition alsacienne au mode de vie Européen. Visitez la nouvelle piscine intérieure ainsi que le centre de remise en forme soigneusement intégré dans ce bâtiment historique avant de diner dans le jardin les soirs d'été.

Encontrará este singular hotel medieval de lo más cautivador. El patio central esta rodeado de 23 cuidadosamente restauradas casas con amplias y luminosas habitaciones, incluyendo 12 nuevas de lujo que son aún más espaciosas y combinan la tradición alsaciana con la vida moderna Europea. Visíte la nueva piscina interior y el centro Wellness que ha sido cuidadosamente incorporado a este edificio histórico, para luego disfrutar de una agradable cena de verano en el jardín.

Our inspector loved: *The new luxurious suites, and fantastic spa area.*

Price Guide: (breakfast €17)
single €119-149
double €149-199
suite/duplex €289

Attractions: Obernai Village, on-site; Alsace Wine Route, on the doorstep; Vosges Lake, 1-hour drive; Black Forest, 1-hour drive

Nearby Towns: Strasbourg, 25km; Colmar, 40km
Airports: Entzheim, 15km; Basel, Switzerland, 1-hour drive; Frankfurt, Germany, 2.5-hour drive

Category: Hotel
Closed: 24th December - 27th January

DOMAINE DE ROCHEVILAINE

POINTE DE PEN LAN, BP 69, 56190 BILLIERS, FRANCE
Tel: +33 2 97 41 61 61 **Fax:** +33 2 97 41 44 85
Web: www.johansens.com/domainerochevilaine **E-mail:** domaine@domainerochevilaine.com

Our inspector loved: *The unrivalled sea views.*

Price Guide: (room only)
single €150-425
double/twin €150-425
suite €400-690

Attractions: Brittany Coastline, on the doorstep; The Morbihan Gulf, 25km

Nearby Towns: Vannes, 30km
Airports: Nantes, 90km

Category: Hotel

Dramatically perched on the edge of the rocky Pointe de Pen Lan, this historic manor house offers unbeaten views across the waterfront. Gaze in awe from the stylish bedrooms, and relax in the comfy lounge with an apéritif, before revelling in Chef Patrice Caillaut's delicious French cooking made from the freshest of local produce.

Perché de manière impressionnante sur la pointe rocheuse de Pen Lan, ce manoir historique offre des vues imprenables sur le bord de mer. Admirez l'élégance des chambres et relaxez-vous dans le salon confortable, en sirotant un apéritif, avant de déguster la délicieuse cuisine française du Chef Patrice Caillaut, réalisée à partir des meilleurs produits locaux.

Encaramado espectacularmente al borde del rocoso Pointe de Pen Lan, esta histórica casa solariega le proporcionará incomparables vistas del frente marino. Contemple sobrecogido el paisaje desde sus elegantes habitaciones y relájese en su cómodo salón con un aperitivo antes de regocijarse con la deliciosa cocina francesa del Chef Patrice Caillaut, confeccionada con los productos más frescos de la zona.

FRANCE / BRITTANY (ST~MALO - LA GOUESNIÈRE)

Château de Bonaban

35350 LA GOUESNIÈRE, FRANCE
Tel: +33 2 99 58 24 50 **Fax:** +33 2 99 58 28 41
Web: www.johansens.com/chateaudebonaban **E-mail:** chateau.bonaban@wanadoo.fr

Time seems to stand still at this idyllic 17th-century Pays Malouin château, surrounded by park and woodland. Guest rooms look out over the pretty pond, and the opulently decorated chapel is ideal for weddings. While in the restaurant, a chef who has studied with the gastronomic greats, creates an ever-changing menu.

Le temps semble s'arrêter dans ce château idyllique du XVIIe siècle en Pays Malouin, entouré de parcs et de forêts. Les chambres donnent sur le ravissant plan d'eau et la chapelle est idéale pour les mariages. Au restaurant le chef, qui a travaillé avec les plus grands, crée un menu toujours nouveau.

En este idílico château Pays Malouin del siglo XVII, rodeado de un parque arbolado, parece ser que el tiempo se ha detenido. Las habitaciones dan a un atractivo estanque y la capilla decorada con opulencia es el lugar ideal para celebrar bodas; al mismo tiempo que en el restaurante un chef que estudió con grandes gastrónomos crea un menú siempre variado.

Our inspector loved: *Walking around the beautiful grounds.*

Price Guide: (room only)
single €100-230
double/twin €100-230
suite €235-300

Attractions: River Rance, 5km; Saint-Malo, 10km; Mont Saint-Michel and Priory, 20km; Dinard British Film Festival, 30km

Nearby Towns: Saint-Malo, 10km; Dinard, 30km; Dinan, 30km; Rennes, 60km
Airports: Dinard, 20km

Category: Hotel

Ti al Lannec & Spa

14 ALLÉE DE MEZO~GUEN, 22560 TREBEURDEN, FRANCE
Tel: +33 2 96 15 01 01 **Fax:** +33 2 96 23 62 14
Web: www.johansens.com/tiallannec **E-mail:** contact@tiallannec.com

Our inspector loved: *The fact that this is the most friendly hotel in France.*

Price Guide: (room only)
single €92-136
double €172-302
suite €200-409

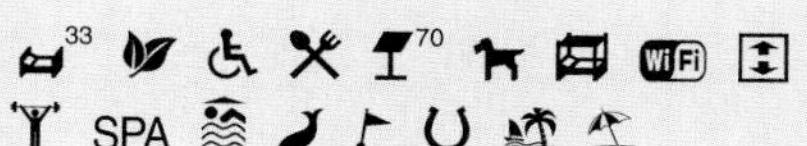

Attractions: The Brittany Coast, 5-min drive

Nearby Towns: The Centre of Trebeurden, 5-min walk; Perros-Guirec, 10km; Lannion, 10km
Airports: Lannion, 12km

Category: Hotel
Closed: Mid-November - 1st March

Lose yourself in the views from this Breton manor house, perched high on a cliff-top overlooking the Rose Granite Coast. Professionalism is key here with a warm welcome from the attentive staff and a keen eye for detail. Many of the comfortable bedrooms have private balconies. A wide range of spa treatments is available.

Laissez-vous emporter par les vues offertes par ce manoir breton, perché sur le haut d'une falaise, surplombant la Côte de Granit Rose. Le professionnalisme est ici un élément clé, avec l'accueil chaleureux d'une équipe attentionnée, à l'œil attentif au moindre détail. La plupart des comfortables chambres ont des balcons privés. Un large éventail de soins de spa est disponible.

Piérdase entre el paisaje de esta casa solariega bretona, encaramada en lo más alto de un acantilado con vistas a la costa Rose Granite. La profesionalidad es su pieza clave, a la que se unen la calurosa bienvenida por parte del atento personal y el gusto por los pequeños detalles. Muchas de las habitaciones cómodas disponen de balcones privados. El spa ofrece una amplia gama de tratamientos.

FRANCE / BURGUNDY - FRANCHE~COMTÉ (BEAUNE / CHAMBOLLE MUSIGNY)

Château Hôtel André Ziltener

RUE DE LA FONTAINE, 21220 CHAMBOLLE - MUSIGNY, FRANCE
Tel: +33 3 80 62 41 62 **Fax:** +33 3 80 62 83 75
Web: www.johansens.com/ziltener **E-mail:** chateau.ziltener@wanadoo.fr

Our inspector loved: *The luxurious suites, the kindness of the staff, and the wine tasting in the cellar!*

Price Guide: (breakfast €18, excluding VAT)
standard €220
double €280-285
apartment suite €380

Attractions: Burgundy Vineyards, on the doorstep; Abbaye de Citeaux, 15km; Beaune, 20km;

Nearby Towns: Dijon, 16km; Beaune, 20km
Airports: Dijon, 15km

Category: Luxury Guest House
Closed: 13th December - 13th March

Wine lovers beware! Upon entering this wonderful château, a former Cistercian abbey, you will not want to leave! Head for the wine bar stocked with the region's specialities and relax in your choice of accommodation whether an apartment, junior suite or double room; each one beautifully elegant and luxuriously appointed.

Amoureux de vins attention! Une fois que vous serez entré dans ce magnifique château, qui fût une ancienne abbaye cistercienne, vous ne voudrez plus en partir! Visitez le bar à vins, remplis des spécialités de la région et relaxez-vous dans l'hébergement de votre choix, que ce soit un appartement, une junior suite ou une chambre double; chacun d'eux superbement élégant et luxueusement agencé.

¡Atentos los amantes del vino! Una vez que entre en este maravilloso château, antigua abadía cisterciense, no querrá salir. Visite la taberna repleta de especialidades de la región y relájese en su alojamiento elegido: apartamento, suite junior o habitación doble. Todas son sumamente elegantes y presentan un lujoso acabado.

ABBAYE DE LA BUSSIÈRE

21360 LA BUSSIÈRE~SUR~OUCHE, CÔTE D'OR, FRANCE
Tel: +33 3 80 49 02 29 **Fax:** +33 3 80 49 05 23
Web: www.johansens.com/abbayedelabussiere **E-mail:** info@abbayedelabussiere.fr

Our inspector loved: *The majesty of the location, and the serenity of the gardens.*

Price Guide: (room only, always check availability of restaurant)
superior €220-260
de luxe €335-390
junior suite €395-450

Awards: 1 Star Michelin

Attractions: Dijon Prenois Racing Circuit, 20km; Burgundy Vineyards, 25km; Hospices de Beaune, 30km

Nearby Towns: Dijon, 20km; Beaune, 30km; Nuits Saint-Georges, 30km
Airports: Dijon, 25km

Category: Hotel
Closed: During January. The bistro is open on Mondays and Tuesdays when the gastronomic restaurant is closed.

Built in the early 12th century by Cistercian monks, this magnificent abbey's frescoes were revealed during its restoration by local craftsmen. Full of romance, no 2 bedrooms are the same, but all enjoy lofty perspectives of the surrounding park. Dinner is a gastronomic treat, and you can gaze longingly at wines in the well-stocked gothic-arched cellar.

Construite au début du XIIe siècle par des moines cisterciens, les magnifiques fresques de cette abbaye furent révélées lors de sa restauration par des artisans locaux. Très romantique, aucune des chambres ne se ressemble mais toutes offrent de superbes vues sur le parc environnant. Les repas sont un délice gastronomique et vous pourrez admirer les vins sous les voûtes gothiques de la cave bien achalandée.

Construida a principios del siglo XII por los monjes cistercienses, los frescos de esta magnífica abadía vieron la luz a manos de artesanos del lugar durante su restauración. Rebosante de romance, no hay 2 habitaciones exactamente iguales, pero todas gozan de sublimes perspectivas del parque que la rodea. La cena es todo una delicia gastronómica. Podrá asimismo mirar con deseo sus vinos en su repleta bodega de arcos góticos.

CHÂTEAU D'ETOGES

51270 ETOGES~EN~CHAMPAGNE, FRANCE
Tel: +33 3 26 59 30 08 **Fax:** +33 3 26 59 35 57
Web: www.johansens.com/etoges **E-mail:** contact@etoges.com

What more could you ask for? Set in the glorious Champagne region, this beautifully renovated château overlooks a moat and has individually appointed bedrooms complemented by 2 dining rooms located in the Orangerie with views of the gardens. An imposing fireplace tells tales of banquets, meetings and celebrations from a medieval past.

Que pouvez-vous demander de plus? Situé dans la superbe région de Champagne, ce château magnifiquement rénové surplombe les douves et possède des chambres individuellement décorées ainsi que 2 salles à manger situées dans l'Orangerie et ayant vue sur les jardins. Une cheminée imposante raconte les récits de banquets, réunions et célébrations de l'époque médiévale.

¿Qué más podría pedirle a este château bellamente renovado con vistas al foso situado en la gloriosa región de Champagne? Sus habitaciones nominadas individualmente se complementan con 2 comedores situados en el Orangerie y vistas a los jardines. Una imponente chimenea recuerda relatos de banquetes, reuniones y celebraciones de un pasado medieval.

Our inspector loved: *The exquisite ambience created by Madame Filliette-Neuville and her team.*

Price Guide: (room only)
single €80-160
double €120-260

Attractions: Champagne Vineyards, 500 metres; Champagne Cellars, 500 metres; Reims Cathedral, 50km

Nearby Towns: Epernay, 20km; Reims, 50km; Troyes, 70km
Airports: Paris-Charles de Gaulle (Roissy), 100km; Paris-Orly, 100km

Category: Hotel
Closed: 24th January - 18th February

Château de Fère

02130 FÈRE~EN~TARDENOIS, FRANCE

Tel: +33 3 23 82 21 13 **Fax:** +33 3 23 82 37 81

Web: www.johansens.com/chateaufere **E-mail:** chateau.fere@wanadoo.fr

Our inspector loved: *The newly refurbished room 12, "Camille Claudel."*

Price Guide: (breakfast €22)
single/double/twin €150-370
suite €310-420

Attractions: Hot-Air Ballooning, on-site; Champagne Cellars and Tastings, 30km

Nearby Towns: Reims, 45km; Paris, 1-hour drive
Airports: Paris-Charles de Gaulle (Roissy), 90km

Category: Hotel
Closed: Early January - early February

Just 1 hour from Paris, this grand 18th-century château sits side-by-side of the impressive ruins of a medieval castle. Guest rooms are tastefully furnished and offer spectacular views. Sneak a look at the Champagne region's secrets on a tour of the cellars, and savour excellent meals in the stylish dining rooms.

A seulement 1 heure de Paris, cet imposant château du XVIIIe siècle se tient à côté des ruines impressionnantes d'une demeure médiévale. Les chambres sont élégamment meublées et offrent de magnifiques vues. Profitez des secrets de la région de Champagne en faisant le tour des caves et dégustez les excellents mets dans les superbes salles à manger.

Este grandioso château del siglo XVIII está a solamente 1 hora de París y linda con las impresionantes ruinas de un castillo medieval. Las habitaciones están amuebladas exquisitamente y ofrecen vistas espectaculares. Descubra los secretos de la región de Champagne en un tour de las bodegas y saboree excelentes comidas en fantásticos comedores.

FRANCE / CHAMPAGNE~ARDENNES (STE~PREUVE - LAON)

Domaine du Château de Barive

02350 SAINTE~PREUVE, FRANCE

Tel: +33 3 23 22 15 15 **Fax:** +33 3 23 22 08 39

Web: www.johansens.com/barive **E-mail:** contact@lesepicuriens.com

Our inspector loved: *The new wellness centre and welcome drink!*

Price Guide: (breakfast €16)
single €120-180
double €140-250
suite €230-450

Attractions: Chemin des Dames, 20km; Champagne Vineyards, 50km; Cathedrals of Picardy, 70km

Nearby Towns: Laon, 18km; Rheims, 50km
Airports: Paris-Charles de Gaulle (Roissy), 100km

Category: Charming Hotel

Step through an ornamental gateway into a manicured garden and courtyard, then take in this picture-book perfect stone-built hotel. Light, airy rooms are modern in style, and though the atmosphere is relaxed, there is amazing attention to detail. Sample the restaurant's classic French cooking and the wares of many local champagne cellars, and take time to visit the magnificent wellness centre, TranSPArence.

Poussez les portes de l'imposant portail, traversez les jardins impeccables et la cour et admirez ce magnifique hôtel digne d'un livre d'images. Claires et aérées les chambres sont de style moderne et bien que l'atmosphère soit décontractée, il y a, à travers tout l'hôtel, une incroyable attention au détail. Goûtez la classique cuisine française du restaurant, dégustez les nombreux champagnes locaux et prenez le temps de visiter le magnifique centre de bien être, TranSPArence.

A través de un decorativo portón, entrará en un exquisito patio y jardín y podrá contemplar este perfecto hotel de postal construido en piedra. El estilo de las espaciosas y frescas habitaciones es moderno y, si bien el ambiente es desenfadado, la atención al detalle se encuentra en todo el hotel. Deguste la clásica cocina francesa del restaurante así como los caldos de numerosas bodegas de champaña del lugar y encuentre tiempo también para visitar TranSPArence, el centro Wellness.

Tiara Yaktsa Cannes

6 BOULEVARD DE L'ESQUILLON, 06590 THÉOULE~SUR~MER, FRANCE
Tel: +33 4 92 28 60 30 **Fax:** +33 4 92 28 46 46
Web: www.johansens.com/tiarayaktsa **E-mail:** reservations.yaktsa@tiara-hotels.com

Our inspector loved: *The luxury bedrooms with all mod cons, free mini-bar and bottle of champagne on arrival.*

Price Guide: (room only, excluding VAT)
classic/de luxe room €300-460
prestige room €660
classic/penthouse suite €860-2,480

Attractions: Massif de l'Esterel, 5-min drive; Théoule-sur-Mer, Exclusive Beaches, 10-min drive; La Croisette, Cannes, 15-min drive

Nearby Towns: Cannes, 15km; Nice, 50km; Saint-Tropez, 85km
Airports: Nice, 45km

Category: Hotel

When you reach Tiara Yaktsa, nestled amongst the hills with breathtaking views over the Mediterranean Sea and the red rocks of Esterel Mountain, you will know you have made an inspired choice. Exuding the refinement of Mediterranean culture, the gardens and pool are exquisite, the food is delicious and the range of beauty treatments is truly indulgent.

Lorsque vous arriverez à Tiara Yaktsa, niché au cœur des collines et offrant des vues à couper le souffle sur la Mer Méditerranée et sur les roches rouges de l'Estérel, vous saurez que vous avez fait le bon choix. L'hôtel respire le raffinement des cultures méditerranéennes, les jardins et la piscine sont ravissants, la cuisine est délicieuse et la gamme de soins est un vrai plaisir.

Cuando llegue a Tiara Yaktsa, situada en medio de colinas con impresionantes vistas al Mar Mediterráneo y a las rocas rojas del monte Esterel, sabrá que su decisión fue un acierto. Rebosantes del refinamiento de la cultura mediterránea, los jardines y la piscina son magníficos, la comida deliciosa y los distintos tratamientos de belleza un verdadero placer.

FRANCE / CÔTE D'AZUR (ÈZE VILLAGE)

CHÂTEAU EZA

RUE DE LA PISE, 06360 ÈZE VILLAGE, FRANCE

Tel: +33 4 93 41 12 24 **Fax:** +33 4 93 41 16 64

Web: www.johansens.com/eza **E-mail:** info@chateaueza.com

1,300ft above the Mediterranean, Château Eza is enchanting, completely refurbished in a contemporary style, yet paying homage to 13th-century houses with original stone walls, oak beams and fireplaces. The sumptuous suites are elegantly decorated with superb fabrics and every modern amenity. Breathtaking views are guaranteed from the terrace and panoramic restaurant.

A 400 mètres au-dessus de la Méditerranée, Château Eza est enchanteur. Complètement rénové dans un style contemporain, l'hôtel a su rendre hommage à ses maisons du XIIIe siècle avec leurs murs de pierres d'origine, leurs poutres en chêne et leurs cheminées. Les suites somptueuses sont élégamment décorées avec de superbes tissus et tout le confort moderne. Des vues à couper le souffle vous sont offertes depuis la terrasse et le restaurant panoramique.

A más de 400 metros de altura sobre el Mediterráneo, Château Eza resulta encantador. Está completamente renovado al estilo contemporáneo sin dejar por ello de rendir homenaje a las casas del siglo XIII, que conservan sus muros de piedra, vigas de roble y chimeneas originales. Sus suntuosas suites están elegantemente decoradas con excelentes telas y todo tipo de modernas instalaciones. Tendrá garantizadas sobrecogedoras vistas desde la terraza y el panorámico restaurante.

Our inspector loved: *The Blue Junior Suite with its superb terrace looking out to stupendous views over the Mediterranean Sea!*

Price Guide: (room only)
double/twin €180-815
suite €460-1,120

Awards: One of Travel & Leisure Magazine's 100 Best Hotels in the World 2009; One of Travel & Leisure Magazine's 500 Best Hotels 2008; 1 Star Michelin

Attractions: Saint-Jean Cap Ferrat, 5km; Villa Ephrussi de Rothschild, 15-min drive; Monaco, 10km; Cannes, 50km

Nearby Towns: Monaco, 10km; Nice, 15km
Airports: Nice, 15km

Category: Hotel

Le Bailli de Suffren

AVENUE DES AMÉRICAINS, GOLFE DE SAINT~TROPEZ, 83820 LE RAYOL – CANADEL~SUR~MER, FRANCE
Tel: +33 4 98 04 47 00 **Fax:** +33 4 98 04 47 99
Web: www.johansens.com/lebaillidesuffren **E-mail:** info@lebaillidesuffren.com

Our inspector loved: *The breathtaking views of the islands and crystal clear sea.*

Price Guide: (room only, excluding VAT)
junior suite €189-443

Attractions: Iles du Levant/Porquerolles, 10-min boat ride

Nearby Towns: Le Lavandou, 15km; Saint-Tropez, 30km; Toulon, 30km
Airports: Toulon-Hyères, 30km; Marseille, 100km; Nice, 120km

Category: Hotel
Closed: 12th October - 12th April

Gaze across the ocean from one of the most beautiful coves of the Saint-Tropez Gulf. Facing the islands of Port-Cros and Levant, junior suites are tastefully decorated in a Provençal style, with balconies and terraces. A pool, fitness room, private beach, yacht and gourmet restaurant are all ingredients for a fantastic holiday.

Cet hôtel contemple la mer depuis l'une des plus belles criques du Golfe de Saint-Tropez. Les suites junior, situées face aux îles de Port-Cros et du Levant, sont décorées avec goût dans un style provençal, avec balcons et terrasses. Une piscine, une salle de remise en forme, une plage privée, un voilier et un restaurant gastronomique, sont les ingrédients pour des vacances fantastiques.

Contemple el océano desde una de las calas más bellas del golfo Saint-Tropez. Situado frente a las Islas de Port-Cros y Levant, las suites júnior están decoradas esmeradamente en un estilo provenzal con balcones y terrazas. Una piscina, sala de fitness, playa privada, yate y restaurante gourmet son todos los ingredientes para pasar unas vacaciones fantásticas.

Hôtel La Pérouse

11 QUAI RAUBA~CAPEU, 06300 NICE, FRANCE

Tel: + 33 4 93 62 34 63 **Fax:** + 33 4 93 62 59 41

Web: www.johansens.com/hotellaperouse **E-mail:** lp@hotel-la-perouse.com

Our inspector loved: *The secluded rooftop solarium with its Jacuzzi, gym and amazing panoramic views.*

Price Guide: (breakfast €21)
classic/superior/de luxe €175-560
junior suite €650-1,000
suite €750-1,500

Attractions: Promedade des Anglais, on-site; Nice Old Town and Flower Market, 2-min walk; Nice Harbour and Opera House, 5-min walk

Nearby Towns: Monaco, 20-min drive; Cannes, 30-min drive; Italy, 30-min drive; Grasse, 40-min drive
Airports: Nice, 20-min drive

Category: Hotel

This is an ideal retreat for guests looking to explore the historic delights of Nice's old town. Upon entering, venture through the corridors and elevators to a hidden Mediterranean garden with olive and lemon trees, and enjoy Provençal meals prepared from the finest local produce. Additional amenities include a secluded pool and sauna at the bottom of the garden.

L'hôtel est le refuge idéal pour ceux qui souhaitent découvrir les délices historiques de la vieille ville de Nice. Dès votre arrivée, aventurez-vous dans les couloirs et ascenceurs, jusqu'à découvrir un jardin méditerranéen caché, rempli d'oliviers et de citronniers, où vous pourrez déguster une cuisine provençale préparée à partir des meilleurs produits locaux. Parmi les services, une piscine extérieure et un sauna isolés, au pied du jardin.

Es el lugar de retiro ideal para quienes buscan explorar las maravillas históricas del casco antiguo de Niza. A su entrada, aventúrese por los pasillos y ascensores hasta llegar a un apartado jardín mediterráneo de olivos y limoneros, y disfrute de las comidas provencales elaboradas con los mejores ingredientes del lugar. Otros servicios incluyen una piscina apartada y sauna al fondo del jardín.

La Ferme d'Augustin

PLAGE DE TAHITI, 83350 RAMATUELLE, NEAR SAINT~TROPEZ, FRANCE
Tel: +33 4 94 55 97 00 **Fax:** +33 4 94 97 59 76
Web: www.johansens.com/fermeaugustin **E-mail:** info@fermeaugustin.com

Our inspector loved: *The relaxing atmosphere and carefree feeling of being on holiday the minute you walk through the door.*

Price Guide: (breakfast €14, excluding VAT)
double/twin €145-310
suite €300-660

Attractions: Bravade Festivities in May; Voiles de Saint-Tropez Sailing Competition in October; Tahiti Beach, 100 metres; Coastal Walks, 100 metres

Nearby Towns: Saint-Tropez, 5-min drive; Toulon, 50km; Cannes, 80km
Airports: Toulon-Hyères, 50km; Nice, 105km; Marseille, 160km

Category: Charming Hotel
Closed: 10th April - 20th October

Should you need to escape the buzz of the Côte d'Azur, this family-run hotel creates the perfect retreat. The Vallets offer traditional French charm and hospitality with magic touches. Pretty bedrooms and suites have antiques and whirlpool baths, while some have private gardens. An outdoor hydrotherapy pool and wonderful cooking complete the picture.

Si vous avez besoin d'échapper au brouhaha de la Côte d'Azur, cet hôtel familial sera le refuge idéal. La famille Vallet propose le charme traditionnel à la française et une hospitalité aux accents magiques. Les chambres et suites sont ravissantes avec leurs meubles anciens et leurs bains bouillonnants; certaines ont même un jardin privé. Une piscine hydrothérapique, à l'extérieur, et une cuisine exceptionnelle viennent compléter le tableau.

Si necesita escaparse del bullicio de la Costa Azul, este hotel de regencia familiar es el lugar perfecto. Los Vallets le ofrecen su tradicional encanto francés y hospitalidad con toques mágicos. Las bonitas habitaciones y suites poseen antigüedades, baños whirlpool y jardines privados, sin olvidar una piscina exterior de hidroterapia y una deliciosa cocina.

FRANCE / CÔTE D'AZUR (ST~RAPHAËL)

La Villa Mauresque

1792 ROUTE DE LA CORNICHE, 83700 SAINT~RAPHAËL, FRANCE
Tel: +33 494 83 02 42 **Fax:** +33 494 83 02 02
Web: www.johansens.com/mauresque **E-mail:** contact@villa-mauresque.com

Our inspector loved: *The location, and the magnificent villas overlooking the sea.*

Price Guide: (room only, excluding VAT)
double €165-440
suite €440-1,100

Attractions: Valescure Golf, 10-min drive; Fréjus Roman Theatre, 10-min drive; Esterel Mountains, 15-min drive

Nearby Towns: Fréjus, 10-min drive; Saint-Tropez, 30-min drive; Cannes, 30-min drive
Airports: Nice, 50km; Toulon-Hyères Nice, 60km; Marseille-Marignane, 105km

Category: Charming Hotel

Breathtaking and romantic, La Villa Mauresque stands in immaculately manicured gardens with seafront views of the Mediterranean. Comprising 2 villas: Boutique Hotel and Spa Hotel, experience comfort and privacy and dinners created by the French chef. Massages and treatments can be arranged and there are heated pools, a gym and personal trainer on request. Visit the private boat-house and rent the 8-seater sailing boat, "Lady Marianna," or motor boat.

Somptueuse et romantique, La Villa Mauresque se dresse au coeur de jardins immaculés et en bord de Méditerranée. Composée de 2 villas: Boutique Hotel et Spa Hotel, vous pourrez expérimenter confort et intimité ainsi que des dîners créés par le Chef français. Des massages et des soins peuvent être organisés et il y a des piscines chauffées, une salle de gym et un entraîneur personnel sur demande. Visitez le boat-house et louez le bateau à voile pouvant accueillir 8 personnes, "Lady Marianna" ou à moteur de l'hôtel.

Imponente y romántica, La Villa Mauresque se sitúa entre impecables jardines con vistas al mar Mediterraneo. En el complejo compuesto de 2 villas, Boutique Hotel y Spa Hotel, podrá disfrutar de confort y intimidad y cenas creadas por el Chef francés. El hotel organiza masajes y tratamientos, y dispone de piscinas climatizadas, un gimnasio y un entrenador personal, bajo petición. Visite el cobertizo privado donde podrá alquilar "Lady Marianna", el barco velero de 8 plazas o una motora.

CHÂTEAU DE FLOURE

1, ALLÉE GASTON BONHEUR, 11800 FLOURE, FRANCE
Tel: +33 4 68 79 11 29 **Fax:** +33 4 68 79 04 61
Web: www.johansens.com/floure **E-mail:** contact@chateau-de-floure.com

Our inspector loved: *The delightful gardens and fantastic views over the "Mont Alaric".*

Price Guide: (room only)
double €110-190
suite €250-280

Attractions: Hiking, on the doorstep; Cycling Route Beside Canal du Midi, on the doorstep; Riding School at Lake Cavayère, 9km; Cathari Castles and Cave Visits, 10km

Nearby Towns: Carcassonne, 9km
Airports: Carcassonne, 12km; Perpignan, 100km; Montpellier, 130km

Category: Charming Hotel

Join the French literati here at this beautiful château, formerly the residence of writer Gaston Bonheur. Lying peacefully in a lush park surrounded by vineyards and exquisite traditional French gardens, its bedrooms are delightful and the 17th-century restaurant, featuring impressive original woodwork, is irresistible. Stroll in the grounds, swim or play tennis.

Rejoignez la littérature française dans ce superbe château, autrefois résidence de l'écrivain Gaston Bonheur. Nichées au cœur d'un parc luxuriant entouré de vignobles et de ravissants jardins à la française, les chambres sont charmantes et la salle de restaurant du XVIIe siècle à l'impressionnante ébénisterie d'origine est magnifique. Promenez-vous dans le parc, nagez ou jouez au tennis.

Codéese aquí con los literatos franceses en este bello château, antaño residencia del escritor Gaston Bonheur. Ubicado en plena edén de tranquilidad en medio de un frondoso parque rodeado de viñedos y distinguidos y tradicionales jardines franceses, sus habitaciones son encantadorás, y su restaurante del siglo XVII con su impresionante ebanistería original, resulta simplemente irresistible. Podrá pasear por su terrenos, practicar la natación o jugar al tenis.

CHÂTEAU DE PRAY

RUE DU CÈDRE, 37530 CHARGÉ~AMBOISE, FRANCE
Tel: +33 247 57 23 67 **Fax:** +33 347 57 32 50
Web: www.johansens.com/chateaudepray **E-mail:** chateau.depray@wanadoo.fr

Our inspector loved: *The wonderfully warm welcome.*

Price Guide: (breakfast €13)
single €120-195
double/twin €120-195
apartment €195-245

Attractions: Loire Valley, on the doorstep; Château d'Amboise, 2km; Châteaux, Gardens and Wine Tastings, 2km; Loire Valley Vineyards, 5km

Nearby Towns: Amboise, 2km; Tours, 28km; Blois, 28km
Airports: Tours, 30km; Paris-Orly, 230km

Category: Hotel
Closed: 4th - 28th January and 15th November - 2nd December

Château de Pray is set on the sunny terraced slopes overlooking the Loire River. An imposing round tower helps you guess at its Renaissance origins, and inside, the wood panelling, heavy beams and rich fabrics perfect the traditional feel. Admire the views from the bedrooms, enjoy a stroll through the peaceful gardens and dine in the award-winning restaurant.

Le Château de Pray se situe sur les coteaux ensoleillés surplombant la Loire. Une tour ronde imposante laisse deviner ses origines de la Renaissance et à l'intérieur les boiseries, les lourdes poutres et les riches étoffes confortent ce sentiment. Admirez les vues depuis les chambres, promenez-vous dans les jardins tranquilles et dégustez la cuisine du restaurant gastronomique.

Château de Pray está ubicado en las soleadas laderas en bancales con vistas al río Loira. Una imponente torre circular le permite adivinar sus orígenes renacentistas, y en su interior, sus paneles de madera, sus pesadas vigas y sus lujosas telas terminan de rematar esa sensación de tradición. Admire sus paisajes desde las habitaciones, disfrute de paseos por sus tranquilos jardines y cene en su galardonado restaurante.

LE MANOIR SAINT THOMAS

1 MAIL SAINT THOMAS, 37400 AMBOISE, FRANCE
Tel: +33 2 47 23 21 82 **Fax:** +33 2 47 23 24 96
Web: www.johansens.com/saintthomas **E-mail:** info@manoir-saint-thomas.com

Our inspector loved: *The very friendly welcome.*

Price Guide: (room only)
single/double €120-190
suite €220-250
duplex €340

Attractions: Historic Amboise, 2-min walk; Loire Valley Châteaux, 1km

Nearby Towns: Amboise, 2-min walk; Chenonceaux, 12km; Tours, 24km
Airports: Tours, 30km; Paris-Orly, 175km

Category: Luxury Guest House

This delightful, newly renovated Loire Valley manor house is set amidst well-kept private gardens and has a wonderfully relaxing atmosphere. Eye-catching modern colours adorn the bedrooms, whilst reminders of the history of Amboise can be found in every nook and cranny, including period fireplaces, a stone turret and beautifully carved woodwork.

Ce ravissant manoir, récemment rénové, est niché au coeur de jardins superbement entretenus et offre une atmosphère merveilleusement relaxante. Des couleurs modernes ornent les chambres tandis que des souvenirs de l'histoire d'Amboise se trouvent dans tous les coins et recoins dont des cheminées d'époques, une tourelle en pierres et de somptueux bois sculptés.

Esta encantadora casa solariega de reciente renovación del Valle de Loira se encuentra rodeada de cuidados jardines particulares y ofrece un encantador y sumamente relajado ambiente. Llamativos y modernos colores adornan las habitaciones, en las que pueden apreciarse vestigios de la historia de Amboise en todos y cada uno de sus rincones y recovecos, entre los que se incluyen hogares de chimenea de época, un torreón de piedra y artesonado de madera de bello labrado.

FRANCE / LOIRE VALLEY (CHAMPIGNÉ)

CHÂTEAU DES BRIOTTIÈRES

49330 CHAMPIGNÉ, FRANCE
Tel: +33 2 41 42 00 02 **Fax:** +33 2 41 42 01 55
Web: www.johansens.com/briottieres **E-mail:** briottieres@wanadoo.fr

Feel the serenity of this magnificent family-owned stately home wash over you, along with the rich perfume of the herbs and flowers from the 360 acres of parkland "à l'anglaise." Classical interiors include immaculate bedrooms, Louis XV antiques and quirky memorabilia. Sample traditional Anjou cuisine in the period dining room.

Laissez-vous envahir par la sérénité de ce magnifique château familial ainsi que par les parfums riches et évocateurs des herbes et fleurs des 140 hectares de jardins à l'Anglaise. Les intérieurs sont classiques, les chambres impeccables et le mobilier Louis XV est agrémenté d'excentriques objets de collection. Les repas traditionnels d'Anjou sont servis dans l'ancienne salle à manger.

Sienta la serenidad de esta magnífica mansión de regencia familiar junto con los sugerentes y ricos perfumes de hierbas y flores procedentes de 140 hectares de parque "à l'anglaise". Su clásico interior incluye habitaciones inmaculadas, antigüedades de Luis XV y peculiares objetos de colección. Disfrute la tradicional cocina de Anjou en el comedor de época.

Our inspector loved: *The peaceful and beautiful gardens.*

Price Guide: (breakfast €15, dinner by reservation €46)
single €150-250
double/twin €150-250
suite €320-350

Attractions: Château du Plessis-Bourré,13km; Solesmes Abbaye (Grégorian Chants), 30km; Distillerie Cointreau, 30km; Wines Routes of the Loire, 30km

Nearby Towns: Château-Gontier, 20km; Sablé, 25km; Angers, 35km
Airports: Nantes, 90km

Category: Hotel

CHÂTEAU DE L'ABBAYE

85450 MOREILLES, FRANCE
Tel: +33 251 56 17 56 **Fax:** +33 251 56 30 30
Web: www.johansens.com/chateaulabbaye **E-mail:** daniellerenard@hotmail.com

Our inspector loved: *The picnic hampers that are provided for guests who choose to go cycling in the Marais.*

Price Guide: (room only)
single €79-109
double €89-159
junior suite €109-189

Attractions: Le Marais Poitevin, on the doorstep; Atlantic Coast Beaches, 20km; La Rochelle, 40km; Puy du Fou, 80km

Nearby Towns: Ile de Ré, 35km; La Rochelle, 40km; Les Sables d'Olonne, 60km; Nantes, 100km
Airports: La Rochelle, 35km; Nantes, 100km

Category: Luxury Guest House

The Renard Family has been welcoming guests to their home for 20 years. A former abbey, their château's history spans 9 centuries and stands in acres of landscaped grounds. Offering 5 rooms and junior suites teeming with personal touches, there are always regional, home-cooked meals on the menu. But for something a little spicier, enjoy Danielle and Korakot's Thai dishes.

La Famille Renard accueille des hôtes dans leur maison depuis plus de 20 ans. Anciennement une abbaye et situé au cœur d'un grand parc entretenu, l'histoire de leur château couvre 9 siècles. Proposant 5 chambres et junior suites fourmillant de touches personnelles, il y a toujours des plats régionaux faits maison au menu. Et pour des choses un peu plus épicées, vous pouvez essayer les plats Thaï de Danielle et Korakot.

La familia Renard llevan más de 20 años recibiendo en casa a sus clientes. Su château, una antigua abadía, abarca 9 siglos de historia y se encuentra situado en una extensa zona ajardinada. Consta de 5 habitaciones y de suites junior repletas de toques personales. En su menú siempre encontrará comidas caseras típicas de la región. Pero si busca algo más picante, pruebe los platos Thai de Danielle y Korakot.

FRANCE / LOIRE VALLEY (ST~CALAIS)

Château de la Barre

72120 CONFLANS~SUR~ANILLE, FRANCE
Tel: +33 2 43 35 00 17
Web: www.johansens.com/delabarre **E-mail:** info@chateaudelabarre.com

Words fail us! This 15th-century château is truly amazing. A lovingly maintained family home for hundreds of years, set in 100 acres of parkland. Guy and Marnie will share their personal treasures with you, and a candle-lit dinner will be an experience second to none. This property will give you a true taste of authentic French living.

Les mots nous manquent! Ce château du XVe siècle est vraiment extraordinaire. Entretenue avec soin depuis des centaines d'années par la même famille, cette demeure est située dans un parc de 40 hectares. Guy et Marnie partageront avec vous leurs trésors personnels et le dîner aux chandelles restera une expérience incomparable. Cette propriété vous fera découvrir le véritable et authentique art de vivre à la française.

¡No hay palabras! Este château del siglo XV es verdaderamente asombroso. Conservado con el mayor cuidado durante siglos, este inmueble de regencia familiar se encuentra situado sobre una superficie de 40 hectares de zona verde. Guy y Marnie compartirán con usted sus tesoros más preciados. La cena a la luz de las velas será una experiencia inolvidable. Este lugar le dará una buena muestra de la verdadera vida francesa.

***Our inspector loved:** The relaxed atmosphere created by the Count and Countess.*

Price Guide: (room only)
single from €150
double €150-300

Awards: 100 Best Hotels in the World, Times Travel Magazine 2008; France's Best Château Guest House, Sunday Times 2007

Attractions: Loire Valley Castles, 55-min drive; Romanesque 12th-Century Chapels, Wineries, Vintage Citroën Hire, Race Car Driving and Hot-Air Ballooning, 25km; The Gardens of Sasnières and Le Petit Bordeaux, 35km; Old City of Le Mans, 38km

Nearby Towns: Vendôme, 28km; Le Mans, 38km; Amboise, 60km; Blois, 60km
Airports: Tours, 65km; Paris Charles de Gaulle (Roissy), 190km

Category: Luxury Guest House

Manoir de Mathan

14480 CRÉPON, FRANCE

Tel: +33 2 31 22 21 73 **Fax:** +33 2 31 22 98 39

Web: www.johansens.com/mathan **E-mail:** manoir.de.mathan@gmail.com

Our inspector loved: *The leisurely atmosphere.*

Price Guide: (room only)
single €95-130
double €160-175
suite €180-260

Attractions: D-Day Beaches, 3km; Mont Saint-Michel, 115km

Nearby Towns: Caen, 20km; Bayeux, 10km
Airports: Caen, 20km

Category: Luxury Guest House

You can tick the "rustic" and "elegant" boxes straight away at this gorgeous 18th-century stone built manor house with its own courtyard and parkland. What could be nicer than waking to birdsong and sunlit breakfasts on the terrace. Unique rooms and suites are prettily decorated, while beams and open fireplaces provide complete homeliness.

Vous pouvez immédiatement cocher les cases "rustique" et "élégant" en parlant de cette superbe ferme en pierre du XVIIIe siècle, de sa cour intérieure et de son domaine. Que peut-on demander de plus que de se réveiller au chant des oiseaux et de prendre son petit-déjeuner au soleil sur la terrasse. Toutes différentes, les chambres et suites sont ravissantes et poutres et cheminées créent une atmosphère accueillante.

Los casilleros "rural" y "elegante" son los que Vd. señalará sin duda alguna para describir esta excepcional mansión rural construida en piedra durante el siglo XVIII, provista de su propio patio y jardines. Nada hay más agradable que despertarse con el canto de las aves y encontrarse el desayuno servido en la soleada terraza privada. Las habitaciones y suites están decoradas con coquetería, mientras que las vigas y hogares de chimeneas proporcionan un ambiente completamente hogareño.

FRANCE / NORMANDY (BAYEUX / PORT~EN~BESSIN)

CHÂTEAU LA CHENEVIÈRE

ESCURES - COMMES, 14520 PORT~EN~BESSIN, FRANCE
Tel: +33 2 31 51 25 25 **Fax:** +33 2 31 51 25 20
Web: www.johansens.com/lacheneviere **E-mail:** reservation@lacheneviere.fr

If you're looking to explore the Normandy coastline, this classical château is the ideal base. It offers traditional hospitality and individually designed bedrooms overlooking lovely parklands. After a day's sightseeing, retire your walking shoes and unwind in the Zanzibar cellar bar before enjoying the regional gastronomic delights in the elegant restaurant.

Ce château est idéal si vous souhaitez explorer les côtes normandes. Il offre une hospitalité traditionnelle et des chambres au décor individuel surplombant les ravissants jardins. Après une journée de visite, relaxez-vous dans le bar cave le Zanzibar avant de savourer des mets gastronomiques régionaux dans l'élégant restaurant.

Si desea Vd. explorar la costa Normanda, este clásico château es el emplazamiento ideal. Pone a su disposición la hospitalidad al estilo más tradicional así como sus habitaciones de diseño individualizado con vistas a encantadoras zonas ajardinadas. Tras un día de visita turística podrá relajarse en la bodega Zanzibar antes de pasar a disfrutar de sus delicias gastronómicas regionales en su elegante restaurante.

Our inspector loved: *The refined elegance of the public rooms.*

Price Guide:
single €223-483
double €244-504
suite €434-504

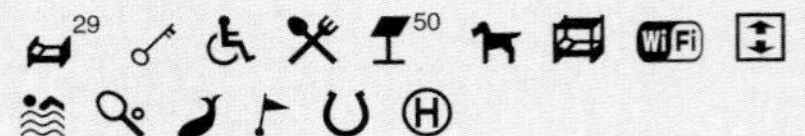

Attractions: The D-Day Beaches, 2km; The Normandy Coast, 2km; Omaha Beach Golf Club, 2km; The Bayeux Tapestry, 10km

Nearby Towns: Port-en-Bessin, 2km; Bayeux, 10km; Caen, 35km
Airports: Caen, 35km; Paris-Charles de Gaulle (Roissy), 280km; Paris-Orly, 280km

Category: Hotel
Closed: During December, January and February

Château de Courcelles

8, RUE DE CHÂTEAU, 02220 COURCELLES~SUR~VESLES (AISNE), FRANCE
Tel: +33 3 23 74 13 53 **Fax:** +33 3 23 74 06 41
Web: www.johansens.com/courcelles **E-mail:** reservation@chateau-de-courcelles.fr

Our inspector loved: *The view of the "jardins à la française" from the junior suite, and the very kind and friendly staff.*

Price Guide: (room only)
single €185-365
double €185-365
apartment or suite €395-455

Awards: 1 Star Michelin

Attractions: Chemin des Dames Battlefield, 10km; Champagne Vineyards, 20km

Nearby Towns: Reims, 35km; Laon, 36km; Epernay, 50km
Airports: Paris-Charles de Gaulle (Roissy), 80km

Category: Hotel

This beautiful 17th-century château is set in vast parkland filled with statues, "French-style gardens" and a canal bordered by 200-year-old plane trees. Gracious period décor accentuates its charming atmosphere and the large bedrooms are the epitome of comfortable country living. The inspired cuisine is a treat that must not be missed!

Ce superbe château du XVIIe siècle se trouve au milieu d'un vaste parc orné de statues, d'un jardin à la française et d'un canal bordé de platanes bicentenaires. Un luxueux décor d'époque accentue l'atmosphère agréable et les chambres représentent la quintessence d'une vie confortable à la campagne. Ne manquez surtout pas la prestigieuse cuisine servie ici!

Este bello château del siglo XVII se encuentra en medio de un extenso parque repleto de estatuas, "jardines al estilo francés" y un canal bordeado por árboles plátanos de 200 años. Su exquisito decorado de época acentúa su encantador ambiente y sus amplias habitaciones constituyen todo un símbolo de la comodidad rural. Su inspirada carta es todo un lujo que no puede permitir perderse.

FRANCE / NORTH - PICARDY (LILLE)

Carlton Hôtel

3 RUE DE PARIS, 59000 LILLE, FRANCE

Tel: +33 3 20 13 33 13 **Fax:** +33 3 20 51 48 17

Web: www.johansens.com/carltonlille **E-mail:** carlton@carltonlille.com

Once you have exhausted Lille's shops, museums and opera, retire to this historic, Louis XV and XVI furnished, city centre hotel. Fitness enthusiasts will love the health and fitness facility and solarium, while others can simply relax in style in the super duplex luxury suite, complete with its own lounge and bar.

Lorsque vous serez venu à bout de l'opéra, des boutiques et musées de Lille, venez vous réfugier dans cet hôtel historique du centre ville, meublé dans le style Louis XV et XVI. Les fanatiques de gym adoreront la salle de remise en forme et le solarium. Vous pouvez également vous reposer avec style dans la superbe et luxueuse suite duplex, qui possède son propre salon et bar.

Después de un día agotador entre compras, museos y ópera en Lille, refúgiese en este céntrico histórico hotel amueblado con los estilos Luis XV y XVI. A los amantes del fitness les encantarán sus instalaciones del centro de salud, del fitness y del solarium; o simplemente relájese en estilo en la súper suite dúplex de lujo, con su propio salón y bar.

Our inspector loved: *The newly refurbished rooms, particularly the suite in the rotunda with its view of the old city and opera house.*

Price Guide: (breakfast €18, excluding €1.10 city tax per day)
single €177-242
double €177-242
luxe bedroom €350-1,280

Attractions: Lille Town Centre, on-site; Lille Christmas Market, 10-min walkOld Lille, 10-min walk

Airports: Lille Lesquin, 15km; Eurostar, 3km

Category: Hotel

CHÂTEAU DE COCOVE

62890 RECQUES~SUR~HEM, FRANCE
Tel: +33 3 21 82 68 29 **Fax:** +33 3 21 82 72 59
Web: www.johansens.com/chateaudecocove **E-mail:** chateaudecocove@hotmail.com

Our inspector loved: *The château's beautiful "parc à l'anglaise."*

Price Guide: (room only, excluding VAT)
single €80-118
double €98-168

Attractions: Le Blockhaus d'Eperlecques, V2 Rocket Site, 5km; Hôtel Sandelin Museum, Saint-Omer, 18km; Cité de la Dentelle à Calais, 20km; Cap Gris Nez et Cap Blanc Nez, 30km

Nearby Towns: Calais, 20km; Lille, 80km
Airports: Eurostar Lille Terminal, 80km; Lille Lesquin, 80km

Category: Hotel
Closed: 24th-25th December

This classically proportioned château promises a gastronomic experience and the carefully planned menus and fine wine selection do not disappoint. Afternoon tea and apéritifs are served on the terrace, while the backdrop for dinner is romantic and candle-lit. Enjoy an evening stroll amidst the 27 acres of pretty parkland.

Ce château classique promet une expérience gastronomique et ni les menus pensés avec attention, ni la sélection de vins fins ne déçoit. Le thé et l'apéritif sont servis sur la terrasse et les dîners ont pour toiles de fond romance et chandelles. En fin de soirée, profitez des 11 hectares du ravissant parc pour vous balader.

Este château clásico promete una experiencia gastronómica y tanto los menús realizados con esmero como una excelente selección de vinos no le defraudarán. El té de la tarde y los aperitivos se sirven en la terraza mientras que el telón de fondo para la cena es romántico y a la luz de las velas. Disfrute de un bonito paseo al atardecer en el magnifico parque de 11 hectáreas.

France (Paris)

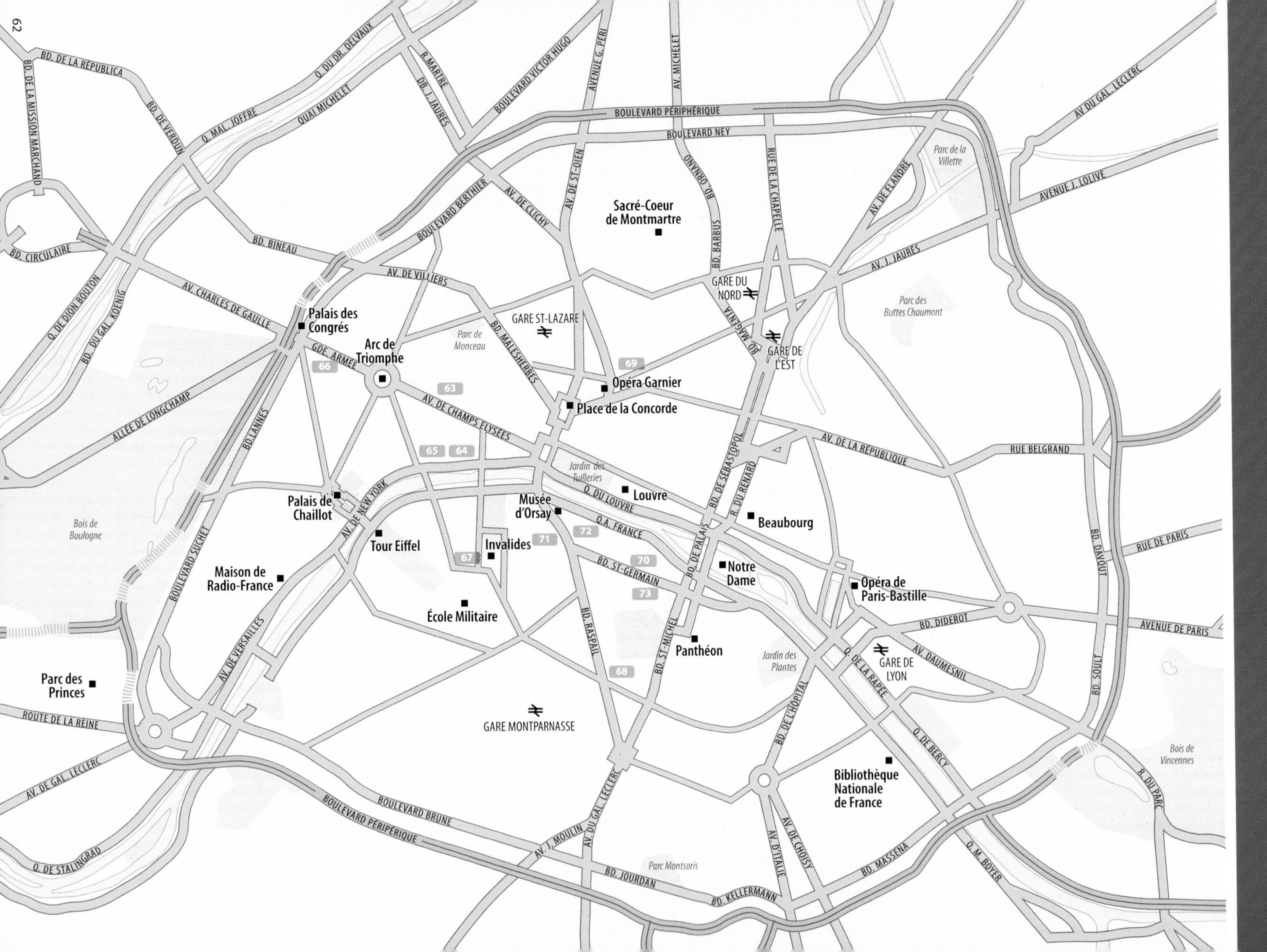

Hospes Lancaster

7, RUE DE BERRI, 75008 PARIS, FRANCE
Tel: +33 1 40 76 40 76 **Fax:** +33 1 40 76 40 00
Web: www.johansens.com/hospeslancaster **E-mail:** reservations@hotel-lancaster.fr

Our inspector loved: *The feeling of entering an elegant and privileged world.*

Price Guide: (room only, excluding VAT)
single €320
double €390-610
suite €707-1,800

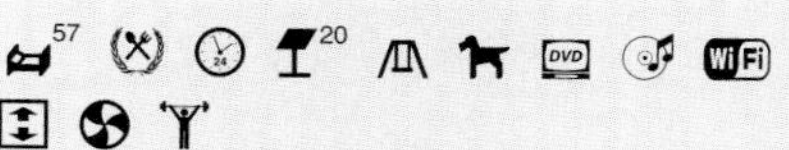

Awards: 1 Star Michelin

Attractions: Arc de Triomphe, 2-min walk; Place de la Concorde, 10-min walk

Airports: Paris-Orly, 25km; Paris-Charles de Gaulle (Roissy), 30km

Category: Hotel

Glamour is Lancaster's middle name, and once you close its heavy doors behind you, the bustling Champs-Elysées seems a million miles away. Run like a home-from-home, drift dreamily between the gasp-worthy salons, the minimalist garden retreat and deliciously intimate restaurant to sample Master Chef Michel Troisgros' exquisite cuisine.

Le mot "chic" est celui qui qualifie le mieux le Lancaster et une fois que vous avez fermé ses lourdes portes derrière vous, le bruit des Champs-Elysées semble être à des milliers de kilomètres. Tout est fait pour que l'on se sente chez soi: flânez agréablement à la découverte des exceptionnels salons, du jardin minimaliste, du délicieux et intime restaurant pour goûter l'exquise cuisine du Chef Michel Troisgros.

Glamour es sinónimo del Lancaster. Cuando se cierren las grandes puertas a sus espaldas, los bulliciosos Campos Elíseos parecerán quedar a millones de quilómetros de allí. Regentado como un hogar privado, podrá dejarse llevar como en un sueño por entre sus increíbles salones y el pacifico jardín minimalista hasta el encantador e intimo restaurante donde degustará la exquisita cocina del Master Chef Michel Troisgros.

FRANCE / PARIS (CHAMPS~ELYSÉES)

HÔTEL SAN RÉGIS

12 RUE JEAN GOUJON, 75008 PARIS, FRANCE

Tel: +33 1 44 95 16 16 **Fax:** +33 1 45 61 05 48

Web: www.johansens.com/sanregis **E-mail:** message@hotel-sanregis.fr

Our inspector loved: *Breakfast in the library restaurant, and the discreet luxury throughout.*

Price Guide: (room only)
single €350
double/twin €465-630
suite €700-1,650

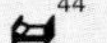 44    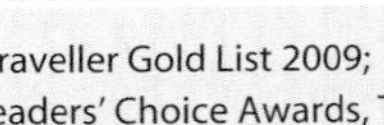

Awards: Condé Nast Traveller Gold List 2009; Condé Nast Traveler Readers' Choice Awards, Top 10 in Paris 2008; Andrew Harper's Hideaway Report, Top City Hotels 2007

Attractions: Grand & Petit Palais, 1-min walk; Avenue Montaigne Shopping, 1-min walk; Place de la Concorde, 1km; Arc de Triomphe, 1km

Airports: Paris-Orly, 25km; Paris-Charles de Gaulle (Roissy), 30km

Category: Hotel

Deep in fashion district lies this intimate and beautifully appointed hotel that dates back to 1857. Relax in one of the lavish rooms adorned with exquisite fabrics, period furniture, works of art and colourful Italian marbles. Enjoy an afternoon tea in the delightful lounges, or a delicious meal in the cozy restaurant that feels more like a private dining room. The décor, together with the discreet service, create a sense of well-being.

Datant de 1857, cet hôtel intime et magnifiquement décoré se cache dans le quartier de la mode. Relaxez-vous dans l'une des somptueuses chambres ornées d'étoffes raffinées, de meubles anciens, d'œuvres d'art et de marbre italien coloré. Dégustez un thé dans les ravissants salons ou un délicieux repas dans le restaurant feutré aux allures de salle à manger privée. Le décor, associé à un service discret, offre un sentiment de bien-être.

En lo profundo del barrio de la moda se encuentra este hotel de bella e intimista factura que data de 1857. Podrá relajarse en alguna de sus fastuosas habitaciones adornadas de exquisitas telas, mobiliario de época, obras de arte y el colorido de sus mármoles italianos. Disfrute de su té de la tarde en sus encantadores salones, o de una deliciosa carta en su acogedor restaurante, tan parecido a un salón-comedor privado. La decoración, junto a su respetuoso personal, proporciona una sensación de bienestar.

LA TRÉMOILLE

14 RUE DE LA TRÉMOILLE, 75008 PARIS, FRANCE

Tel: +33 1 56 52 14 00 **Fax:** +33 1 40 70 01 08

Web: www.johansens.com/tremoille **E-mail:** reservation@hotel-tremoille.com

Our inspector loved: *The hatch in the bedroom, ideal for discrete room service!*

Price Guide: (room only)
double/twin €485-630
suite €700-1,150

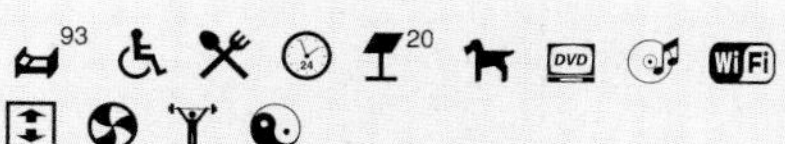

Attractions: Champs-Elysées, 5-min walk; Arc de Triomphe, 5-min walk; Eiffel Tower, 15-min walk

Airports: Paris-Orly, 25km; Paris-Charles de Gaulle (Roissy), 30km

Category: Hotel

This boutique-style hotel is the epitome of 21st-century elegance. Bedrooms are beautifully designed in muted tones with inspiring use of fabric, and public spaces house a superb collection of artwork. The restaurant and bar, Le Louis^{2}, a truly chic and elegant venue, is one of the hottest spots on Paris' Right Bank.

Ce boutique hôtel est la quintessence de l'élégance du XXIe siècle. Les chambres aux couleurs douces sont superbement décorées avec une utilisation véritablement inspirée des tissus. Les parties communes accueillent une splendide collection d'œuvres d'art. Le restaurant et bar Le Louis^{2} s'est d'ores et déjà imposé comme une adresse incontournable du "Triangle d'Or."

Este hotel de estilo tan distinguido encarna la elegancia del siglo XXI. Sus habitaciones están maravillosamente diseñadas a base de tonos tenues mediante un sugerente uso de la tela. Los salones comunes albergan una magnífica colección de obras de arte. El bar restaurante Le Louis^{2}, un lugar verdaderamente elegante, es uno de los sitios más de moda del "Triangle d'Or."

FRANCE / PARIS (ETOILE - PORTE MAILLOT)

Hôtel Duret

30 RUE DURET, 75116 PARIS, FRANCE
Tel: +33 1 45 00 42 60 **Fax:** +33 1 45 00 55 89
Web: www.johansens.com/hotelduret **E-mail:** reservation@hotelduret.com

This refined Parisian hotel prides itself on its extraordinary service and welcoming ambience. Soak up the city atmosphere before retiring to the inviting rooms decorated with bold splashes of colour and striking dark wood in cutting-edge styles. You'll enjoy the gourmet buffet breakfasts and the variety of cocktails served in the lounge bar.

Cet hôtel parisien raffiné peut s'enorgueillir de son excellent service et de son accueil chaleureux. Imprégnez-vous de l'atmosphère de la ville puis réfugiez-vous dans les chambres aux notes de couleurs chatoyantes contrastant avec le mobilier moderne en bois sombre. Vous apprécierez le buffet gourmand du petit-déjeuner et le choix de cocktails servis dans le bar lounge.

Este refinado hotel parisino se enorgullece de su extraordinario servicio y sugerente ambiente. Empápese del ambiente de la ciudad para luego retirarse a sus acogedoras habitaciones impregnadas de atrevidos salpicados de colores y sorprendente madera oscura de modernísimos estilos. Le encantarán los desayunos buffet-gourmet y la variedad de cócteles que se sirven en el salón-bar.

***Our inspector loved:** The dining room with its elegant table, ideal for breakfast meetings.*

Price Guide: (breakfast €16)
double €240-330
suite €450-470

Attractions: Arc de Triomphe, 10-min walk; Champs-Elysées, 1km; Concorde, 2.5km; Louvre Museum, 3km

Airports: Paris-Orly, 24km; Paris-Charles de Gaulle (Roissy), 27km

Category: Charming Hotel

HÔTEL LE TOURVILLE

16 AVENUE DE TOURVILLE, 75007 PARIS, FRANCE
Tel: +33 1 47 05 62 62 **Fax:** +33 1 47 05 43 90
Web: www.johansens.com/tourville **E-mail:** hotel@tourville.com

Our inspector loved: *The beautiful suites equipped with exceptional bathrooms.*

Price Guide: (breakfast €15, excluding VAT)
double/twin €180-270
junior suite €350-470

Attractions: Les Invalides, 2-min walk; Eiffel Tower, 5-min walk; Saint-Germain, 15-min walk

Airports: Paris-Orly, 20km; Paris-Charles de Gaulle (Roissy), 35km

Category: Charming Hotel

Within striking distance of the Eiffel Tower this neoclassical hotel is refined and tranquil, with a wealth of antique furniture and paintings gracing its salons and bedrooms. Guests will love the luxury toiletries in the marble bathrooms and the delicious breakfasts served in the vaulted cellar room.

A quelques pas de la Tour Eiffel, cet hôtel néoclassique est raffiné et tranquille; les salons et les chambres sont décorés de meubles antiques et de tableaux anciens. Les hôtes apprécieront les luxueux produits de toilette dans les salles de bain en marbre ainsi que les délicieux petit déjeuners servis dans la cave voûtée.

A corta distancia de la Torre de Eiffel, este hotel neoclásico rezuma refinamiento y tranquilidad. Dispone de un gran despliegue de muebles y lienzos antiguos que honran sus salones y habitaciones. A sus clientes les encantarán los lujosos tocadores de los cuartos de baño de mármol y los deliciosos desayunos servidos en su bodega abovedada.

Hôtel des Académies et des Arts

15 RUE DE LA GRANDE CHAUMIÈRE, 75006 PARIS, FRANCE

Tel: +33 1 43 26 66 44 **Fax:** +33 1 40 46 86 85

Web: www.johansens.com/hoteldesacademies **E-mail:** reservation@hoteldesacademies.com

Our inspector loved: *The amazing breakfast, and new tea room that serves a superb selection of teas and delicious Pierre Hermé macaroons.*

Price Guide: (room only, excluding VAT)
double €189-294

 20   

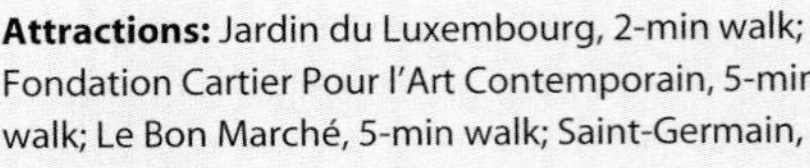

Attractions: Jardin du Luxembourg, 2-min walk; Fondation Cartier Pour l'Art Contemporain, 5-min walk; Le Bon Marché, 5-min walk; Saint-Germain, 10-min walk

Airports: Paris-Orly, 30-min drive; Paris-Charles de Gaulle (Roissy), 1-hour drive

Category: Charming Hotel

The owners of this boutique hotel are passionate art lovers and trusted artists Jérôme Mesnager and Sophie de Watrigant to "dress" their hotel. Jérôme's signature white bodies and Sophie's sculptures are truly captivating. 4 themes pervade the guest rooms: the Parisienne, the Comédienne, the Man Ray and the Ruhlmann. Each simple, stylish and striking all at once.

Les propriétaires de ce boutique hôtel sont passionnés d'art et ont donné carte blanche aux artistes Jérôme Mesnager et Sophie de Watrigant pour leur établissement. Les "corps blancs", signature de Jérôme, et les sculptures de Sophie sont absolument fascinants. Les chambres sont décorées sur 4 thèmes: la Parisienne, la Comédienne, la Man Ray et la Ruhlmann. Toutes simples, élégantes et fascinantes à la fois.

Los propietarios de este hotel boutique son los apasionados amantes del arte y han confiado a los reconocidos artistas Jérôme Mesnager y Sophie de Watrigant la misión de "vestir" su hotel. Los cuerpos blancos característicos de Jérôme y las esculturas de Sophie son verdaderamente cautivadoras. 4 son los temas que dominan en las habitaciones: el parisino, el comediante, el Man Ray y el Ruhlmann. Cada uno de ellos simple, elegante e impactante a la vez.

Hotel Banke

20 RUE LA FAYETTE, 75009 PARIS, FRANCE
Tel: +33 1 55 33 22 22 **Fax:** +33 1 55 33 22 23
Web: www.johansens.com/hotelbanke **E-mail:** banke@derbyhotels.com

Our inspector loved: *The amazing glass ceiling and the "Hispanic" atmosphere.*

Price Guide: (room only, excluding VAT)
double €580
suite €1,265

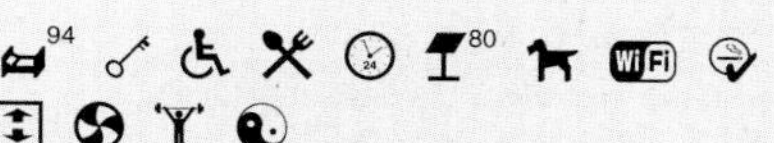

Attractions: Galeries Lafayette and Printemps Department Stores, 2-min walk; Opéra and Palais Garnier, 5-min walk; Louvre Museum, 10-min walk; Place Vendôme, 10-min walk

Airports: Paris Charles de Gaulle (Roissy), 30km; Paris Orly, 25km

Category: Hotel

Within a short walk of the city's leading department stores and the Opera House, this beautiful Parisian building is luxuriously and elegantly refined with a wealth of artwork from a variety of cultures. Guests will love this new hotel's "Eiffel" style design, avant-garde interior, the exquisite spacious bedrooms with dark wooden floors, superb lamps and spectacular panoramic views.

A quelques pas des grands magasins et de l'Opéra, ce magnifique bâtiment parisien est élégamment et luxueusement raffiné avec une abondance d'œuvres d'arts venant de nombreuses cultures. Les clients vont adorer ce nouvel hôtel dans le style "Eiffel" avec ses intérieurs avant-gardiste, ses ravissantes et spacieuses chambres aux parquets en bois foncé et aux vues panoramiques.

A un corto paseo de los famosos almacenes de la ciudad y de la Opéra, este bello edificio parisino está elegante y refinadamente decorado con todo lujo con un verdadero despliegue de obras de arte de las más variadas culturas. Los clientes quedarán seducidos por el estilo "Eiffel" del diseño de este nuevo hotel, sus interiores vanguardistas, sus exquisitas y amplias habitaciones de oscuras solerías de madera, espectaculares lámparas y excepcionales vistas panorámicas.

FRANCE / PARIS (ST~GERMAIN~DES~PRÉS)

HÔTEL DE BUCI

22 RUE DE BUCI, 75006 PARIS, FRANCE

Tel: +33 1 55 42 74 74 **Fax:** +33 1 55 42 74 44

Web: www.johansens.com/hotelbuci **E-mail:** reservations@buci-hotel.com

Experience the vibrancy of the Parisian lifestyle at Hôtel de Buci, a delightful hotel located in the heart of Saint-Germain-des-Pres, surrounded by old cobbled streets, shops and restaurants. Take time to admire the traditional French-style décor presenting beautiful fabrics and rare paintings, and enjoy a hearty welcome that will make your stay a memorable one.

Venez partager la foisonnante vie parisienne à l'Hôtel de Buci, un charmant hôtel situé au coeur de Saint-Germain-des-Prés, entouré de vieilles rues pavées, de boutiques et de restaurants. Prenez le temps d'admirer le style français traditionnel du décor avec ses magnifiques tissus et ses peintures originales et appréciez l'accueil chaleureux qui rendra votre séjour inoubliable.

Sienta la vitalidad de la vida parisina en Hôtel de Buci, un hotel encantador situado en el corazón de Saint-Germain-des-Pres y rodeado de antiguas calles adoquinadas, de tiendas y restaurantes. Admire la decoración tradicional francesa con sus magnificas telas y cuadros valiosos y disfrute de la calurosa bienvenida que hará memorable su estancia.

Our inspector loved: *Its ideal location in the heart of the lively streets of Saint-Germain-des-Prés.*

Price Guide:
single €195-235
double €220-435
suite €430-570

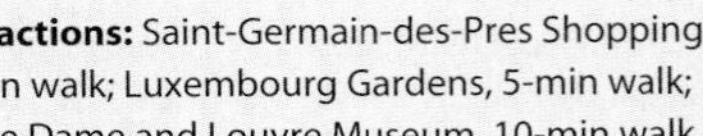

Attractions: Saint-Germain-des-Pres Shopping, 1-min walk; Luxembourg Gardens, 5-min walk; Notre Dame and Louvre Museum, 10-min walk

Airports: Paris-Orly, 25km; Paris-Charles de Gaulle (Roissy), 30km

Category: Charming Hotel

HÔTEL DUC DE SAINT~SIMON

14 RUE DE SAINT~SIMON, 75007 PARIS, FRANCE
Tel: +33 1 44 39 20 20 **Fax:** +33 1 45 48 68 25
Web: www.johansens.com/saintsimon **E-mail:** duc.de.saint.simon@wanadoo.fr

Our inspector loved: *The blue bedroom with view of the hotel's pretty Parisian town house garden.*

Price Guide: (room only)
double €225-290
suite €385-395

 34  

Attractions: Saint-Germain-des-Prés, 5-min walk; Musée d'Orsay, 10-min walk; Notre-Dame de Paris, 15-min walk

Airports: Paris-Orly, 15km; Paris-Charles de Gaulle (Roissy), 30km

Category: Charming Hotel

Just a small plaque indicates the existence of this elegant home-from-home, hidden in a quiet street in central Paris. Join the ranks of celebrities and Nobel Prize winners and seek sanctuary, as the focus is guests' well-being. Some rooms have private terraces, and you can enjoy a relaxing drink in the 17th-century wine cellar bar.

Une simple plaque indique l'existence de cette élégante maison, cachée dans une rue calme au centre de Paris, où l'on se sent comme chez soi. Rejoignez la liste des célébrités et Prix Nobel venus chercher refuge ici, car on y privilégie le bien-être des invités. Certaines chambres ont des terrasses privées. Vous apprécierez les boissons servies au bar situé dans la cave à vin du XVIIe siècle.

Sólo una pequeña lápida indica la existencia de esta elegante "segunda casa" que se esconde en una tranquila calle del centro de París. Únase a las filas de famosos y de ganadores del premio Nóbel y busque en él santuario, pues su meta es proporcionar bienestar a sus clientes. Algunas habitaciones disponen de terrazas privadas. También podrá Vd. disfrutar de una relajante copa en su bodega-bar del siglo XVII.

FRANCE / PARIS (ST~GERMAIN~DES~PRÉS)

LE BELLECHASSE

8 RUE DE BELLECHASSE, 75007 PARIS, FRANCE
Tel: +33 1 45 50 22 31 **Fax:** +33 1 45 51 52 36
Web: www.johansens.com/lebellechasse **E-mail:** info@lebellechasse.com

Behind a beautiful white classical façade is this feast for the senses: a Christian Lacroix designed interior bursting with colour, Bohemian spirit and innovation. Bedrooms are fantastical creations, designed to reflect one of 7 "universes" invented by Lacroix, inspired by the works of fictional novelist Jules Verne and many other free-thinking artists.

Derrière une magnifique façade classique blanche se cache un plaisir pour les sens: un intérieur décoré par Christian Lacroix offrant explosion de couleurs, esprit bohémien et innovation. Les chambres sont de fantastiques créations, décorées autour des 7 univers créés pas Lacroix et inspirés par les travaux du romancier de fiction Jules Verne et de nombreux artistes libre penseurs.

Tras una bella y blanca fachada clásica hay todo un festín para los sentidos: un interior con diseño de Christian Lacroix rebosante de color, espíritu bohemio e innovación. Las habitaciones son fantásticas creaciones, diseñadas para reflejar uno de los 7 "universos" inventados por Lacroix, inspirados en las obras del novelista Julio Verne y otros muchos artistas librepensadores.

***Our inspector loved:** The 7 different "universes" that take guests into different worlds.*

Price Guide: (room only, excluding VAT)
double €240-390

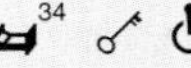   

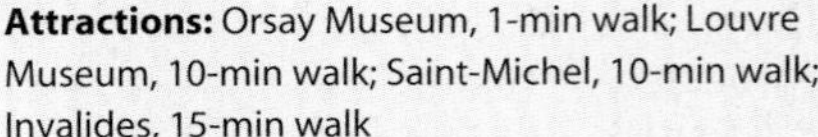

Attractions: Orsay Museum, 1-min walk; Louvre Museum, 10-min walk; Saint-Michel, 10-min walk; Invalides, 15-min walk

Airports: Paris-Orly, 25km; Paris-Charles de Gaulle (Roissy), 30km

Category: Charming Hotel

FRANCE / PARIS (ST~GERMAIN~DES~PRÉS) 

ODÉON SAINT~GERMAIN

13 RUE DE SAINT~SULPICE, 75006 PARIS, FRANCE
Tel: +33 1 43 25 70 11 **Fax:** +33 1 43 29 97 34
Web: www.johansens.com/parishotelodeon **E-mail:** reservation@paris-hotel-odeon.com

Our inspector loved: *The "plafond à la française" (beamed ceiling) in most of the bedrooms.*

Price Guide: (room only, excluding VAT)
single €195
double €260-330
junior suite €370

 27   

Attractions: Saint-Germain Church, 5-min walk; Notre Dame de Paris, 10-min walk; Panthéon, 15-min walk

Airports: Paris-Orly, 25km; Paris-Charles de Gaulle (Roissy), 30km

Category: Charming Hotel

Within walking distance of the Place Saint-Sulpice and church of Saint-Germain, designer Jacques García has created interiors that ooze intimacy, filled with warm colours, thick carpets, taffetas and velvets. Bedrooms are cosy while the breakfast/tea room overlooks a restful, tiny tree-shaded inner courtyard.

Proche de la Place Saint-Sulpice et de l'église Saint-Germain, le designer Jacques García a créé des intérieurs qui respirent l'intimité; remplis de tons chauds, de moquettes épaisses, de taffetas et de velours. Les chambres sont chaleureuses et la salle du petit déjeuner/salon de thé regarde la délicieuse petite cour intérieure arborée.

A un paso de la Place Saint-Sulpice y de la iglesia de Saint-Germain, el diseñador Jacques García ha sabido crear unos interiores que rebosan intimidad y cálidos colores, mullidas alfombras, tafetanes y terciopelos. Las habitaciones son acogedoras y su salón de desayuno/té, da a un pequeño sereno y umbrío patio interior arbolado.

FRANCE / POITOU~CHARENTES (LA ROCHELLE)

HÔTEL "RÉSIDENCE DE FRANCE"

43 RUE MINAGE, 17000 LA ROCHELLE, FRANCE
Tel: +33 5 46 28 06 00 **Fax:** +33 5 46 28 06 03
Web: www.johansens.com/residencedefrance **E-mail:** info@hotel-larochelle.com

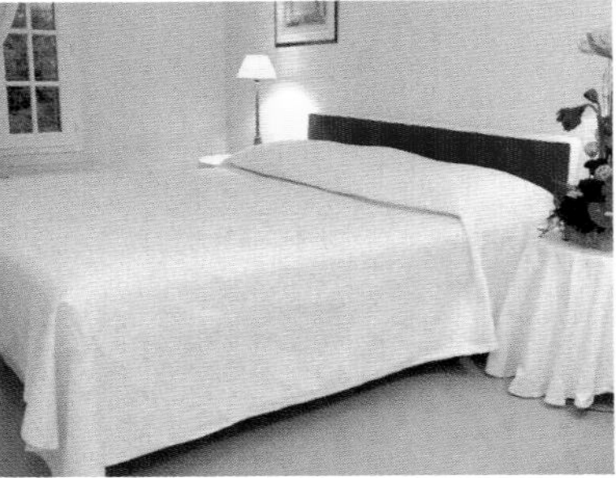

Our inspector loved: *The cool and spacious public rooms located around a peaceful courtyard with pool, fountains and mature trees, right in the middle of La Rochelle.*

Price Guide: (excluding tax)
single/double €110-170
suite €150-425

Attractions: Old Harbour, 5-min walk; Water Sports, 5-min walk; Maritime Museum and Aquarium, 10-min drive; Il de Ré, 30-min boat ride

Nearby Towns: Il de Ré, 8km; Rochefort, 34km; Niort, 54km; Cognac, 106km
Airports: La Rochelle, 5km

Category: Hotel

Set around a courtyard with pool and mature trees, this 16th-century stone building has been transformed into a retreat evocative of an art gallery, as there are sculptures, paintings and contemporary furnishings everywhere. A choice of classic, affordable dishes is available in the restaurant, and after a dinner of inventive cuisine based on local fresh fish and seafood, stroll along La Rochelle's harbour, with its famous 3 towers.

Construit autour d'une cour intérieure avec piscine et arbres anciens, ce bâtiment en pierres du XVIe siècle a été transformé en un refuge évocateur d'une galerie d'art car l'on trouve dans chaque recoin des sculptures, des tableaux et du mobilier moderne. Un chevalet expose les plats, classiques et abordables, qui sont disponibles au restaurant et après la dégustation d'une cuisine inventive à base de poissons et de fruits de mer locaux pour le dîner, promenez-vous sur le port de la Rochelle avec ses fameuses 3 tours.

Construido alrededor de un patio con piscina y arboles adultos, este edificio de piedra del siglo XVI ha sido convertido en un refugio que recuerda a una galería de arte, pues por todas partes se encuentran esculturas, cuadros y muebles contemporáneos. Sobre un caballete encontrara la carta con una selección de platos clásicos asequibles, y después de una cena inventiva a base de pescado y marisco fresco del lugar, puede pasear por el puerto de la Rochelle y ver sus 3 célebres torres.

La Coquillade

DOMAINE DE LA COQUILLADE, 84400 GARGAS, PROVENCE, FRANCE
Tel: +33 4 90 74 71 71 **Fax:** +33 4 90 74 71 72
Web: www.johansens.com/coquillade **E-mail:** info@coquillade.fr

Our inspector loved: *The 360° breathtaking views over the Luberon.*

Price Guide: (room only)
chambre de charme and junior suite €240-360
suite de charme and suite superieure €350-535
suite de luxe €470-1,210

Attractions: Garden of Arts with Amphitheatre, Walking, Hiking, Aureto Tasting and Vineyard Tours, Hire of BMC Mountain Bikes, Racing Bikes and Electric Flyer Bikes, on-site; Shopping, nearby

Nearby Towns: Apt, 5km; Roussillon, 8km; Lacoste, 13km; Bonnieux, 14km
Airports: Avignon, 38km; Marseille, 82km

Category: Hotel
Closed: January - mid-March

Surrounded by vineyards, this hillside hamlet has a long and successful Aureto wine producing history. Sample the produce in the wine tasting cellar or during a meal in one of the 2 restaurants: gastronomic and traditional. Chic bedrooms and suites feature high-tech, eco-friendly facilities; 2 large suites are located in a stone villa within the grounds. One has an outdoor Jacuzzi and the other boasts a private pool.

Entouré de vignes, ce hameau se dresse au sommet d'une colline et offre un long et glorieux passé de production de vins. Goûtez la production dans la cave de dégustation ou lors d'un repas dans l'un des 2 restaurants: gastronomique ou traditionnel. Les chambres et suites sont chics offrent des équipements de haute technologie et écologiques. 2 grandes suites sont situées dans villa en retrait du domaine: l'une est équipée d'un jacuzzi extérieur, l'autre d'une piscine privée.

Rodeada de viñedos, esta aldea situada sobre una colina, tiene una larga y celebrada trayectoria de producción de vino Aureto. Pruebe estos caldos en la bodega de catas o durante alguna comida en uno de sus 2 restaurantes: el gastronómico y o el tradicional. Las elegantes habitaciones y suites, ponen a su disposición instalaciones de alta tecnología y eco-amigables. 2 amplias suites, una con Jacuzzi exterior y la otra con piscina privada, se encuentran dentro de una villa construida en piedra que forma parte de la finca.

LA MAISON DU PARADOU

ROUTE DE SAINT~ROCH, 13520 LE PARADOU, FRANCE
Tel: +33 4 90 54 65 46 **Fax:** +33 4 90 54 85 83
Web: www.johansens.com/maisonduparadou **E-mail:** reservations@maisonduparadou.com

Formerly the village post house and now a private boutique hotel, Nick and Andrea Morris invite you to their unique retreat in the sunny south of France. Spend time on the shaded terrace, relax by the pool, watch a film in the library on its giant screen or visit the many local attractions that await your discovery.

Anciennement un relais de poste et dorénavant un boutique hôtel privé, Nick et Andrea Morris vous invite dans leur refuge unique dans le sud ensoleillé de France. Profitez des terrasses ombragées, relaxez-vous près de la piscine, regardez un film dans la bibliothèque sur l'écran géant ou visitez les nombreuses attractions locales qui vous attendent.

El que antaño fuera la casa de postas de la aldea es en la actualidad un hotel boutique privado. Nick y Andrea Morris les invita a su singular lugar de retiro en el soleado sur de Francia. Podran descansarse a la sombra en la terraza, relajarse junto a la piscina, ver una película en la biblioteca en pantalla gigante o visitar las numerosas atracciones locales que esperan ser descubiertas.

Our inspector loved: *The romantic "Secret Garden" room.*

Price Guide: (room only)
double from €265

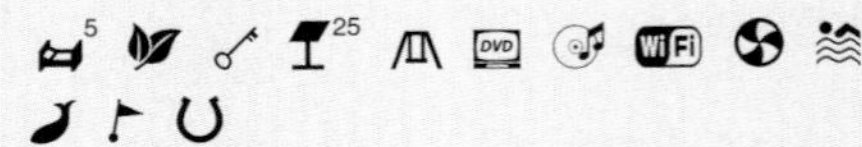

Awards: Condé Nast Traveller Hot List 2009; Tatler Travel Awards, Top 101 Hotels 2009

Attractions: Les Baux de Provence, 1km; La Camargue, 18km

Nearby Towns: Saint-Rémy-de-Provence, 12km; Arles, 17km; Avignon, 32km
Airports: Nimes, 25km; Avignon, 32km; Marseille, 42km

Category: Charming Hotel

DOMAINE LE HAMEAU DES BAUX

CHEMIN DE BOURGEAC, 13520 LE PARADOU, FRANCE
Tel: +33 4 90 54 10 30 **Fax:** +33 4 90 54 45 30
Web: www.johansens.com/hameaudesbaux **E-mail:** reservation@hameaudesbaux.com

Our inspector loved: *The beautiful setting, the amazing atmosphere and the feeling of exclusivity.*

Price Guide: (room only)
double €195-280
suite €270-545

Attractions: Les Baux-de-Provence, 5-min drive; Saint-Rémy-de-Provence, 10km; La Camargue, 30-min drive

Nearby Towns: Arles, 18km; Avignon, 30km
Airports: Nîmes, 47km; Marseille, 65km

Category: Hotel
Closed: During January and February

Tucked into the Alpilles Mountains this quintessential Provençal hamlet's farmhouse, barn, cottage, chapel and mill are built from local stone, and terraces lead from most guest rooms onto the garden. You'll sense that the Swiss owners have done their very best to create a "family home" ambience, with an eclectic mix of contemporary art and fabrics with period architecture, original wooden doors and furniture.

Situés au coeur des Alpilles, la ferme, la grange, la chapelle et le moulin de ce hameau typiquement provençal sont construits en pierre locale. Les terrasses de la plupart des chambres ouvrent sur le jardin. Vous comprendrez que les propriétaires suisses ont tout fait pour créer l'ambiance d'une maison familiale, en mêlant art et tissus contemporains à l'architecture d'époque, aux portes en bois et aux meubles originaux.

Situada en las montañas Alpilles, este prototipo de granja de aldea provenzal con su granero, casita, capilla y molino está totalmente construida en piedra de la zona, y las terrazas de la mayoría de las habitaciones dan al jardín. Percibirá que los propietarios suizos han echo todo lo posible para crear un ambiente de "casa familiar", utilizando una mezcla ecléctica de telas y arte contemporáneo con arquitectura de época, puertas originales y muebles antiguos.

FRANCE / PROVENCE (LE THOR)

La Bastide Rose

99 CHEMIN DES CROUPIÈRES, 84250 LE THOR, PROVENCE, FRANCE

Tel: + 33 4 90 02 14 33 **Fax:** + 33 4 90 02 19 38

Web: www.johansens.com/bastiderose **E-mail:** contact@bastiderose.com

This charming family-run guest house and cottage nestles on the edge of the River Sorgue. More like a friend's home, completely unwind and reside in a room or suite in the house or hire the cottage, located on the riverbank. Breakfasts are served on the terrace or veranda, whilst innovative, Mediterranean flavoured lunches and dinners are prepared upon request.

Cette charmante maison d'hôtes familiale et son cottage sont nichés sur les bords de la rivière Sorgue. Plus conçue comme une maison d'amis, relaxez-vous totalement et séjournez dans une chambre ou une suite de la maison ou louez le cottage, situé sur la berge. Les petits déjeuners sont servis sur la terrasse ou dans la véranda, tandis que des déjeuners et diners innovants aux saveurs méditerranéennes sont préparés sur demande.

Esta encantadora combinación de casa de huéspedes y cottage rural de regencia familiar se encuentra a orillas del río Sorgue. Siéntase como en casa de un amigo y relájese por completo en una de las habitaciones o suites de la casa, o bien alquile el cottage sito en la ribera del río. Los desayunos se sirven en la terraza o en la veranda, mientras que los innovadores almuerzos y cenas a base de sabor mediterráneo se preparan a petición del cliente.

Our inspector loved: *The interesting photos displayed throughout the house and the on-site museum that pays tribute to Pierre Salinger, the former owner, and the Kennedys.*

Price Guide: (excluding €1.16 local tax per person per night)
double €160-200
suite €200-280

Attractions: Pierre Salinger Museum and Exhibition, on-site; Isle-sur-la-Sorgue, 15-min drive; Festival of Avignon and Châteauneuf-du-Pape, 20-min drive; Festival of Aix, 45-min drive

Nearby Towns: Avignon, 20-min drive; Gordes, 30-min drive; Aix en Provence, 45-min drive
Airports: Marseille, 55-min drive; Nice, 2.5-hour drive

Category: Luxury Guest House
Closed: Mid-January - mid-March

L'Estelle en Camargue

ROUTE DU PETIT RHÔNE, 13460 LES SAINTES~MARIES~DE~LA~MER, FRANCE
Tel: +33 4 90 97 89 01 **Fax:** +33 4 90 97 80 36
Web: www.johansens.com/lestelle **E-mail:** reception@hotelestelle.com

Our inspector loved: *The new Jacuzzi with panoramic views over the lake.*

Price Guide: (room only, excluding VAT)
double €190-390
suite €290-570

Attractions: Camargue, on-site; Saintes-Maries-de-la-Mer, 5-min drive; Aigues-Morte and The Salins, 30-min drive

Nearby Towns: Arles, 30km; Montpellier, 45km
Airports: Montpellier, 50km; Nîmes, 65km; Marseille, 125km

Category: Hotel
Closed: 3rd January - 26th March and 21st November - 22nd December

Located in 7 acres of the wild Camargue and overlooking its very own lake, the setting of this gorgeous hotel is magical. The surrounding wildlife, including the well-renowned Camargue horses, is in full view from bedroom and bathroom windows, while the terrace has an amazing vantage point of the lake and pool.

Situé au cœur de 3 hectares de Camargue sauvage et surplombant son propre lac, l'emplacement de ce magnifique hôtel est magique. La faune et la flore environnantes, qui comprit les fameux chevaux camarguais, peuvent être observéer depuis les chambres et les fenêtres des salles de bain. La terrasse est un point de vue idéal sur le lac et la piscine.

Situado en 3 hectáreas del silvestre Camargue y con vistas a su propio lago, el emplazamiento de este espléndido hotel resulta mágico. Su fauna salvaje de sus alrededores, entre los que se incluyen los afamados caballos de Camargue, está al alcance de su vista desde su habitación y las ventanas del cuarto de baño. Su terraza dispone de un sorprendente punto estratégico desde el que contemplar el lago y la piscina.

FRANCE / PROVENCE (PORT CAMARGUE)

Le Spinaker

POINTE DU MÔLE, PORT-CAMARGUE 30 240, LE GRAU DU ROI, FRANCE
Tel: +33 4 66 53 36 37 **Fax:** +33 4 66 53 17 47
Web: www.johansens.com/spinaker **E-mail:** spinaker@wanadoo.fr

Our inspector loved: *The superb circular swimming pool surrounded by verdant greenery and boat masts.*

Price Guide: (breakfast €14)
comfort room €88-120
room with living room €99-149
suite €119-265

Awards: 15/20 Gault Millau

Attractions: Camargue, 5-min drive; Aigue Mortes, 10-min drive; Montpellier, 30-min drive; Nîmes, 40-min drive

Nearby Towns: Montpellier, 30km; Nîmes, 40km
Airports: Montpellier, 20km; Nîmes, 45km

Category: Charming Hotel
Closed: Hotel and restaurant closed during the Christmas week and 3 weeks in January.

In the heart of the marina lies this magical and charming oasis of greenery, pine and palm trees. Relax by the swimming pool whose water appears bluer than the nearby sea, and adjourn to your lovely individually-styled bedroom with décor inspired by Africa, Morocco or Provence and private terrace overlooking the harbour. The enchanting Carré des Gourmets restaurant invites you to discover the flavours of the South. New suites and a spa are due to open soon.

Au milieu du port de plaisance se cache un oasis magique et charmant rempli de verdure, de palmiers et de pins. Relaxez- vous près de la piscine dont l'eau semble être plus bleue que la mer voisine et profitez de votre chambre individuellement décorée avec des inspirations africaines, marocaines ou provençales et de sa terrasse privée qui donne sur la marina. Le restaurant Le Carré des Gourmets est un enchantement et une invitation à découvrir les arômes du sud. De nouvelles suites et un spa doivent ouvrir prochainement.

En el centro del puerto deportivo se ubica este oasis de vegetación, palmeras y pinos. Descanse al lado de la piscina, cuyas aguas son mas azules que las del mar, para luego retirarse a su encantadora habitación de diseño personal con inspiración africana, marroquí o provenzal, que se abre a una terraza privada con vistas al puerto. El restaurante Le Carré des Gourmets es un encanto y una invitación a degustar los sabores del sur. Dentro de poco se abrirán nuevas suites y un spa.

Château de Bagnols

69620 BAGNOLS, FRANCE

Tel: +33 4 74 71 40 00 **Fax:** +33 4 74 71 40 49

Web: www.johansens.com/bagnols **E-mail:** info@chateaudebagnols.fr

Our inspector loved: *The majestic restaurant, Salle des Gardes, and its 15th-century fireplace, France's largest gothic fireplace.*

Price Guide:
double €428-€655
junior suite €668-€760
château suite €792-€990

Awards: 1 Star Michelin; Condé Nast Traveller Gold List 2007; Fodor's Choice, Pudlo Award 2007

Attractions: Vineyards and Beaujolais Villages, on the doorstep; Lyon, 28km

Nearby Towns: Lyon, 28km
Airports: Lyon Saint-Exupéry, 50-min drive

Category: Hotel

Part of von Essen hotels and a Relais & Châteaux member, this 13th-century château, with soaring towers, moat, drawbridge and surrounding vineyards, is considered one of the most impressive hotels in France; our inspector says that it is simply beautiful. Restored to its splendour, its breathtaking historical features have been highlighted throughout, from the bedrooms to the dining room. The cuisine is exquisite.

Partie de von Essen hotels et membre de la chaîne Relais & Châteaux, ce château du XIIIe siècle, avec ses hautes tours, ses douves, son pont-levis et son vignoble environnant, est considéré comme l'un des hôtels les plus impressionnants de France ; notre inspecteur dit qu'il est tout simplement magnifique. Restauré afin de lui rendre toute sa splendeur, ses extraordinaires caractéristiques historiques ont été partout mises en valeur, des chambres à la salle à manger. La cuisine est incomparable.

Parte de von Essen hotels y miembro de Relais & Châteaux, este château del siglo XIII con vertiginosos torreones, foso, puente levadizo y rodeado de viñedos es considerado uno de los hoteles más impresionantes de Francia; nuestro inspector asegura que es una preciosidad. Ha sido restaurado en todo su esplendor y las impresionantes características históricas destacan en todo el edificio desde las habitaciones al comedor. La cocina es exquisita.

FRANCE / RHÔNE~ALPES (CONDRIEU)

Le Beau Rivage

2 RUE DU BEAU~RIVAGE, 69420 CONDRIEU, FRANCE
Tel: +33 4 74 56 82 82 **Fax:** +33 4 74 59 59 36
Web: www.johansens.com/beaurivage **E-mail:** infos@hotel-beaurivage.com

On the banks of the Rhône, close to the hills of Côte Rôtie, this former fishermen's house has been magnificently renovated and extended. Some rooms have a private terrace, and in summer you can eat Lyonnaise-style cuisine al fresco and enjoy some of the finest wines of the Rhône Valley.

Sur les rives du Rhône, près des collines de Côte-Rôtie, cette ancienne maison de pêcheurs a été somptueusement rénovée et agrandie. Certaines chambres possèdent leur propre terrasse privée. En été, vous pouvez goûter la cuisine lyonnaise en plein air et déguster les vins les plus raffinés de la vallée du Rhône.

A orillas del Ródano y cerca de las colinas de Côte Rôtie, esta antigua casa de pescadores ha sido magníficamente renovada y ampliada. Algunas de las habitaciones tienen terraza, en verano podrá disfrutar de la cocina al estilo de Lyon servida al aire libre y degustar los mejores vinos del Valle del Ródano.

***Our inspector loved:** The bedrooms with balconies overlooking the river.*

Price Guide:
double €155-200
suite €270-290

Awards: 1 Star Michelin

Attractions: Vineyards of Condrieu and Côte Rotie, on the doorstep; The Rigotte Fair (1st May), on the doorstep; Ampuis Wine Market (end of January), on the doorstep

Nearby Towns: Lyon, 35km; Valence, 75km
Airports: Lyon Saint-Exupery, 40km

Category: Hotel

FRANCE / RHÔNE~ALPES (LES GÊTS) 

Chalet Hôtel La Marmotte

61 RUE DU CHÊNE, 74260 LES GÊTS, FRANCE
Tel: +33 4 50 75 80 33 **Fax:** +33 4 50 75 83 26
Web: www.johansens.com/marmotte **E-mail:** info@hotel-marmotte.com

Our inspector loved: *The direct access to the slopes and the central location in the heart of the village.*

Price Guide: (half board, per person)
standard room €149-205
superior room €170-236
chalet €187-253

Attractions: Portes du Soleil Ski Area, on-site; Lac de Baignade, 1km; Golf des Gêts, 3km

Nearby Towns: Geneva, 55km; Chamonix, 60km; Annecy, 80km; Lyon, 185km
Airports: Geneva, Switzerland, 55km; Lyon Saint-Exupery, 170km

Category: Charming Hotel
Closed: Mid-April - end of June and end of August - mid-December

Family-orientated, this friendly hotel is set amid the beautiful alpine trails and ski slopes of the French Alps. Everyone will appreciate the range of activities on offer; if you're seeking an adrenaline rush you can ski, play golf or visit nearby Lac de Baignade. Guests seeking relaxation will love the hotel spa.

Idéal pour les familles, cet accueillant hôtel se situe au milieu des magnifiques sentiers alpins et des pistes de ski des Alpes françaises. Tous apprécieront la gamme d'activités proposées ; si vous recherchez des activités physiques, vous pouvez skier ou vous rendre au lac voisin de Baignade et ceux qui souhaitent se relaxer vont adorer le spa.

Este hotel acogedor, ideal para familias, se encuentra entre bellos senderos alpinos y pistas de ski en los Alpes franceses. Todos disfrutarán las diversas actividades que ofrece; los amantes del deporte pueden esquiar o visitar el lago Baignade y a los que deseen relajarse les encantará el spa.

FRANCE / RHÔNE~ALPES (LES MENUIRES)

Chalet Hôtel Kaya

VILLAGE DE REBERTY, LES MENUIRES, 73440 SAINT~MARTIN~DE~BELLEVILLE, FRANCE
Tel: +33 4 79 41 42 00 **Fax:** +33 4 79 41 42 01
Web: www.johansens.com/hotelkaya **E-mail:** info@hotel-kaya.com

Our inspector loved: *The spaciousness of the bedrooms and the superb family rooms.*

Price Guide: (half board, per person)
double room €168-201
junior suite €198-243
family suite or prestige €290-442

Grab your skis and head to the magnificent Three Valleys ski resort. Revel in the comfort of this exceptional chalet hotel where the use of natural materials has created a modish sanctuary amidst 25 peaks that span 600km of skiing. Enjoy the privacy of your spacious bedroom or suite while taking advantage of the inviting Lounge, Bar, Library and exceptional Le K restaurant.

Attrapez vos skis et rendez vous dans le somptueux domaine des Trois Vallées. Délectez-vous du confort de cet hôtel contemporain où les matériaux naturels ont créés un sanctuaire à la mode au coeur de 25 sommets qui couvrent 600 kms de pistes. Savourez l'intimité de votre chambre ou de votre suite tout en profitant de l'accueillant lounge, du bar et du délicieux restaurant Le K.

Coja sus esquís y diríjase a la magnífica estación de Tres Valles. Regocíjese en la comodidad de este excepcional chalet hotel, un santuario de moda creado con materiales naturales y ubicado entre 25 picos que abarcan 600 km de pistas de esquí. Deléitese en la intimidad de su amplia habitación o suite, pero disfrute también del acogedor salón, bar, biblioteca y de su excepcional restaurante Le K.

Attractions: Skiing at Méribel and Val Thorens, on-site; Snow Scooters, Lugelaud, 10-min walk; Dog Sleigh Outings and Farm Visits, 15-min drive

Nearby Towns: Annecy, 90km; Chambéry, 100km
Airports: Chambéry, 100km; Grenoble, 130km; Geneva, 130km

Category: Hotel
Closed: Mid-April - mid-December

Le Fer à Cheval

36 ROUTE DU CRÊT D'ARBOIS, 74120 MEGÈVE, FRANCE

Tel: +33 4 50 21 30 39 **Fax:** +33 4 50 93 07 60

Web: www.johansens.com/cheval **E-mail:** fer-a-cheval@wanadoo.fr

Our inspector loved: *The bar area with its cosy corners and roaring fire, ideal for lunch or tea and delicious home-made cake.*

Price Guide: (including dinner)
single €255-310
double €355-640
suite upon request

Attractions: Downhill and Cross-Country Skiing, on-site; Hiking Trails, Dog Sledding, Curling, Paragliding, Golfing, Casino, Historical Village and Vallée Blanche, 30km

Nearby Towns: Chamonix, 30km; Geneva, 70km
Airports: Geneva, 70km

Category: Hotel

Traditional chalets form this magical hotel within the heart of the Megève Ski Resort. After a day on the slopes, relax in the spa, retreat to the warm timber interiors with roaring fires and experience gourmet meals in the hotel's 2 restaurants. Special events can be arranged upon request all year round at the hotel's chalet, "Les Molliettes" located 1,500 metres up in the mountains.

Un ensemble de chalets traditionnels forme cet hôtel magique au coeur de la station de ski de Megève. Après une journée sur les pistes, détendez-vous dans le spa ou profitez des chaleureux intérieurs en bois, des beaux feux de cheminée et dégustez la cuisine des 2 restaurants de l'hôtel. Toute l'année, sur demande, découvrez le chalet d'alpage "Les Molliettes" à 1 500 m d'altitude où des événements spéciaux peuvent être organisés.

Este mágico hotel ubicado en el corazón del Megève Ski Resort está compuesto por cabañas tradicionales. Tras un día en las laderas, relájese en el spa, retírese a los cálidos interiores de madera provistos de chispeantes hogueras y saboree sus platos gourmet en los 2 hoteles del restaurante. Se pueden concertar celebraciones especiales a petición del cliente durante todo el año en la cabaña del hotel, "Les Mollietes", situado en plena montaña a 1.500 metros de altitud.

Château les Merles

TUILIÈRES, 24520 MOULEYDIER, DORDOGNE, NEAR BERGERAC, FRANCE
Tel: +33 5 53 63 13 42 **Fax:** +33 5 53 63 13 45
Web: www.johansens.com/lesmerles **E-mail:** info@lesmerles.com

Jan van Grinsven and his family invite you to stay at their dream home surrounded by the Liorac forest and Bergerac vineyards. Beyond the 19th-century façade, the interior will surprise you with its minimalist, modern elegance that is both cosy and intimate. A popular wedding venue and golfing destination, the château also offers exceptional dining at the gourmet La Bruyère Blanche and the relaxed al fresco Bistrot.

Jan van Grinsven et sa famille vous invitent à séjourner dans leur maison de rêve, entourée par la forêt de Liorac et les vignobles de Bergerac. Derrière la façade du XIXe siècle, les intérieurs vous surprendront par leur élégance minimaliste et moderne mais aussi accueillante et intime. Destination courue pour les mariages et le golf, le château propose également une cuisine exceptionnelle au restaurant gastronomique La Bruyère Blanche ou plus relaxé au Bistrot pour un repas en plein air.

Jan van Grinsven y su familia le invitan a su hogar de ensueño en medio del bosque Liorac y de los viñedos de Bergerac. El interior que se esconde tras su fachada del siglo XIX le sorprenderá por su minimalismo así como por su moderna, acogedora e íntima elegancia. Lugar muy de moda para celebraciones de bodas, el château ofrece comidas excepcionales en el restaurante gastronómico La Bruyère Blanche o al aire libre en el apacible Bistrot.

Our inspector loved: *The blend of warm informality, perfect service, chic décor and the traditional ambience of a Dordogne château.*

Price Guide: (breakfast €15)
room €120-185
suite €150-205
apartment €220-290

14 120 WiFi

Awards: 15/20 Gault Millau

Attractions: Cookery Lessons, on-site; Dordogne Châteaux, on the doorstep; Bergerac Wine Tasting, on-site and 5-40km

Nearby Towns: Bergerac, 12km; Sarlat, 65km; Bordeaux, 145km
Airports: Bergerac, 12km; Bordeaux, 145km

Category: Charming Hotel

Hôtel du Palais

1 AVENUE DE L'IMPÉRATRICE, 64200 BIARRITZ, FRANCE
Tel: +33 5 59 41 64 00 **Fax:** +33 5 59 41 67 99
Web: www.johansens.com/palais **E-mail:** manager@hotel-du-palais.com

Our inspector loved: *Watching the sunset over the Atlantic Ocean and Biarritz beaches from the magnificent rotunda restaurant.*

Price Guide: (breakfast €32-42)
single €300-375
double/twin €600-1,750
suite €600-4,000

Awards: Condé Nast Johansens Most Excellent European Spa Hotel 2008; 1 Star Michelin

Attractions: Water Sports, 2-min walk; Tennis and Squash, 15-min drive

Nearby Towns: Bayonne, 8km; Saint-Jean-de-Luz, 17km; San Sebastien, 50km
Airports: Biarritz, 5km; Bordeaux, 200km

Category: Hotel

You can't fail to be impressed by the auspicious history of this 19th-century residence, echoing proudly around marble pillars and chandeliers adorning its palatial foyer. Enjoy the antique furnishings and lovely surroundings, visit the chic bars, the 2 swimming pools, the vast heated outdoor sea-water pool and large indoor pool. Get pampered at the magnificent Guerlain spa and dine at the Michelin-starred restaurant.

Vous ne pouvez qu'être impressionné par l'histoire incroyable de cette résidence du XIXe siècle qui se reflète autour des piliers en marbre et des chandeliers qui ornent le hall de ce palais. Admirez l'élégant mobilier ancien, profitez des bars chics, des 2 piscines : l'immense piscine d'eau salée chauffée extérieure et la grande piscine intérieure. Faites-vous dorloter dans le magnifique spa Guerlain et dînez dans le restaurant étoilé Michelin.

No podrá evitar quedar impresionado por la fascinante historia de esta residencia del siglo XIX que transpiran con orgullo tanto sus columnas de mármol como las arañas de cristal que decoran el vestíbulo palaciego. Deléitese en el elegante mobiliario antiguo, tómese una copa en uno de los chic bares y disfrute de las 2 piscinas: la enorme piscina exterior con agua de mar climatizada y la amplia piscina interior. Dejese mimar en el magnifico Spa de Guerlain y cene en el restaurante galardonado con una estrella Michelín.

Great Britain

LUTON HOO HOTEL, GOLF & SPA

THE MANSION HOUSE, LUTON HOO, LUTON, BEDFORDSHIRE LU1 3TQ, ENGLAND
Tel: +44 1582 734437 **Fax:** +44 1582 485438
Web: www.johansens.com/lutonhoo **E-mail:** reservations@lutonhoo.com

Our inspector loved: *The splendour of the marble panelled Wernher Restaurant.*

Price Guide:
double £220-525
suite £395-850

Attractions: Cathedral City of St Albans, 20-min drive; Hatfield House and Gardens, 25-min drive; Knebworth House, 25-min drive; Woburn Safari Park, 30-min drive

Nearby Towns: London, 30-min train/metro; Milton Keynes, 30-min drive; Bedford, 30-min drive; Hitchin, 16km
Airports: Luton Parkway Train Station, 10-min drive; Luton, 10-min drive; Heathrow, 30-min drive

Category: Hotel

Centred around the Grade I listed Mansion House, this luxury hotel is the result of a loving restoration to one of Britain's greatest stately homes. No expense has been spared with the interior furnishings and the guest rooms have many original features including marble fireplaces and silk-lined and panelled walls. 2 restaurants, 2 bars, an 18-hole golf course and spa complete the 1,065-acre estate.

Manoir classé de Grade I, cet hôtel luxueux est le résultat d'une restauration attentionnée de l'une des plus extraordinaire demeure d'Angleterre. Rien n'a été oublié pour les aménagements intérieurs et les chambres possèdent de nombreux éléments originaux, notamment des cheminées en marbre, des murs tendus de soie et des boiseries. 2 restaurants, 2 bars, un golf 18 trous et un spa complètent cette propriété de 431 hectares.

Este hotel de lujo es el resultado de una cuidadosa restauración de Mansion House, una de las más espléndidas casas solariegas de Gran Bretaña, edificio protegido por considerarse patrimonio histórico. No se ha reparado en gastos en el mobiliario de su interior y las habitaciones poseen muchos de los rasgos originales, entre los cuales se incluyen chimeneas de mármol y paredes recubiertas de seda y madera. 2 restaurantes, 2 bares, un campo de golf de 18 hoyos y un spa completan esta hacienda de 431 hectáreas.

GREAT BRITAIN / ENGLAND (BERKSHIRE)

THE FRENCH HORN

SONNING~ON~THAMES, BERKSHIRE RG4 6TN, ENGLAND

Tel: +44 1189 692 204 **Fax:** +44 1189 442 210

Web: www.johansens.com/frenchhorneuro **E-mail:** info@thefrenchhorn.com

A superb base from which to explore the River Thames, this riverside hotel has offered hospitality for over 150 years. Conveniently located for London and Gatwick Airport, head to this romantic getaway where the mix of French and English cooking provides an unforgettable dining experience. Take the time to peruse the wine list, amongst the finest in Europe.

Base idéale pour explorer la Tamise, cet hôtel installé au bord de la rivière offre son hospitalité depuis plus de 150 ans. Commodément situé à proximité de Londres et de l'aéroport de Gatwick, il préside à une échappée romantique où le mélange des cuisines française et anglaise donne une expérience culinaire inoubliable. Prenez le temps de lire attentivement la carte des vins, réputée pour être parmi les meilleurs en Europe.

Una base perfecta para explorar el río Tamesis, este hotel lleva ofreciendo alojamiento y restauración a orillas del río durante más de 150 años. Convenientemente ubicado cerca de Londres y también del aeropuerto de Gatwick, es un lugar ideal para una escapada romántica donde la mezcla de cocina francesa e inglesa transformara su cena en una experiencia inolvidable. Tómese el tiempo también para estudiar la carta de vinos, que es una de las mejores de Europa.

Our inspector loved: *The warm and genuine welcome, and the beautiful grounds where the attention to detail is really quite remarkable!*

Price Guide:
single £125-170
double/twin £160-215

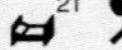 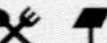   

Awards: 2 AA Rosettes 2007-2008

Attractions: Riverside Walk Along the River Thames, on the doorstep; Mapledurham House, 6km; Windsor Castle, 16km; Ascot and Legoland, 19km

Nearby Towns: Reading, 5km; Henley, 8km; Windsor, 16km; Oxford, 32km

Airports: London Heathrow, 32km; London Gatwick, 93km

Category: Charming Hotel

GREAT BRITAIN / ENGLAND (HAMPSHIRE) 

Tylney Hall

ROTHERWICK, HOOK, HAMPSHIRE RG27 9AZ, ENGLAND
Tel: +44 1256 764881 **Fax:** +44 1256 768141
Web: www.johansens.com/tylneyhalleuro **E-mail:** reservations@tylneyhall.com

Our inspector loved: *The outstanding service at this majestic country house hotel that offers the best afternoon tea in Hampshire!*

Price Guide:
double/twin £205-340
suite £385-500

Awards: AA 4 Red Stars; 2 AA Rosettes

Attractions: Antiques at Hartley Wintney and West Green House and Gardens, 7km; Jane Austen's House, 20km; Winchester Cathedral, 42km; Watercress Line Steam Railway, 48km

Nearby Towns: Basingstoke, 11km; Fleet, 18km; Farnborough, 19km
Airports: Farnborough, 19km; London Heathrow, 52km

Category: Hotel

Approaching floodlit Tylney Hall by night it's easy to imagine you're arriving for a party in a private stately home. The hotel is surrounded by rolling countryside, and the wood-panelled interiors create a cosy atmosphere that is enhanced by crackling open fires and lovely antiques. Dining is a treat, and the bedrooms are the ultimate in comfort.

En approchant Tylney Hall illuminé de nuit, il est facile d'imaginer que l'on arrive à une soirée dans une superbe demeure privée. L'hôtel est entouré d'une campagne vallonnée et les intérieurs en bois créent une ambiance douillette renforcée par le crépitement des feux de cheminées et de jolis objets anciens. Les dîners sont un vrai bonheur et les chambres bénéficient du nec plus ultra en matière de confort.

Cuando uno se acerca al iluminado Tylney Hall por la noche resulta fácil creer que llega a una fiesta de una mansión privada. El hotel está rodeado de ondulada campiña y sus interiores recubiertos en madera le proporcionan un ambiente acogedor intensificado por chispeantes chimeneas y encantadoras antigüedades. Las cenas son una delicia y las habitaciones son el último grito en confort.

GREAT BRITAIN / ENGLAND (LONDON)

JUMEIRAH CARLTON TOWER

ON CADOGAN PLACE, LONDON SW1X 9PY, ENGLAND

Tel: +44 20 7235 1234 **Fax:** +44 20 7235 9129

Web: www.johansens.com/carltontowereuro **E-mail:** JCTinfo@jumeirah.com

Located in the heart of Knightsbridge, the famously luxurious Jumeirah Carlton Tower boasts 220 rooms and suites, featuring panoramic city views. The Peak Health Club & Spa offers an indoor stainless-steel pool, a fully-equipped fitness facility, state-of-the-art Golf Simulator and spa treatments. Seek out The Rib Room's mouth-watering Aberdeen Angus beef or sip something sparkly at the exclusive GILT Champagne Lounge.

Situé au coeur de Knightsbridge, le fameusement luxueux Jumeirah Carlton Tower propose 220 chambres et suites offrant des vues panoramiques sur la ville. Le Peak Health Club & Spa offre une piscine intérieure en acier, une salle de gym parfaitement équipée, un simulateur de golf de premier ordre et des soins de Spa. Découvrez les délicieux steaks Aberdeen Angus du Rib Room ou dégustez quelque-chose de pétillant dans le très fermé GILT Champagne Lounge.

Ubicado en el corazón de Knightsbridge, el famoso y lujoso Jumeirah Carlton Tower ostenta 220 habitaciones y suites con vistas panorámicas de Londres. El Peak Health Club y Spa ofrece una piscina interior de acero inoxidable, un gimnasio totalmente equipado, modernísimo simulador del golf y tratamientos de Spa. Descubra los sabrosos filetes Aberdeen Angus que sirven en el Rib Room o beba unas burbujas en el exclusivo GILT Champagne Lounge.

Our inspector loved: *The relaxing spa and great location in the heart of Knightsbridge, perfect for business and pleasure.*

Price Guide: (excluding VAT)
double from £239
suite from £449

Awards: Best UK Business Hotel 2008, Condé Nast Traveller Readers' Travel Awards; Condé Nast Traveller Gold List 2007

Attractions: Harvey Nichols and Harrods, 5-min walk; Hyde Park, 1km; Buckingham Palace, 2km; Natural History Museum, 5-min drive

Airports: Knightsbridge Underground, 5-min walk; London Heathrow, 24km; London Gatwick, 48km

Category: Hotel

GREAT BRITAIN / ENGLAND (LONDON) 

Jumeirah Lowndes Hotel

21 LOWNDES STREET, KNIGHTSBRIDGE, LONDON SW1X 9ES, ENGLAND
Tel: +44 20 7823 1234 **Fax:** +44 20 7235 1154
Web: www.johansens.com/lowndeseuro **E-mail:** JLHinfo@jumeirah.com

Our inspector loved: *The exquisite Mimosa Bar & Restaurant, sampling the speciality cocktails, and dining at the Terrace.*

Price Guide: (room only, excluding VAT)
double from £199
suite from £349

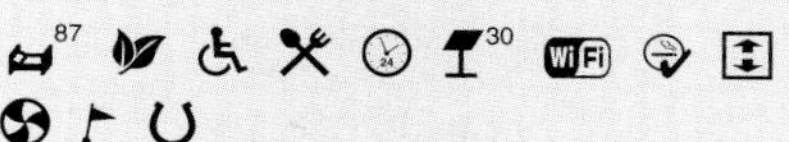

Attractions: Harvey Nichols, 3-min walk; Spa at Jumeirah Carlton Tower and Harrods, 5-min walk; Natural History Museum, 5-min drive; Buckingham Palace, 10-min drive

Airports: London Heathrow, 15 miles; London Gatwick, 30 miles

Category: Hotel

This chic boutique retreat in Belgravia offers 87 rooms including 14 suites complemented by the finest Temple Spa amenities. It is beautifully finished in contemporary design, enhanced by light and space to create an inviting and intimate atmosphere. The Mimosa Bar & Restaurant serves modern European cuisine with al fresco dining at the "Terrace" as well as brunch on Saturday and Sundays. Indulge in cocktails and light bites at the welcoming bar.

Ce boutique hôtel chic du quartier de Belgravia offre 87 chambres dont 14 suites auxquelles sajoutent les excellents équipements du Spa Temple. La lumière et l'espace mettent en valeur le splendide décor contemporain et créent une atmosphère intime et accueillante. Le Bar & Restaurant Mimosa sert une cuisine européenne moderne et des dîners en extérieur á la "Terrasse" ainsi que des brunchs les samedis et dimanches. Laissez-vous par des cocktails et des apéritifs à l'agréable bar.

Este elegante hotel boutique en Belgravia dispone de 87 habitaciones, 14 de ellas suites, que se completan con los mejores productos de tocador de Temple Spa. Un bello acabado en estilo contemporáneo saca el máximo partido a la luz y al espacio para crear un ambiente íntimo y acogedor. En el Mimosa Bar & Restaurant se sirve cocina moderna europea con la posibilidad de cenar al abierto en la Terraza, y ofrece "brunches" los sábados y domingos. Aprecie unos cócteles y las comidas ligeras que se sirven en el acogedor bar.

GREAT BRITAIN / ENGLAND (LONDON)

THE MAYFLOWER HOTEL

26-28 TREBOVIR ROAD, LONDON SW5 9NJ, ENGLAND

Tel: +44 20 7370 0991 **Fax:** +44 20 7370 0994

Web: www.johansens.com/mayflowereuro **E-mail:** info@mayflower-group.co.uk

Our inspector loved: *The first and second-floor bedrooms; so elegant and restful.*

Price Guide:
double £120-155
family room £130-195

 48  25  

Awards: 4 AA Rosettes 2007-2008

Attractions: Earl's Court Exhibition Centre, 2-min walk; Harrods and Hyde Park, 1.6km; Madame Tussauds, 4.9km; London Eye, 7.5km

Nearby Towns: Windsor, 34km; Oxford, 94km; Cambridge, 101km
Airports: London Heathrow, 21km; London Gatwick, 58km; London Stansted, 62km

Category: Charming Hotel

You'll struggle to choose your favourite feature of this stylishly renovated hotel: the Eastern influences, must-have modern technology, vibrant fabrics or Indian and Oriental antiques? Guest rooms are cosy and feature clever design that has maximised each inch of space to incorporate every modern amenity. Request one of the larger first-floor bedrooms for that little bit of extra luxury.

Vous aurez du mal à choisir ce que vous préférez dans cet hôtel rénové avec style - ses influences orientales, sa technologie moderne dernier cri, ses tissus vifs ou ses antiquités orientales et indiennes? Les chambres sont confortables et proposent un design intelligent où chaque centimètre carré a été maximisé pour incorporer tout l'équipement moderne possible. Demandez l'une des larges chambres au première étage pour ce petit luxe supplémentaire.

Le costará decir cuál es su característica favorita de este hotel elegantemente renovado: las influencias orientales, la tecnología de último modelo, las vivas telas o las antigüedades hindúes y orientales. Habitaciones acogedoras e inteligentemente diseñadas para aprovechar cada espacio, incorporan todas las comodidades modernas. Si desea aún más lujo, pida una de las habitaciones del primero piso que son más amplias.

GREAT BRITAIN / ENGLAND (LONDON) 

THE NEW LINDEN HOTEL

58-60 LEINSTER SQUARE, NOTTING HILL, LONDON W2 4PS, ENGLAND

Tel: +44 20 7221 4321 **Fax:** +44 20 7727 3156

Web: www.johansens.com/newlindeneuro **E-mail:** newlindenhotel@mayflower-group.co.uk

Our inspector loved: *The location, right in the heart of London's trendy Notting Hill.*

Price Guide: (room only, excluding VAT)
single £89-110
double £120-155
suite £130-195

 49     

Attractions: Whiteleys of Bayswater, 5-min walk; Madame Tussauds, 5-min walk; Hyde Park and Kensington Palace Gardens, 5-min walk; Portobello Road Market, 10-min walk

Airports: London Heathrow, 30-min train ride; London Gatwick, 1-hour train ride; London Stansted, 1-hour train ride

Category: Charming Hotel

Behind the beautiful white-fronted town house façade is a contemporary and chic interior. Stylish and utterly informal, this hotel very much reflects its lively and vibrant location. Compact and well-designed bedrooms mix Eastern beds with leather rugs, trendy fabrics and beige walls against accents of brighter colours. 2 of the first-floor bedrooms have balconies overlooking Notting Hill.

Derrière la jolie façade pâle de cette maison de ville se trouve un intérieur chic contemporain. Elégant et parfaitement informel, cet hôtel est à l'image de son emplacement, dans un quartier animé et plein de vie. Compactes et bien décorées, les chambres mélangent lits orientaux et tapis de cuir, tissus tendances et des murs beiges qui contrastent avec des accents de couleurs vives. 2 des chambres du premier étage ont des balcons qui donnent sur Notting Hill.

Tras la bella y blanca fachada principal de esta casa unifamiliar encontrará un refinado interior contemporáneo. Este elegante pero plenamente informal hotel es un verdadero reflejo de la animación y el bullicio del lugar en que se encuentra ubicado. Las habitaciones, bien diseñadas y compactas, combinan las camas orientales con las alfombras de piel y las telas modernas al tiempo que las paredes de color beige contrastan con otros tonos más vivos. 2 de las habitaciones del primer piso disponen de balcones con vistas al Notting Hill.

 GREAT BRITAIN / ENGLAND (LONDON)

TWENTY NEVERN SQUARE

20 NEVERN SQUARE, LONDON SW5 9PD, ENGLAND
Tel: +44 20 7565 9555 **Fax:** +44 20 7565 9444
Web: www.johansens.com/twentynevernsquareeuro **E-mail:** hotel@twentynevernsquare.co.uk

Sumptuously restored with an emphasis on natural materials, this elegant town house overlooks Nevern Square. Intimate bedrooms hint at Asian and European influences, and beautiful hand-carved beds are draped in natural linens, cotton and silks. The Ottoman Suite, with its white and cream colour scheme and striking use of turquoise accents, is a large, dramatic room with rolltop bath and 3 sets of French doors that look out to the square.

Somptueusement restauré en privilégiant les matériaux naturels, cet élégant hôtel particulier surplombe Nevern Square. Les chambres intimes ont des accents aux influences asiatiques et européennes et les magnifiques lits artisanaux sculptés sont garnis de draps en lins naturels, coton et soie. La Suite Ottomane, aux tons blanc et crème avec des touches marquées de turquoise, est une suite spacieuse et spectaculaire avec une baignoire à pieds et 3 portes-fenêtres qui donnent sur le place.

Suntuosamente restaurada con especial interés en los materiales naturales, esta elegante casa urbana, tiene vistas a plaza Nevern. Sus íntimas habitaciones sugieren influencias asiáticas y europeas con bellas camas talladas artesanalmente y revestidas con telas naturales en lino, algodón y seda. La Suite Ottoman, decorada en blanco y crema con acentos turquesa, es una habitación grande y dramática con original bañera y 3 puerta-ventanas que miran a la plaza ajardinada.

Our inspector loved: *The fantastic location opposite a quiet leafy square yet so close to central London!*

Price Guide:
double/twin £130-165
suite £275

Awards: 4 AA Rosettes 2007-2008

Attractions: Victoria and Albert Museum, 1km; Natural History Museum, 1km; Harrods and Hyde Park, 1.6km; London Eye, 7.5km

Nearby Towns: Windsor, 34km; Oxford, 94km; Cambridge, 101km
Airports: London Heathrow, 21km; London Gatwick, 58km; London Stansted, 62km

Category: Charming Hotel

GREAT BRITAIN / ENGLAND (EAST SUSSEX) 

Ashdown Park Hotel and Country Club

WYCH CROSS, FOREST ROW, EAST SUSSEX RH18 5JR, ENGLAND
Tel: +44 1342 824 988 **Fax:** +44 1342 826 206
Web: www.johansens.com/ashdownparkeuro **E-mail:** reservations@ashdownpark.com

Our inspector loved: *The open fires, and masses of fresh flowers throughout the public rooms.*

Price Guide:
double/twin £190-360
suite £400-445

Awards: 4 Red Stars; 2 AA Rosettes

Attractions: Bluebell Railway, 15-min drive; Lingfield Park Racecourse, 20-min drive; Wakehurst Place, 20-min drive; Hever Castle, 30-min drive

Nearby Towns: East Grinstead, 15-min drive; Haywards Heath, 15-min drive; Tunbridge Wells, 25-min drive; Brighton, 45-min drive
Airports: London Gatwick, 20-min drive; London Heathrow, 1-hour drive

Category: Hotel

A grand old character amidst acres of landscaped gardens, this 19th-century mansion has a charming, informal atmosphere. Bring out your romantic side and stay in a room with a four poster, and take your time over carefully compiled menus and good wines. Leisure facilities include an 18-hole par 3 golf course, woodland walks and spa.

Ancien édifice de caractère parmi des hectares de jardins paysagers, ce manoir du XIXe siècle possède une atmosphère charmante et informelle. Laissez parler votre côté romantique dans une chambre à lit à baldaquin et prenez votre temps pour découvrir les menus soigneusement compilés et les vins délicieux. Les activités de loisirs comprennent un parcours 18 trous par 3, promenades dans le bois et un spa.

Ejemplo de veterana grandiosidad sita entre hectáreas de paisajísticos jardines es esta mansión del siglo XIX, que ofrece un ambiente encantador y desenfadado. Dé rienda suelta a su vertiente romántica en una habitación con baldaquín y tómese el tiempo que desee para ver sus cuidadosamente elaboradas cartas de platos y buenos vinos. Entre sus instalaciones para el ocio se incluye un campo de golf de 18 hoyos, paseos por el bosque y un spa.

GREAT BRITAIN / ENGLAND (EAST SUSSEX)

THE GRAND HOTEL

KING EDWARD'S PARADE, EASTBOURNE, EAST SUSSEX BN21 4EQ, ENGLAND

Tel: +44 1323 412345 **Fax:** +44 1323 412233

Web: www.johansens.com/grandeastbourneeuro **E-mail:** reservations@grandeastbourne.com

A grand old Victorian dame with panoramic sea views, The Grand's majestic façade hides bedrooms of vast proportions, impressive leisure facilities and a good choice of restaurants and bars. The Mirabelle in particular excels itself when it comes to food. If you're seeking a peaceful retreat you'll slip easily into Eastbourne's tranquil atmosphere.

Vieille dame imposante offrant des vues mer panoramiques, la façade majestueuse du Grand Hôtel cache des chambres très spacieuses, d'impressionnants équipements de loisirs et un grand choix de bars et de restaurants. Le Mirabelle en particulier excelle sur le plan de la cuisine. Si vous êtes à la recherche d'une adresse tranquille, vous vous laisserez facilement emporter par l'atmosphère sereine d'Eastbourne.

Grandiosa y veterana dama provista de panorámicas vistas al mar, la majestuosa fachada del Grand Hotel esconde tras de sí habitaciones de vastas proporciones, impresionantes instalaciones para el ocio y una excelente selección de restaurantes y bares. El Mirabelle en particular se supera a sí mismo en lo que se refiere a su carta. Si desea Vd. encontrar un lugar de retiro tranquilo, no tendrá dificultades en integrarse con facilidad en la tranquilidad del ambiente de Eastbourne.

Our inspector loved: *The warm welcome, and extensive facilities for families with children.*

Price Guide:
double/twin £190-335
suite £380-535

Awards: 2 AA Rosettes 2009-2010; AA 5 Stars

Attractions: Beachy Head, 2km; Sovereign Harbour, 5km; Drusillas Zoo and English Wine Centre, 15km; Glyndebourne Opera, 20km

Nearby Towns: Lewes, 25km; Battle, 25km; Brighton, 35km

Airports: London Gatwick, 1-hour drive; London Heathrow, 2-hour drive

Category: Hotel

SERBIA
Pristina
Sofia
BULGARIA
Plovdiv
Edirne
BLACK SEA
Istanbul
Izmit
TURKEY
SEA OF MARMARA
Skopje
FORMER YUGOSLAV REPUBLIC OF MACEDONIA
Tirana
ALBANIA
Vlore
Komotini
Xanthi
Drama
Kavala
Alexandroupoli
Serres
Samothraki
Thasos
Thessaloniki
Kalamaria
Veroia
Polygyros
Katerini
Kosani
Limnos
Agios Efstratios
Lesvos (Lesbos)
TURKEY
Larisa
Ioannina
Trikala
Volos
Kerkyra (Corfu)
Skyros
Izmir
Antipsara
Chios
Lamia
Paxoi
Antipaxoi
Evvoia (Euboea)
IONIAN SEA
106
105
Lefkada (Leucade)
Chalkida
Samos
AEGEAN SEA
Andros
Athens
100
Ikaria
Tinos
Patra
Korinthos
110
Patmos
107
108
109
Mykonos
Kefallonia
Kea
Syros
Agios Georgios
Kythnos
Naxos
Kalymnos
Pyrgos
Paros
Kos
Symi
Rodos
Zakynthos (Zante)
Tripoli
Spetses
Serifos
Astypalaia
Sikinos
Ios
Tilos
Milos
112
111
Santorini
Rodos (Rhodes)
Kalamata
SEA OF CRETE
Karpathos
Kythira
Kasos
Kriti (Crete)
101
102
104
103
Chania
Irakleio
MEDITERRANEAN SEA
Gavdos

GREECE (ATHENS)

ROYAL OLYMPIC

28-34 ATHANASIOU DIAKOU STREET, 11743 ATHENS, GREECE
Tel: +30 210 928 8400 **Fax:** +30 210 923 3317
Web: www.johansens.com/royalolympic **E-mail:** info@royalolympic.com

Our inspector loved: *The spectacular view over the ancient Temple of Zeus from the Athenian rooms.*

Price Guide:
deluxe double €140-350
suite €650-850

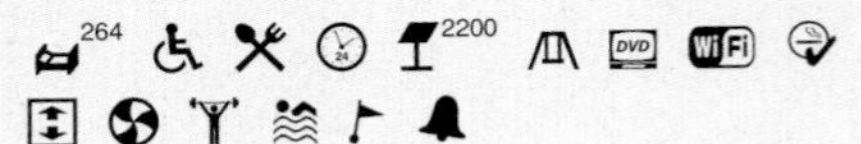

Attractions: Temple of Zeus, 50 metres; Shopping, 50 metres; Acropolis, 1km; Constitution Square (Syntagma), 5-min walk

Nearby Towns: Pireus (Old Town), 8km
Airports: Athens-Elefterios Venizelos, 27km

Category: Hotel

This is a magical place, not only because of its spectacular location but for its 21st-century modernity and opulent accommodation. Visit the Library overlooking the Temple of Zeus, relax at the Pool Bar or recline in the cosy Lounge Bar before enjoying superior food and carefully chosen wine at the Roof Garden Gourmet Restaurant, well known for its breathtaking view.

C'est un endroit magique, non seulement par sa situation exceptionnelle mais également pour sa modernité du XXIe siècle et son hébergement opulent. Visitez la Bibliothèque surplombant le Temple de Zeus, relaxez-vous au Pool Bar ou retirez-vous dans le confortable Lounge Bar avant de déguster la délicieuse cuisine et les vins attentivement choisis du Roof Garden Gourmet Restaurant, réputé pour sa vue époustouflante.

He aquí un lugar mágico, no sólo por su espectacular emplazamiento sino también por su modernidad propia del siglo XXI y por la opulencia de sus habitaciones. Visite la Biblioteca con vistas al Templo de Zeus, relájese en el Pool Bar, o en el acogedor Lounge Bar antes de disfrutar de una excelente cena y un vino meticulosamente escogido en el Roof Garden Gourmet Restaurant, lugar conocido por sus magnificas vistas.

GREECE (CRETE) 

DOMES OF ELOUNDA, ALL SUITES AND VILLAS SPA RESORT

ELOUNDA, 72053 CRETE, GREECE
Tel: +30 2310 810624 **Fax:** +30 2310 810634
Web: www.johansens.com/domesofelounda **E-mail:** info@domesofelounda.com

Our inspector loved: *The total luxury, and picture-perfect views.*

Price Guide:
suite €115-630
villa €420-5,040

Awards: 1 Star Michelin

Attractions: Archaeological Museum of Aghios Nikolaos, 15-min drive; Aghios Nikolaos Port and Lake, 15-min drive; Spinalonga Island, 10-min boat ride; Knossos Palace, 85km

Nearby Towns: Aghios Nikolaos, 8km; Heraklion, 75km
Airports: Heraklion, 75km

Category: Hotel
Closed: 1st November - 15th April

Standing high on a hillside setting, spectacular views of Spinalonga Island are seen from every direction. These spacious villas have large private terraces and pools, are fitted with high-tech amenities and contain modern furniture, natural light and colourful fabrics. Indulge in full spa treatments at Domes Spa, and fine dining in the restaurants or at the private jetty.

Grâce à une situation sur les hauteurs d'un coteau, on dispose partout de vues spectaculaires sur l'île de Spinalonga. Les spacieuses villas qui ont de larges terrasses et des piscines, possèdent des équipements high-tech et offrent meubles modernes, lumière naturelle et tissus colorés. Faites-vous plaisir avec les soins complets du Spa Domes Spa et un délicieux repas dans les restaurants ou sur la jetée privée.

Su emplazamiento en la cima de un paisaje montañoso permite la contemplación de espectaculares vistas a la isla de Spinalonga desde todas las posibles direcciones. Las espaciosas villas disponen de amplias terrazas y piscinas privadas, están provistas de instalaciones de alta tecnología así como de moderno mobiliario, luz natural y telas de generoso colorido. Disfrute de sus completos tratamientos de spa en Domes Spa, excelentes cenas en sus restaurantes o en su embarcadero privado.

GREECE (CRETE)

Paradise Island Villas

ARISTOPHANI STREET, ANISSARAS HERSONISSOS, 70014 CRETE, GREECE

Tel: +30 28970 22893 **Fax:** +30 28970 21655

Web: www.johansens.com/paradiseisland **E-mail:** info@paradiseislandvillas.gr

An island experience to savour: comprising elegant and stylish villas and a charming boutique hotel, this hillside location looks out to sea and mountain views. Celebrate a special occasion here at the unique pool area and stay in one of the villas where comfort and style are synonymous. Each features ethnic furnishings and luxury amenities as well as private pools, Jacuzzis and gardens. A true haven of relaxation.

Savourez l'expérience de la vie sur une île composée d'élégante villas stylées et d'un ravissant boutique hôtel dont l'emplacement à flanc de colline est tourné vers la mer et les montagnes. Célébrez une occasion particulière ici autour de la piscine et séjournez dans l'une des villas où confort et élégance sont synonymes. Chacune offre des meubles ethniques et des équipements luxueux ainsi que piscines privées, Jacuzzis et jardins. Un véritable paradis de relaxation.

Esta es una experiencia isleña para disfrutar que consta de elegantes chalets llenos de estilo y un encantador boutique hotel, ubicados en la ladera de una colina con vistas al mar y a la montaña. Un lugar ideal para celebrar un evento especial en la original zona de piscina, con estancia en uno de los chalets donde el confort y el estilo son sinónimos. Cada uno esta decorado con muebles étnicos y provisto de complementos de lujo, así como piscina privada, Jacuzzi y jardín. ¡Un verdadero oasis de relajación!

Our inspector loved: *Enjoying the serene atmosphere by the pool after watching the sunset.*

Price Guide: (excluding breakfast)
senior villa €229-376
executive villa €330-472
superior villa €436-592

Attractions: Traditional Villages of Old Hersonissos and Koutouloufari, 10-min drive; Crete Golf Club, 10-min drive; Aquarium, 15-min drive; Knossos Palace, 27km

Nearby Towns: Hersonissos, 2km; Heraklion, 20-min drive; Elounda, 40-min drive
Airports: Heraklion, 22km

Category: Charming Hotel
Closed: 31st October - April

Pleiades Luxurious Villas

PLAKES, 72100 AGHIOS NIKOLAOS, CRETE, GREECE
Tel: +30 2310 810624 **Fax:** +30 2310 810634
Web: www.johansens.com/pleiades **E-mail:** pleia@otenet.gr

Our inspector loved: *Each villa's privacy, comfort and luxury.*

Price Guide: (self-catering)
2-bedroom €212-497
2-bedroom superior €278-647
3-bedroom €283-684

Awards: Condé Nast Johansens Most Excellent European Guest House 2007; Luxury Family Hotel Winner, World Luxury Hotel Awards 2007

Attractions: Domes Spa at Domes of Elounda, 10-min drive; Old Town Cafés, Restaurants and Shopping, 5-min drive; Spinalonga Island, 30-min boat ride; Aquaworld at Hersonissos, 45km

Nearby Towns: Aghios Nickolaos, 3-min drive; Elounda, 10-min drive; Heraklion, 70km
Airports: Heraklion, 65km

Category: Luxury Guest House

Here you can treat yourself and friends to the quiet location and beautiful views over the Mirabello Gulf, as each villa sleeps 4-6 people and has spacious living areas, a fireplace, kitchen, dining room and pool. A daily maid service is included, and there is a gym, sauna and steambath. Condé Nast Johansens guests receive a complimentary bottle of wine and fruit.

Ici vous pouvez vous faire plaisir ainsi qu'à vos amis, grâce au calme de l'emplacement, aux vues splendides sur le golf de Mirabello, et parce que chaque villa, qui accueille 4 à 6 personnes, possède des espaces de vie très spacieux, une cheminée, une cuisine, une salle à manger et une piscine. Le ménage est fait quotidiennement et on y trouve un espace de gymnastique, un sauna et un bain de vapeur. Les hôtes qui se recommandent de Condé Nast Johansens reçoivent gratuitement une bouteille de vin et des fruits.

Aquí podrán Vd. y sus amigos disfrutar de un tranquilo emplazamiento y de bellas vistas al golfo de Mirabello, ya que cada villa puede alojar de 4 a 6 personas y disponen de amplio espacio, chimenea, comedor y piscina. Se incluye el servicio diario de limpieza de habitaciones a cargo de una doncella. Dispone asimismo de gimnasio, sauna y baños de vapor. Los clientes de Condé Nast Johansens son obsequiados con una botella de vino y fruta.

GREECE (CRETE)

St Nicolas Bay Resort Hotel & Villas

PO BOX 47, 72100 AGHIOS NIKOLAOS, CRETE, GREECE
Tel: +30 28410 25041 **Fax:** +30 28410 24556
Web: www.johansens.com/stnicolasbay **E-mail:** stnicolas@otenet.gr

Surrounded by flower-filled gardens with olive, lemon and orange trees, this exclusive, discreet and elegant hotel is set on a quiet seafront with private sandy beach. Savour a cocktail at The Blue Bay bar before dining in one of the restaurants where à la carte, Cretan and international dishes are available. Try the dreamy Poseidon Spa with Elemis treatments before retiring to your room or suite with private pool and stunning views.

Entouré de jardins remplis de fleurs, d'oliviers, de citronniers et d'orangers, cet hôtel exclusif, discret et élégant est installé au calme, en bord de mer, avec une plage de sable privée. Savourez un cocktail au Blue Bay bar avant de dîner dans l'un des restaurants où vous seront servis des plats à la carte, une cuisine crétoise ou internationale. Essayez le formidable Spa Poseidon et ses traitements signés Elemis avant de vous retirer dans votre chambre ou suite avec piscine privée et de somptueuses vues.

Rodeado de floridos jardines con olivos, limoneros y naranjos, este discreto, elegante y exclusivo hotel está situado al borde del mar en una tranquila playa privada de fina arena. Tome un cocktail en el bar The Blue Bay antes de cenar en uno de los restaurantes donde podrá elegir entre platos cretense, internacionales o a la carta. Visíte el ensoñador Poseidon Spa con tratamientos Elemis antes de retirarse a su habitación o suite provista de piscina privada y espectaculares vistas.

Our inspector loved: *The lush gardens, relaxed ambience and helpful staff.*

Price Guide:
classic double/twin sea view €250-470
classic de luxe suite sea view €340-650
executive suite with private pool and sea view €850-1,300

Attractions: Aghios Nikolaos Old Town Cafés, Restaurants and Shops, 5-min drive; Spinalonga Island, 30-min boat ride; Vai Palm Beach and Toplou Monastery, 65km; Knossos Palace Archaeological Site, 75km

Nearby Towns: Aghios Nikolaos, 2km; Elounda, 6km; Heraklion, 70km
Airports: Heraklion, 65km

Category: Hotel
Closed: November - April

Meli Traditional House

DRAGANO, 310 82 LEFKADA, IONIAN ISLANDS, GREECE
Tel: +30 69 4526 2123 **Fax:** +30 21 0710 0099
Web: www.johansens.com/melilefkada **E-mail:** info@meli-lefkada.com

Our inspector loved: *The chilled out ambience, and the beautiful courtyard with barbecue.*

Price Guide:
room €90-150
villa €200-500

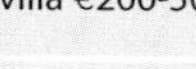

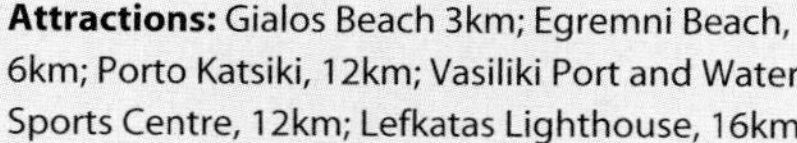

Attractions: Gialos Beach 3km; Egremni Beach, 6km; Porto Katsiki, 12km; Vasiliki Port and Water Sports Centre, 12km; Lefkatas Lighthouse, 16km

Nearby Towns: Vasiliki, 12km; Lefkada, 35km
Airports: Harbour and Ferry, 12km; Aktion/Preveza Airport, 48km

Category: Luxury Guest House

Built from local stone and wood, this traditional mansion is surrounded by natural forest, mountains and farmland. The interiors are full of character, using earthy colours and a wonderful combination of rustic charm and modern convenience. You will love the thoughtful attention to detail and the traditional wood-burning stove and built-in barbecue that are perfect for outdoor dining.

Construit à partir de pierres et de bois locaux, cette demeure traditionnelle est entourée de forêt naturelle, de montagnes et de terres fermières. Les intérieurs sont empreint de caractère, avec des couleurs de terre et un mélange ravissant de charme rustique et d'équipement moderne. Vous adorerez les délicates attentions aux détails et le four à bois traditionnel et le barbecue encastré sont parfaits pour les dîners en extérieur.

Construida con madera y piedra del lugar, esta tradicional mansión está rodeada de un bosque natural, montañas y tierras de labranza. Los interiores son de una gran personalidad a base de colores sencillos y de una maravillosa combinación entre el encanto rústico y las comodidades modernas. Le encantarán el esmerado gusto por el detalle, el horno de leña tradicional así como su incorporada barbacoa ideales para una cena al aire libre.

GREECE (LEFKADA)

Pavezzo Country Retreat

KATOUNA, LEFKADA, IONIAN ISLANDS, GREECE
Tel: +30 26450 71782 **Fax:** +30 26450 71800
Web: www.johansens.com/pavezzo **E-mail:** info@pavezzo.gr

Pavezzo means "home of the good life," and you certainly get a taste of that here. The 9 restored Venetian houses and honeymoon villa with private pool, are perfect for a romantic break or a relaxing few days away. In the restaurant, Chef Mrs Evi Voutsina creates gourmet meals. The beautiful island of Lefkada is just a walk away.

Pavezzo signifie "maison de la bonne vie" et vous en goûterez certainement la saveur ici. Les 9 maisons vénitiennes restaurées et la villa dédiée aux lunes de miel avec sa piscine privée, sont parfaites pour une halte romantique ou un séjour au calme. Dans le restaurant, la chef, Madame Evi Voutsina, crée des plats gastronomiques. La magnifique île de Lefkada se situe tout près.

Pavezzo significa "hogar de la buena vida" y seguro que aquí lo va a notar. Las 9 casas venecianas restauradas y la villa "luna de miel" con piscina privada son perfectas para un descanso romántico o para relajarse unos días. La chef Sra. Evi Voutsina crea comidas gourmet en el restaurante. La hermosa isla de Lefkada está a tan sólo un paso de aquí.

Our inspector loved: *The small but fully-equipped wellness centre, with its charming mini-splash pool.*

Price Guide:
suite €105-370

9 50

Attractions: Skorpios, Private Island of Aristotelis Onasis, 10-min boat ride; Meganisi, Kalamos and Kastos Sailing, 15-min drive; Porto Katsiki Award-Winning Beaches, Egremnoi, Kathisma and Archaeological Site of Nikopolis, 40-min drive; Ithaca and Kefalonia Islands, 75-min boat ride

Nearby Towns: Katouna Village, 5-min walk; Ligia Village, 5-min drive; Lefkada, 15-min drive
Airports: Aktion Preveza, 30-min drive

Category: Charming Hotel
Closed: October - April

APANEMA

TAGOO, MYKONOS, GREECE
Tel: +30 22890 28590 **Fax:** +30 22890 79250
Web: www.johansens.com/apanema **E-mail:** mail@apanemaresort.com

Our inspector loved: *The relaxed and comfortable atmosphere. The Mykonos sunset is not to be missed!*

Price Guide:
single €135-240
double €150-330
suite €250-525

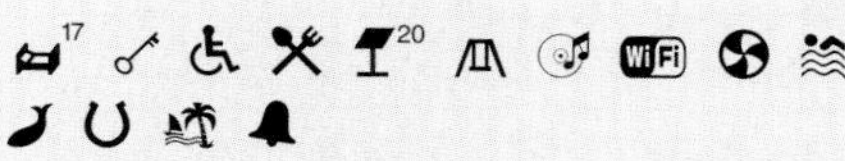

Attractions: Little Venice, 10-min walk; Mykonos Centre, Restaurants and Night-life, 10-min walk; Ornos Bay, 10-min drive; Paradise Beach, 15-min drive

Nearby Towns: Delos Island, 20-min boat ride
Airports: Mykonos, 5-min drive

Category: Charming Hotel
Closed: November - April

If you prefer a more private, bijou location, this boutique hotel is a retreat from the island's vibrant lifestyle. A very homely and casual place, Apanema is set on the waterfront and enjoys amazing views of the sunsets. Bedrooms offer all the amenities of a large hotel, including a choice of a soft or hard mattress, Azzaro or Molton Brown bath products, and breakfast is served until 1pm.

Si vous préférez un emplacement exclusif et ravissant, ce boutique hôtel est un refuge intime loin de la vie trépidante de l'île. Très accueillant et relaxant, Apanema est situé en bord de mer et offre de superbes couchers de soleil. Les chambres ont tous les services d'un grand hôtel tels que le choix d'un matelas dur ou mou, des produits de salle de bain Azzaro ou Molton Brown et le petit-déjeuner servi jusqu'à 13 heures.

Si prefiere un enclave de ensueño más íntimo, este hotel boutique constituye un lugar de retiro del bullicioso ambiente de la isla. Apanema, acogedor y relajado, esta ubicado en primera línea de playa y sus crepúsculos son impresionantes. Las habitaciones proporcionan todas las comodidades de un gran hotel, como la elección de colchones blandos o duros, productos para el baño Azzaro o Molton Brown y servicio de desayunos hasta las 1 de la tarde.

GREECE (MYKONOS)

Cavo Tagoo Hotel

84600 MYKONOS, GREECE
Tel: +30 22890 20100 **Fax:** +30 22890 20150
Web: www.johansens.com/cavotagoo **E-mail:** reservations@cavotagoo.gr

A unique, high-class hotel in which to relax and be seen. Considered by some to shortly become a status symbol, this haven of luxury is built into an impressive cliff-side. Oozing style and elegance that encompasses a certain chicness and accommodation minimalism, upscale service, a spa, private pools and Jacuzzi tubs are yours to enjoy.

Un hôtel unique et haut de gamme dans lequel se relaxer et être vu. Ce havre de luxe est construit à flanc de falaise et certains considèrent qu'il deviendra bientôt une marque de prestige. Débordant de classe et d'élégance avec une pointe de chic et un hébergement minimaliste, le service de premier ordre, le spa, les piscines privées et les jacuzzis n'attendent que vous.

Un hotel de primera clase y único donde podrá relajarse y ser visto. Los hay que piensan que está cerca de convertirse en todo un símbolo de clase. Este paraíso del lujo está construido en la ladera de un impresionante acantilado. Su rebosante estilo y elegancia van paralelos a su cierta distinción. El minimalismo de sus alojamientos junto a un servicio exclusivo, el spa, las piscinas privadas y las bañeras jacuzzi están a disposición para disfrute del cliente.

Our inspector loved: *The chic pool area.*

Price Guide: (includes American buffet breakfast)
classic room €240-480
deluxe room €290-590
golden villa with pool €760-2,500

80 SPA

Attractions: Bars and Restaurants, Clubs and Shops, 10-min walk; Beaches, 15-min drive; Panagia Paraportiani Church, 15-min walk; Little Venice, 20-min walk

Nearby Towns: Mykonos Town, 10-min walk; Delos, 30-min boat ride
Airports: Mykonos, 8-min drive

Category: Charming Hotel
Closed: November - April

THARROE OF MYKONOS

MYKONOS TOWN, ANGELICA, 84600 MYKONOS, GREECE
Tel: +30 22890 27370 **Fax:** +30 22890 27375
Web: www.johansens.com/tharroe **E-mail:** info@tharroeofmykonos.gr

Our inspector loved: *The home-away-from-home feeling, and friendly, cheerful staff.*

Price Guide:
single €115-350
double €125-450
suite €195-1,500

Attractions: Ornos Beaches, 5-min drive; Little Venice, 5-min drive; Archaeological Museum, 5-min drive; Mykonos Night-life, 5-min drive

Nearby Towns: Delos Island, 20-min boat ride
Airports: Mykonos, 5-min drive

Category: Hotel
Closed: November - April

This hilltop hotel enjoys breathtaking sunsets over the Aegean. Savour views of the town from the recently renovated breakfast room, and in the evening sample traditional Greek and Mediterranean cuisine with organic wines in the Barbarossa restaurant. The newly refurbished bedrooms have Jacuzzis and luxurious amenities. And Calypso Well Being Salon offers an extended menu of treatments.

Cet hôtel au sommet d'une colline, offre des couchers de soleil sur la mer Egée à couper le souffle. Admirez les vues sur la ville depuis la salle du petit-déjeuner récemment rénovée, et dans la soirée, goûtez la cuisine traditionnelle grecque et méditerranéenne et les vins biologiques au restaurant Barbarossa. Les chambres, récemment redécorées, ont des jacuzzis et des aménagements luxueux. Le Calypso Well Being Salon propose un large éventail de soins de beauté et de traitements.

Este hotel situado sobre una colina y deleita a sus huéspedes con espectaculares puestas de sol al mar Egeo. Paladee vistas de la ciudad desde comedor de desayunos recientemente renovado, y por la noche pruebe la tradicional cocina griega y mediterránea acompañada de vinos ecológicos en el restaurante Barbarossa. Las habitaciones recientemente reformadas, disponen de jacuzzis y lujosos productos de tocador. El Calypso Well Being Salon ofrece una amplia variedad de tratamientos.

GREECE (PATMOS)

PETRA HOTEL

GRIKOS, 85500 PATMOS, GREECE

Tel: +30 22470 34020 **Fax:** +30 22470 32567

Web: www.johansens.com/petrahotel **E-mail:** info@petrahotel-patmos.com

Discover Petra Hotel, Patmos' best kept secret, situated in the peaceful fishing village of Grikos. Overlooking breathtaking sea views, the stylish interior combines traditional whitewashed walls with simple, luxury details. Its décor features exquisite textiles and unique artifacts. You'll also enjoy the home-made breakfasts and dinners, served on the main terrace with even more spectacular views!

Découvrez l'Hôtel Petra, le secret le mieux gardé de Patmos, situé au paisible village de pêcheurs de Grikos. Offrant des vues exceptionnelles sur la mer, l'intérieur élégant associe murs de chaux blancs traditionnels et détails simples et luxueux. Sa décoration est composée de textiles délicats et d'objets d'art unique. Vous apprécierez également les petits-déjeuners et repas faits maison, servis sur la terrasse qui offre encore d'autres vues spectaculaires !

Descubra el secreto mejor guardado de Patmos: el Petra Hotel, situado en el tranquilo pueblo pesquero de Grikos. Con una vista impresionante al mar, el elegante interior del hotel combina sus muros blanqueados con sencillos y lujosos detalles. La decoración muestra exquisitas telas y piezas únicas. Asimismo disfrutará de los desayunos y cenas caseras que se sirven en la terraza principal de donde se puede contemplar aún más vistas espectaculares.

Our inspector loved: *The romantic atmosphere and personal service.*

Price Guide:
de luxe double €175-275
suite €220-580

Attractions: Grikos Beach, 70 metres; Monastery of St John, 4km; Cave of the Apocalypse, 7km; Island Hopping by Private Boat

Nearby Towns: Chora, 4km; Skala, 4.5km
Airports: Leros, Kos, and Samos, 40-min flight from Athens and 1-2.5-hour boat connection to Patmos

Category: Charming Hotel
Closed: November - April

Andronis Luxury Suites

OIA, 84702 SANTORINI, GREECE
Tel: +30 22860 72041/2/3 **Fax:** +30 22860 72044
Web: www.johansens.com/andronissuites **E-mail:** info@andronis-suites.com

Our inspector loved: *The friendly welcome, and very romantic atmosphere.*

Price Guide:
suite €460-2,000

Awards: Top 10 Lists, World's Best Cliff-side Hotels, Luxury Travel Magazine 2009; Condé Nast Traveller Hot List 2008

Attractions: Naval Museum, 2-min walk; Ammudi Seaside Restaurants, 5-min drive; Nea Kammeni, 10-min boat ride

Nearby Towns: Oia, 1-min walk; Fira, 30-min drive
Airports: Santorini, 35-min drive; Port, 40-min drive

Category: Charming Hotel
Closed: November - March

The ideal honeymoon destination or romantic break, this cliff-top boutique hotel has it all: style, intimacy, comfort and stunning panoramic views. Not to mention tasteful furnishings and discreet, personalised service. Practising an "organic philosphy," all meals are created from unprocessed ingredients, mini-bars are stocked with natural soft drinks and the pool is chlorine free. Relax at the spa or browse in nearby shops and art galleries.

Idéal pour une lune de miel ou un séjour romantique, ce boutique hôtel situé au sommet d'une colline, possède tout ce qu'il faut: style, intimité, confort et de magnifiques vues panoramiques. Sans parler de l'élégant et impeccable mobilier ou du service personnalisé. Suivant la «philosophie biologique», tous les plats sont réalisés à partir d'ingrédients non traités, les minis bars sont remplis de boissons naturelles et la piscine est sans chlore. Relaxez-vous dans le spa ou promenez-vous dans les boutiques et galeries d'arts voisines.

El lugar ideal para su luna de miel o para una escapada romántica, este boutique hotel lo tiene todo: estilo, intimidad, confort y espectaculares vistas panorámicas paro no hablar del atractivo mobiliario e el servicio discreto y personalizado. Fieles a la filosofía orgánica, todas las comidas son elaboradas con ingredientes sin procesar, los mini-bars contienen zumos naturales y la piscina no contiene cloro. Relájese en el Spa o de un paseo por las tiendas y galerías de arte cercanas.

GREECE (SANTORINI)

IKIES TRADITIONAL HOUSES

OIA, 84702 SANTORINI, GREECE
Tel: +30 22860 71311 **Fax:** +30 22860 71953
Web: www.johansens.com/ikies **E-mail:** info@ikies.com

Our inspector loved: *Breakfast, which is a real feast! The views are stunning and the staff are just fantastic.*

Price Guide:
studio €200-465
maisonette €300-415
suite €450-1,200

Designed in the traditional multi-level Greek way, Ikies commands spectacular views from exclusive stone-carved hideaways in the Caldera cliffs. This is an intimate and romantic place where the service is discrete and personalised. Tastefully and impeccably furnished accommodations are available in 3 categories: apartments, maisonettes and suites. Thinking of where to spend your honeymoon? Think no more...

Conçu sur plusieurs niveaux, à la manière grecque traditionnelle, Ikies dispose de vues spectaculaires depuis ses "refuges" creusés dans la roche de la Caldera. C'est un endroit intime et romantique où le service est discret et personnalisé. Meublés impeccablement et avec goût, les hébergements sont disponibles en 3 catégories : appartements, maisonnettes et suites. Vous réfléchissiez à l'endroit où vous alliez passer votre lune de miel ? Vous avez trouvé…

Diseñadas al estilo multinivel griego tradicional, Ikies dispone de espectaculares vistas desde las peculiares cuevas esculpidas en piedra situadas en los acantilados de Caldera. Se trata de un lugar íntimo y romántico con un servicio discreto y personalizado. Los alojamientos, amueblados con elegante e impecable gusto, están a su disposición en tres categorías: apartamentos, duplex y suites. ¿Está pensando dónde pasar su luna de miel? No lo piense más…

Attractions: Ammoudi Beach, 20-min walk; Wineries, 10-min drive; Boat Trip to Volcano from Port, 15-min boat ride; Akrotiri, 40-min drive

Nearby Towns: Imerovigli, 8km; Firostefani, 10km; Fira, 12km
Airports: Santorini, 18km; Athinios Port, 22km

Category: Charming Hotel
Closed: November - March

POLAND
Budapest
Budapest
II. kerület
Budapest
VI. kerület
114
Budapest VII. kerület
Budapest
XII. kerület
Budapest
IX. kerület
Budapest
XI. kerület
Kraków
CZECH
REPUBLIC
Kofice
UKRAINE
SLOVAKIA
Miskolc
Nyíregyháza
Eger
BRATISLAVA
VIENNA
Debrecen
Gyor
Tatabánya
BUDAPEST
Sopron
Szolnok
Oradea
AUSTRIA
Székesfehérvár
Kecskemét
Szombathely
Veszprém
Dunaújváros
Békéscsaba
Lake Balaton
Zalaegerszeg
Hódmezovásárhely
Szeged
Kaposvár
ROMANIA
Timiçoara
Pécs
Koprivnica
ZAGREB
Osijek
SERBIA
CROATIA
Novi Sad
Karlovac
Vukovar
BELGRADE
BOSNIA-HERZEGOVINA
SARAJEVO

HUNGARY (BUDAPEST)

CORINTHIA HOTEL BUDAPEST

ERZSÉBET KORUT 43-49, 1073 BUDAPEST, HUNGARY
Tel: +36 1 479 4000 **Fax:** +36 1 479 4333
Web: www.johansens.com/corinthiabudapest **E-mail:** budapest@corinthia.com

Enter this imposing hotel beyond the beautiful façade through to an equally spectacular interior where tradition and elegance meets the 21st-century. Behind the hotel is the Royal Residence, a complex of modern apartments perfect for longer stays. The breathtaking, state-of-the-art spa first opened here in 1886 and is now restored to its full glory.

Pénétrez dans cet imposant hôtel et retrouvez derrière la magnifique façade un intérieur spectaculaire où la tradition et l'élégance rencontre le XXIe siècle. Derrière l'hôtel se trouve la Royal Residence, un complexe d'appartements modernes parfaitement adaptés aux longs séjours. Le somptueux spa, à la pointe de la technologie, ouvert en 1986, a été complètement rénové.

Cruce la bella fachada de este imponente hotel y entre a un interior no menos espectacular donde la tradición y la elegancia se dan cita con el siglo XXI. Detrás del hotel se encuentra el Royal Residence, un complejo de modernos apartamentos ideales para estancias más largas. El sobrecogedor spa de última generación, cuya inauguración se remonta a 1886, ha sido restaurado para recuperar todo su esplendor.

Our inspector loved: *The variety of conference facilities, spa treatments and restaurants, and the central location in the heart of Budapest.*

Price Guide: (room only, excluding VAT)
double €160-380
suite €530-3,000

Attractions: Theatres, Pesti Broadway, 1km; Parliament, 2.5km; Buda Castle, 3km; Margaret Island, 3.5km

Airports: Budapest, 18km; Pozsony, 204km; Vienna, Austria, 247km

Category: Hotel

Bern
SWITZERLAND
Geneva
St Moritz
Innsbruck
Lienz
AUSTRIA
HUNGARY
Klagenfurt
Zalaegerszeg
Maribor
Ljubljana
SLOVENIA
Zagreb
CROATIA
Rijeka
BOSNIA-H.
Split
Sarajevo
Trentino~Alto Adige
Bolzano
Trento
Belluno
Friuli-Venezia
Udine
Aosta
Valle d'Aosta
Lombardy
Como
Bergamo
Novara
Milan
Brescia
Veneto
Treviso
Vicenza
Verona
Trieste
Torino
Padua
Venice
Piemonte
Alessandria
Piacenza
Cuneo
Parma
Ferrara
Liguria
Genoa
Bologna
Ravenna
Emilia~Romagna
ONACO
San Remo
La Spezia
Cannes
Rimini
LIGURIAN SEA
Pisa
Florence
SAN MARINO REPUBLIC
Livorno
Ancona
Tuscany
Marche
Perugia
Umbria
Grosseto
Corsica
Terni
ADRIATIC SEA
Lazio
Pescara
Rome
Abruzzo
Frosinone
Molise
Latina
Campobasso
Sassari
Olbia
Foggia
Nuoro
Benevento
Naples
Campania
Bari
Oristano
Salerno
Potenza
Matera
Puglia
Brindisi
Sardinia
Basilicata
Taranto
Cagliari
Lecce
TYRRHENIAN SEA
Cosenza
Calabria
MEDITERRANEAN SEA
Catanzaro
Aeolian Islands
Trapani
Palermo
Messina
Reggio di Calabria
IONIAN SEA
Sicily
Caltanissetta
Catania
Tunis
Agrigento
Ragusa
Siracusa
TUNISIA
ANCE
137 141 145 146 207 142 143 149 138 139 140 209 208 211 213 169 212 164 165 166 167 168 170 210 214 147 148 144 120 119 122 118 121 131 133 135 136 132 134 177 152 171 206 200 201 205 199 204 198 203 202 130 123 124 154 155 153 150 116 151 117 156 161 160 159 162 163 157 158

ITALY / CAMPANIA (FURORE, AMALFI COAST)

Furore Inn Resort & Spa

VIA DELL'AMORE, 84010 FURORE, AMALFI COAST, ITALY
Tel: +39 089 830 4711 **Fax:** +39 089 830 4777
Web: www.johansens.com/furoreinn **E-mail:** information@furoreinn.it

As you arrive at this beautiful stretch of Italy's coastline, you're in for a treat. The welcome you receive is instant, and continues as you enjoy 3 stunning pools, an elegant wellness area, and one of the best gourmet restaurants on the coast. Activities on offer include exclusive escorted tours of the area, wine tasting tours - the hotel's cellars are amazing - and private boat excursions.

Dès l'instant où vous arrivez dans cette ravissante partie de la côte italienne, vous aurez une bonne surprise. La qualité de l'accueil est immédiate et se prolonge pour votre plaisir avec les 3 sensationnelles piscines, un spa élégant et l'un des meilleurs restaurant de la côte. Les activités comprennent des visites exclusives et accompagnées de la région, des circuits de dégustation de vins – la cave de l'hôtel est impressionnante – et des excursions en bateau privé.

Al llegar a este bello trecho de la costa italiana le espera una agradable sorpresa. El excelente trato que recibirá sera instantáneo, y lo seguirá siendo durante su estancia, mientras disfruta de las 3 impresionantes piscinas, la elegante zona Spa y uno de los mejores restaurantes gastronómicos de la costa. Exclusivos viajes guiados de la zona, rutas de degustacíon de vinos- las bodegas del hotel son excepcionales - y excursiones privadas en barco, son algunas de las actividades a las que se puede apuntar.

***Our inspector loved:** The romantic ambience.*

Price Guide:
single €180-320
double €260-460
suite €390-750

Awards: Condé Nast Johansens Most Excellent European Romantic Hotel Award 2008; Italy's Leading Boutique Hotel, World Travel Awards 2007

Attractions: Lover's Path, 5-min walk; Pompei, 38km; Capri, 50-min hydrofoil ride; Ischia, 1-hour hydrofoil ride

Nearby Towns: Amalfi, 7km; Ravello,14km; Positano, 17km; Pompei, 38km
Airports: Naples Capodichino, 60km; Rome Ciampino, 230km; Rome Fiumicino, 290km

Category: Hotel
Closed: December - March

Il Cannito

VIA CANNITO, 84047 LOC. CAPACCIO, PAESTUM (SALERNO), ITALY
Tel: +39 0828 196 2277 **Fax:** +39 0828 796 2276
Web: www.johansens.com/ilcannito **E-mail:** info@ilcannito.com

Our inspector loved: *Enjoying the sunset from the pool terrace.*

Price Guide: (including transfer to and from Il Cannito and Lido in Tela Beach)
double room €187-385

Attractions: UNESCO Paestum, 5km; Private Beach, 5km; Cilento Natural Reserve, 20km; Amalfi Coast, 50km

Nearby Towns: UNESCO Paestum, 5km; Amalfi Coast, 50km; Sorrento, 65km
Airports: Naples, 101km; Rome Ciampino, 320km; Rome Fiumicino, 350km

Category: Charming Hotel

Welcome to the Gorga family's charming hideaway, surrounded by wild Mediterranean nature. With great respect for the environment, this modernistic retreat was built with local materials and traditions, and serves local dishes prepared from produce grown on-site. This fantastic location overlooks Capri, the UNESCO ruins of Paestum, and has access to a private beach.

Bienvenue dans le charmant refuge de la famille Gorga, entouré par une nature méditerranéenne sauvage. Avec un respect marqué pour l'environnement, ce lieu moderniste fut construit selon les traditions et matériaux locaux et l'on y sert des plats régionaux préparés à partir de produits cultivés sur place. Ce magnifique endroit surplombe Capri, les ruines de l'UNESCO de Paestum et offre un accès à une plage privée.

Bienvenido al encantador escondite de la familia Gorga, rodeado de salvaje naturaleza mediterránea. Plenamente respetuoso con el medio ambiente, este modernista lugar de retiro se construyó con materiales locales y con fidelidad a las tradiciones. Pone a su disposición platos locales preparados con ingredientes cultivados en las propias instalaciones. Este fantástico emplazamiento incluye vistas a Capri, las ruinas de Paestum de la UNESCO así como acceso a una playa privada.

Il Convento dei Fiori di Seta

VIA ORFEO 34/4, 40124 BOLOGNA, ITALY
Tel: +39 051 272039 **Fax:** +39 051 2759001
Web: www.johansens.com/silkflowersnunnery **E-mail:** info@silkflowersnunnery.com

Intimate and charming, this 15th-century Jesuit nunnery church has undergone a sensitive revamp successfully implementing modern-day elements and design whilst respecting its ancient architecture and religious heritage. Oozing romance, bedrooms are chic and stylised; 4 are located in the original apse. Breakfast is served in the altar area and meal orders are taken in the sacristy!

Intime et charmant, cet ancien couvent jésuite du XVe siècle a subi un remaniement délicat par l'implantation réussi d'éléments modernes et de design tout en conservant et en respectant son ancienne architecture et son héritage religieux. Débordant de poésie, les chambres sont chics et stylées ; 4 sont situées dans l'abside d'origine. Le petit-déjeuner est servi autour de l'autel et les commandes des repas sont pris dans la sacristie !

Intimista y encantador, esta iglesia-convento jesuita del siglo XV ha experimentado una sensible modernización que logra combinar con éxito elementos y diseño de hoy día a la vez que respeta su arquitectura antigua y patrimonio religioso. Rebosante de romance, sus habitaciones son de lo más chic y elegantes, 4 de las cuales se encuentran ubicadas en el ábside original. ¡El desayuno se sirve en la zona del altar y los pedidos de su carta se realizan en la sacristía!

***Our inspector loved:** The intimate, charming atmosphere and the original, sacred fresco in the lounge.*

Price Guide:
double €145-250
junior suite €160-320
suite €300-480

Attractions: Queen Margherita Gardens, Cathedrals, Medieval Buildings, Monuments, Museums, Art Galleries and Shopping, 2-min walk; Ravenna and Dante's Tomb, 97km; Rimini and the Adriatic Coast, 118km

Nearby Towns: Ferrara, 54km; Ravenna, 75km; Parma, 97km; Florence, 100km
Airports: Bologna - Marconi, 13km; Forlì, 75km

Category: Charming Hotel

Palazzo Dalla Rosa Prati

STRADA AL DUOMO 7, 43100 PARMA, ITALY
Tel: +39 0521 386 429 **Fax:** +39 0521 502 204
Web: www.johansens.com/palazzodallarosaprati **E-mail:** info@palazzodallarosaprati.it

Our inspector loved: *The historical setting in the heart of Parma and the new "Temporary Shop" and "Coffee Library."*

Price Guide: (room only)
suite €180-310

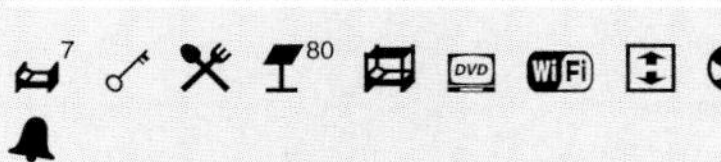

Attractions: Duomo Battistero and Teatro Regio, 1-min walk; Cibus and Mercanteinfiera Exhibitions, 15-min drive; Visits to Parma Ham, Parmesan Cheese and Balsamic Vinegar Producers, 10km; Terre Verdiane (Verdi's House), 25km

Nearby Towns: Bologna, 90km; Milan, 120km; Verona, 130km; Florence, 200km
Airports: Parma, 5km; Bologna, 90km; Milan Malpensa, 120km

Category: Luxury Guest House

Experience how the other half live, namely the Marquis Dalla Rosa Prati whose family has owned this palace since the 15th century. Its exclusive suites combine modern comforts with original architectural features and look out to views of the main city monuments and Duomo Square. Discover La Violetta di Parma perfumes and soaps, and ancient books and maps in the "Temporary Shop."

Vivez comme les grands de ce monde, à savoir le Marquis Dalla Rosa Prati, dont la famille est propriétaire de cet extraordinaire palais depuis le XVe siècle. Ses suites très sélectes, qui combinent confort moderne et élément originaux d'architecture, ont des vues sur les principaux monuments de la ville et Duomo Square. Découvrez les savons et parfums La Violetta di Parma ainsi que d'anciens livres et cartes au "Temporary Shop."

Experimente cómo viven los ricos, concretamente el Marqués Dalla Rosa Prati, a cuya familia pertenece este extraordinario palacio desde el siglo XV. Sus exclusivas suites combinan las comodidades modernos con elementos arquitectónicos originales y proporcionan vistas a los principales monumentos de la ciudad y Duomo Square. Descubre los jabones y per fumes de La Violetta di Parma así como libros y mapas antiguos en la "Temporary Shop."

ITALY / EMILIA ROMAGNA (PIACENZA - BORGO DI RIVALTA)

Torre di San Martino - Historical Residence

LOC. BORGO DI RIVALTA, 29010 GAZZOLA, PIACENZA, ITALY
Tel: +39 0523 972002 **Fax:** +39 0523 972030
Web: www.johansens.com/torredisanmartino **E-mail:** info@torredisanmartino.it

Overlooking a magnificent castle rising from the banks of Trebbia River, this stylish B&B has friendly staff who welcome you into luscious guest rooms. Antiques, four posters and beamed ceilings mix with modern creature comforts. Nearby restaurants serve traditional food and you can immerse yourself in history on guided tours of the castle.

Surplombant le fantastique château qui s'élève sur les berges de la rivière Trebbia, cet élégant B&B est tenu par un personnel amical qui vous accueille dans des chambres avenantes. Objets anciens, lits à baldaquin, poutres apparentes aux plafonds, sont mélangés aux conforts modernes. Juste à côté, des restaurants servent une cuisine traditionnelle. Vous pouvez vous plonger dans l'histoire en suivant les visites guidées du château.

Con vistas a un magnífico Castillo que se eleva sobre las orillas del río Trebbia, este elegante Bed & Breakfast (Alojamiento y Desayuno) tiene un afable personal que le dará la bienvenida a sus suntuosas habitaciones. Las antigüedades, los baldaquinos y los techos de vigas comparten espacio con los modernas instalaciones. Los restaurantes de las cercanías sirven cartas tradicionales y podrá sumergirse en la historia gracias a las visitas guiadas del castillo.

Our inspector loved: *The view of the castle from the rooms.*

Price Guide:
single €180-250
double €230-300
suite €350-600

 10 200    

Awards: Condé Nast Johansens Most Excellent European Guest House 2008

Attractions: Golf Course, 3-min drive; Wineries, 5-min drive; The Castles of The Duchy of Parma and Piacenza, 8km-135km; Adventure Park, 20-min drive

Nearby Towns: Piacenza, 10km; Cremona, 40km; Parma, 60km; Mantova, 100km
Airports: Milan Linate, 70km; Bergamo Orio al Serio, 91km; Milan Malpensa, 120km

Category: Luxury Guest House

Hotel Villa Roncuzzi

VIA M. SILVESTRONI, 6/10, 48026 RUSSI - FRAZ. SAN PANCRAZIO, RAVENNA, ITALY
Tel: +39 0544 534776 **Fax:** +39 0544 535437
Web: www.johansens.com/villaroncuzzi **E-mail:** info@villaroncuzzi.it

Our inspector loved: *The precious and colourful pieces of art.*

Price Guide:
de luxe (single occupancy) €120-150
junior suite €180-230
suite €230-280

Attractions: Ravenna's Mosaics, Byzantine Churches, Dante, Ravenna Festival Vs Riccardo Muti, International Ceramic Museum of Faenza, 15km; Natural Park of the Po Delta, 20km; Amusement Parks and Sandy Beaches on the Adriatic Coast, 20km

Nearby Towns: Ravenna, 10km; Faenza, 15km; Bologna, 60km; Ferrara, 110km
Airports: Forlì, 23km; Rimini, 74km; Bologna, 90km

Category: Luxury Guest House

You will certainly enjoy the refined elegance of this delightful guest house, close to the sea and verdant hills. Stone walls and wooden beams enrich the many beautiful frescoes, sculptures and contemporary artworks, while outside, the pool is inviting and the pleasing gardens are perfect for reading a book and relaxing in.

Vous apprécierez certainement l'élégance raffinée de cette délicieuse maison d'hôtes, près de la mer et des collines verdoyantes. Murs de pierre et poutres en bois enrichissent la plupart des magnifiques fresques, sculptures et œuvres d'art contemporaines alors qu'à l'extérieur, la piscine vous tend les bras et les jardins semblent faits pour lire et se détendre.

Ciertamente disfrutará de la refinada elegancia que ofrece esta deliciosa casa de huéspedes próxima al mar y a verdes colinas. Las paredes de piedra y vigas de madera enriquecen los muchos y bellos frescos, las esculturas y las piezas de arte contemporáneo. En su exterior, la piscina invita al baño y los apacibles jardines se convierten en un lugar perfecto para la lectura y el descanso.

ITALY / EMILIA ROMAGNA (REGGIO EMILIA)

Hotel Posta (Historical Residence)

PIAZZA DEL MONTE, 2, 42100 REGGIO EMILIA, ITALY
Tel: +39 05 22 43 29 44 **Fax:** +39 05 22 45 26 02
Web: www.johansens.com/hotelposta **E-mail:** info@hotelposta.re.it

Our inspector loved: *The hotel's heritage and traditional hospitality.*

Price Guide:
double (single occupancy) €108-165
double €152-205
suite €184-280

Within the historical centre, this impressive building boasts a long history. Discover the past centuries throughout the interior, from the delightful bar with its refined, unusual atmosphere, to the splendid Salone del Capitano. Located in the farmhouse, where balsamic vinegar is traditionally produced and aged, the gourmet restaurant serves mouth-watering local dishes. Excursions to parmesan cheese factories can be organised.

Situé au cœur du centre historique, cet impressionnant bâtiment possède une longue histoire. Vous découvrirez les siècles passés partout à l'intérieur, depuis le charmant bar à l'ambiance raffinée et unique, jusqu'au splendide Salone del Capitano. Situé dans le corps de ferme où le vinaigre balsamique est produit et vieilli, le restaurant gastronomique sert de délicieux plats locaux. Des excursions dans les fabriques qui produisent le parmesan peuvent être organisées.

Situado en el corazón del centro histórico, este impresionante edificio tiene tras de sí una larga historia. Puede descubrir los siglos pasados a través de su interior, desde el encantador bar de ambiente distinguido y singular hasta el espléndido Salone del Capitano. En la casa de labranza,donde se produce y envejece el vinagre balsámico al modo tradicional, encontrará también el restaurante gastronomico, que ofrece platos locales exquisitos. Se organizan excursiones a fábricas donde se elabora el queso parmesano.

Attractions: Balsamic Vinegar and Parmesan Cheese Factories and Enogastronomic Tours, 10km; Ferrari Shop and Museum, Maranello, 18km; Max Mara Factory Store and Fashion Outlets, 40km; Salsomaggiore Spa & Thermal Baths, 74km

Nearby Towns: Modena, 25km; Parma, 27km; Verona, 80km; Florence, 160km
Airports: Parma, 27km; Bologna, 60km; Milan Linate, 150km

Category: Charming Hotel
Closed: 2 weeks in August and 1 week during the Christmas period

La Posta Vecchia

PALO LAZIALE, 00055 LADISPOLI, ROME, ITALY
Tel: +39 0699 49501 **Fax:** +39 0699 49507
Web: www.johansens.com/lapostavecchia **E-mail:** info@lapostavecchia.com

Our inspector loved: *The location so close to Rome, yet so secluded and private.*

Price Guide:
double €320-590
suite €550-1,600

Awards: 1 Star Michelin

Attractions: WWF Oasis, 5-min walk; Etruscan Necropolis, 20-min drive

Nearby Towns: Ceri Etruscan City, 15-min drive; Lake Bracciano, 25-min drive; Rome City Centre, 40-min drive; Viterbo, 45-min drive
Airports: Rome Fiumicino, 30-min drive; Rome Ciampino, 45-min drive

Category: Hotel

Built on ancient Roman foundations and overlooking the sea, original stone doorways and fireplaces remain, and the delicate colour schemes are warm and welcoming. Enjoy the Michelin-starred cuisine, treatments at the wellness area, in the vast surrounding park or in your own room. Take a day trip to Rome by private chauffeur or a helicopter ride along the Tuscan coast.

Construit sur d'anciennes fondations romaines, dominant la mer, cet endroit possède encore ses embrasures de portes en pierre et ses cheminées d'origine. La délicatesse des combinaisons de couleurs est chaleureuse et accueillante. Dégustez la cuisine étoilée au Michelin, profitez des soins au centre de remise en forme ainsi que du grand parc environnant ou tout simplement de votre chambre. Offrez-vous une sortie à Rome dans une voiture avec chauffeur ou un vol en hélicoptère le long de la côte toscane.

Construida sobre antiguos cimientos romanos y con vistas al mar, conserva aún las antiguas entradas de piedra y chimeneas. Las delicadas combinaciones de color dan al ambiente un toque cálido y acogedor. Disfrute de la exquisita cocina, galardonada con estrella Michelin, y de los tratamientos que se ofrecen en el centro wellness, al aire libre dentro de los enormes jardines o en su propia habitacion. Haga una excursión a Roma con chófer privado o un viaje en helicóptero a lo largo de la costa toscana.

Italy (Rome)

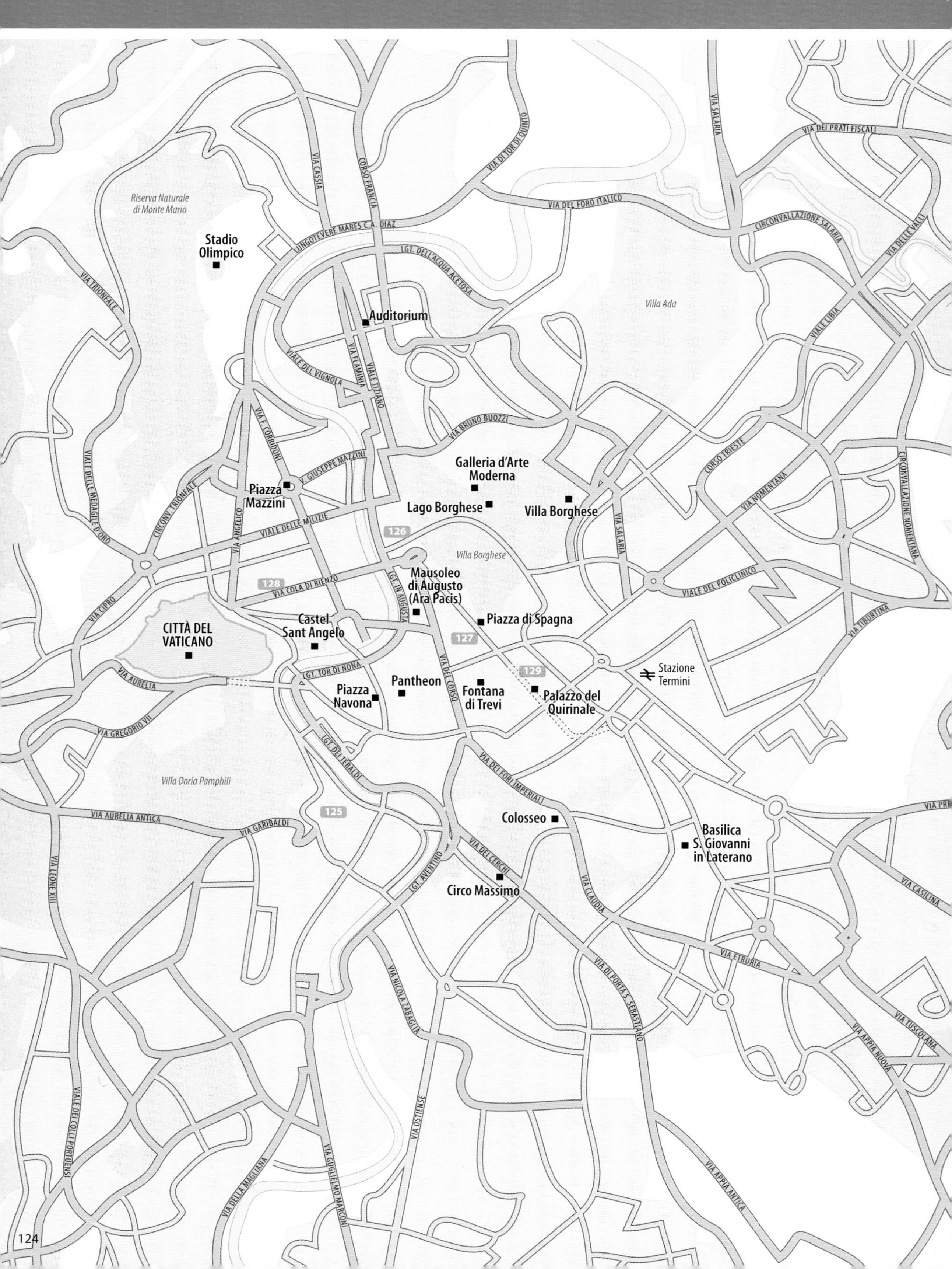

Riserva Naturale di Monte Mario
Stadio Olimpico
Auditorium
Piazza Mazzini
Galleria d'Arte Moderna
Lago Borghese
Villa Borghese
Villa Ada
Mausoleo di Augusto (Ara Pacis)
Piazza di Spagna
Castel Sant Angelo
CITTÀ DEL VATICANO
Pantheon
Piazza Navona
Fontana di Trevi
Palazzo del Quirinale
Stazione Termini
Villa Doria Pamphili
Colosseo
Basilica S. Giovanni in Laterano
Circo Massimo
VIA CASSIA
CORSO FRANCIA
VIA DI TOR DI QUINTO
VIA SALARIA
VIA DEI PRATI FISCALI
VIA DEL FORO ITALICO
LUNGOTEVERE MARES C.A. DIAZ
LGT. DELL'ACQUA ACETOSA
CIRCONVALLAZIONE SALARIA
VIA DELLE VALLI
VIA TRIONFALE
VIALE LIBIA
VIALE DEL VIGNOLA
VIA FLAMINIA
VIALE TIZIANO
VIA BRUNO BUOZZI
VIA F. CORRIDONI
V. GIUSEPPE MAZZINI
VIALE DELLE MEDAGLIE D'ORO
CIRCONV. TRIONFALE
VIA ANGELICO
VIALE DELLE MILIZIE
CORSO TRIESTE
VIA NOMENTANA
CIRCONVALLAZIONE NOMENTANA
126
128
VIA COLA DI RIENZO
LGT. IN AUGUSTA
VIA CIPRO
VIALE DEL POLICLINICO
VIA TIBURTINA
127
129
VIA AURELIA
LGT. TOR DI NONA
VIA DEL CORSO
VIA GREGORIO VII
LGT. DEI TEBALDI
VIA DEI FORI IMPERIALI
125
VIA AURELIA ANTICA
VIA GARIBALDI
VIA PRE
VIA DEI CERCHI
LGT. AVENTINO
VIA CLAUDIA
VIA CASILINA
VIA LEONE XIII
VIA ETRURIA
VIA NICOLA ZABAGLIA
VIA DI PORTA S. SEBASTIANO
VIA TUSCOLANA
VIA APPIA NUOVA
VIALE DEI COLLI PORTUENSI
VIA OSTIENSE
VIA APPIA ANTICA
VIA DELLA MAGLIANA
VIA GUGLIELMO MARCONI

Buonanotte Garibaldi

VIA GARIBALDI 83, 00153 ROME, ITALY
Tel: +39 06 58 330 733 **Fax:** +39 06 58 335 682
Web: www.johansens.com/garibaldi **E-mail:** info@buonanottegaribaldi.com

Our inspector loved: *The magical world of colours and fabrics created by owner Luisa Longo.*

Price Guide:
double €230-280

Attractions: Trastereve District, 2-min walk; Piazza Trilussa, 5-min walk; Pantheon and Navona Square, 15-min walk; Campo de' Fiori Square, 15-min walk

Airports: Rome Fiumicino, 40-min drive; Rome Ciampino, 40-min drive

Category: Luxury Guest House

Charming beyond expectations, owner Luisa Longo, also an artist and fashion designer, has opened her own house and atelier to selected guests who will appreciate her sophisticated touch in furnishings, décor and comfort. You will love breakfasting on the beautiful, shaded patio, and this very exclusive B&B's location in the amazing area of Trastevere, the real heart of town.

Charmante au-delà de toute attente, la propriétaire Luisa Longo, qui est aussi artiste et styliste, a ouvert sa propre maison et son atelier à des hôtes privilégiés, qui sauront apprécier sa touche raffinée en matière d'ameublement, de décoration et de confort. Vous adorerez prendre votre petit-déjeuner dans le magnifique patio ombragé ainsi que la situation de ce B&B, dans l'extraordinaire quartier du Trastevere, au coeur même de la ville.

Más encantadora de lo pudiera imaginarse, la propietaria Luisa Longo, también artista y diseñadora de moda, ha abierto su propia casa y taller a clientes selectos que apreciarán su sofisticado gusto en mobiliario, decoración y confort. Le encantará desayunar a la sombra en el bello patio, y el emplazamiento de este exclusivo Bed & Breakfast (Alojamiento y Desayuno) ubicado en el fabuloso Trastevere, el verdadero corazón de la ciudad.

ITALY / LAZIO (ROME)

CASA MONTANI - LUXURY TOWN HOUSE

PIAZZALE FLAMINIO 9, 00196 ROME, ITALY
Tel: +39 06 3260 0421 **Fax:** +39 06 32504 117
Web: www.johansens.com/casamontani **E-mail:** info@casamontani.com

Looking for an exclusive hideaway in the heart of Rome? Then this third-floor town house retreat is the place for you. Lavishly decorated with locally commissioned furnishings and the finest Italian and French designer furniture and fabrics, this owner-managed property offers a personalised and intimate service.

Vous recherchez un refuge unique au coeur de Rome? Alors ce paradis situé au troisième étage d'une maison de ville est l'endroit pour vous. Somptueusement décorée avec des ameublements commandés localement et avec les meubles et tissus des plus prestigieuses marques françaises et italiennes, cette maison gérée par les propriétaires offre un service personnalisé et intime.

¿Busca Vd. un escondite exclusivo en pleno corazón de Roma? Entonces esta residencia sita en una tercera planta es el lugar de retiro ideal para Vd. Este establecimiento gestionado por su propietario, generosamente decorado con accesorios encargados a artesanos del lugar y con los más selectos muebles y telas de diseño italiano y francés, le ofrece todo un servicio personalizado e intimista.

Our inspector loved: *The unbeatable location.*

Price Guide: (some private, fee-paying garages are available nearby)
double de luxe €140-200
junior suite €160-220
suite €180-240

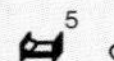   

Attractions: Spanish Steps, 5-min walk; Vatican, 15-min walk; Trevi Fountain, 15-min walk; Navona Square and Pantheon, 15-min walk

Airports: Rome Fiumicino, 40-min drive; Rome Ciampino, 40-min drive

Category: Luxury Guest House

Hotel dei Borgognoni

VIA DEL BUFALO 126 (PIAZZA DI SPAGNA), 00187 ROME, ITALY
Tel: +39 06 6994 1505 **Fax:** +39 06 6994 1501
Web: www.johansens.com/borgognoni **E-mail:** info@hotelborgognoni.it

Our inspector loved: *The new interior design. The hotel attracts a very hip clientele!*

Price Guide:
single €225-247
double €290-325
suite upon request

 51    60  

Attractions: Trevi Fountain, 2-min walk; Spanish Steps, 5-min walk; Navona Square, 10-min walk; Campo dè Fiori, 10-min walk

Airports: Rome Ciampino, 40-min drive; Rome Fiumicino, 50-min train/metro

Category: Charming Hotel

Hidden in a "vicolo," a short walk from the Trevi Fountain and Spanish Steps, this quiet, newly redecorated hotel is elegant and secluded. Peep out from your bedroom window to the enclosed terrace garden with its relaxing sunchairs, stay in one of the rooms that enjoy a private terrace or people watch from the lovely new lounge. This is a super hotel away from the city crowds, perfect for both business and pleasure.

Caché dans un "vicolo" à quelques pas de la Fontaine de Trévi et des Marches Espagnoles, cet hôtel nouvellement rénové est élégant et retiré. Jetez un coup d'oeil depuis la fenêtre de votre chambre sur le jardin clos et ses chaises longues, séjournez dans l'une des ravissantes chambres qui offrent une spacieuse terrasse ou regardez les gens passer depuis le ravissant nouveau salon. C'est un formidable hôtel loin de la foule urbaine, idéal aussi bien pour les affaires que pour le plaisir.

Escondido en un "vicolo", a corta distancia de la Fontana di Trevi y de la Plaza de España, este tranquilo hotel, recientemente re-decorado es elegante y exclusivo. Asomese a la ventana de su habitación para contemplar el patio-jardín con su relajantes butacas para tomar el sol, o puede alojarse en una de las bonitas habitaciones que disponen de terrazas privadas, o quedese mirando a la gente que pasa desde el bonito nuevo salón. Este es un hotel encantador, alejado del gentío de la ciudad y perfecto tanto para estancias de negocios como de placer.

Hotel dei Consoli

VIA VARRONE 2/D, 00193 ROME, ITALY
Tel: +39 0668 892 972 **Fax:** +39 0668 212 274
Web: www.johansens.com/deiconsoli **E-mail:** info@hoteldeiconsoli.com

Ideally located for shopping and visiting the Vatican, this classic, intimate hotel, dating back to the 19th century, is peaceful with ornate public rooms featuring stucco decorations, Murano chandeliers, antique furniture, fresh flowers and excellent paintings. Many guest rooms overlook St Peter's dome and the roof garden affords a great vantage point of the city. You will find yourself ideally placed for exploring Rome and its magical delights.

Idéalement situé pour faire du shopping et visiter le Vatican, cet hôtel classique et intime, qui remonte au XIXe siècle, est un lieu paisible, avec des salons ornés de décorations en stuc, des lustres de Murano, des meubles anciens, des fleurs fraîches et de beaux tableaux. De nombreuses chambres donnent sur le dôme de Saint-Pierre et le jardin sur le toit offre de merveilleuses vues sur la ville. Vous apprécierez d'être idéalement placé pour explorer Rome et ses lieux magiques.

Situado en lugar ideal para hacer compras y visitar el Vaticano, este hotel clasico e intimo que data del siglo XIX, es de lo más tranquilo, con salones decorados de estuco, lámparas araña de Murano, muebles antiguos, flores naturales y magníficos lienzos. Desde muchas de las habitaciones se ve la Cúpula de San Pedro y la terraza-jardín en el último piso proporciona vistas priviligiadas de la ciudad . Una ubicación ideal para explorar Roma y todos sus encantos.

Our inspector loved: *The roof terrace with its amazing view over St Peter's dome and the loveliest breeze in town!*

Price Guide:
single €220
superior/de luxe €300-320
junior suite €380-480

Attractions: Vatican, 2-min walk; Sistine Chapel, 2-min walk; Spanish Steps, 20-min walk; Pantheon, 20-min walk

Airports: Rome Fiumicino, 40-min drive; Rome Ciampino, 50-min drive

Category: Charming Hotel

VILLA SPALLETTI TRIVELLI

VIA PIACENZA 4, 00184 ROME, ITALY
Tel: +39 06 48907934 **Fax:** +39 06 4871409
Web: www.johansens.com/villaspallettitrivelli **E-mail:** info@villaspallettitrivelli.com

Our inspector loved: *The fact that this luxury villa is the best kept secret in town!*

Price Guide:
luxe romantic €880
de luxe prestige €1,100
junior suite/suite €1,430-1,705

Attractions: Trevi Fountain, 10-min walk; Spanish Steps, 10-min walk; Designer Shops, Colosseum and Roman Forum, 15-min walk; Navona Square, 20-min walk

Airports: Rome Fiumicino, 30-min drive; Rome Ciampino, 45-min drive

Category: Charming Hotel

This magnificent example of a 19th-century "urban villa" is frequented by the rich and famous and VIPs seeking seclusion within the city. Antiques, a Liberty wrought-iron staircase and flower-designed balcony are just for starters, while the UNESCO Cultural Heritage Bond-awarded library reveals beautiful bookcases filled with valuable, ancient books. Private dining is available in the vast garden, and spa treatments in the popular, luxurious spa.

Ce magnifique exemple de "villa urbaine" du XIXe siècle est fréquentée par les riches, les célébrités et les VIP à la recherche d'isolement dans la ville. Les antiquités, l'escalier circulaire en fer forgé et le balcon au décor floral d'Edoardo Gioja ne sont que des mises en bouche. La bibliothèque reconnue comme Héritage Culturel par l'UNESCO est remplie de magnifiques livres anciens de valeur. Il est possible de dîner en privé dans le vaste jardin et de profiter des soins dans le luxueux spa.

Este magnífico ejemplar de "villa urbana" del siglo XIX es frecuentada por ricos, famosos y otros VIPs que buscan tranquilidad dentro de la ciudad. Entre las primeras galas del lugar se encuentran diversas piezas de anticuario, una escalera Liberty de hierro forjado y un balcón de diseño floral, mientras que en la biblioteca, nombrada Patrimonio Cultural por UNESCO, podrá admirar las bellas librerías repletas de antiquísimos valiosos libros. En el enorme jardín se sirven cenas privadas y el lujoso y popular Spa ofrece tratamientos de todo tipo.

Villa La Cerretana

STRADA ORTANA 40, BAGNAIA, 01100 VITERBO, LAZIO, ITALY
Tel: +39 0761 1762565 **Fax:** +39 0761 370263
Web: www.johansens.com/villalacerretana **E-mail:** info@villalacerretana.it

This welcoming villa is surrounded by an incredible peony scented botanical garden, set in the beautiful Alto Lazio region with views of rolling hills and vineyards. A former family retreat, there are 3 rooms, which still retain their original character with an eclectic mix of ancient pieces and modern touches, and relaxing garden and pool areas. Guided tours and wine and oil tasting excursions can be arranged nearby.

Cette accueillante villa est entourée par un jardin botanique vaste et coloré, situé dans la belle région du Alto Lazio, avec vues sur les collines vallonnées et les vignobles. Cette ancienne maison de famille possède 3 chambres qui ont gardé leurs caractéristiques d'origine avec un mélange éclectique de meubles anciens et de notes modernes, ainsi que des jardins et des endroits près de la piscine où se relaxer. Des visites guidées et des dégustations de vins et d'huiles d'olives peuvent être organisées.

Esta acogedora villa rodeada por un precioso jardín botánico con olor a peonias está situada en la bella región del Alto Lazio donde las vistas son de onduladas colinas y viñedos. Antiguo lugar de descanso familiar, 3 de sus habitaciones aún conservan , con una eclectica combinacion de piezas antiguas y detalles modernos, su carácter original, así como el relajante jardin y la zona de piscina. Se pueden concertar recorridos guiados y excursiones para probar vinos y aceite de oliva.

Our inspector loved: *The homely atmosphere. The owners live on the premises and guests are made to feel like family!*

Price Guide:
room €120-185

Attractions: Villa Lante di Bagnaia, 3km; Viterbo Roman Thermal Bath, 10km; Bomarzo Monster Park, 10km; Siena, 150km

Nearby Towns: Viterbo, 5-min drive; Bolsena Lake, 20-min drive; Orvieto, 35-min drive; Siena, 90-min drive
Airports: Rome Ciampino, 105km; Rome Fiumicino, 120km; Florence International, 205km

Category: Luxury Guest House

Hotel Punta Est

VIA AURELIA 1, 17024 FINALE LIGURE (SV), ITALY
Tel: +39 019 600611 **Fax:** +39 019 600611
Web: www.johansens.com/puntaest **E-mail:** info@puntaest.com

Our inspector loved: *The charming Ligurian ambience, the sea view from the restaurant's terrace and the hydromassage in the natural grotto.*

Price Guide:
single €120-200
double/twin €220-300
suite €270-500

Attractions: Medieval Village and Castle, on-site; Genova's Harbour and Aquarium, 70km; Sanremo Casino, 80km; Côte d'Azur, 100km

Nearby Towns: Genova, 70km; Sanremo, 80km; Portofino, 100km; Monte Carlo, Monaco, 120km
Airports: Genova, 70km; Nice, 130km

Category: Charming Hotel
Closed: Mid-October - mid-April

This elegant 18th-century villa was once a private summer residence. Today, it is a unique hotel nestled in its own park. Guests can wander the shaded pathways and olive groves and admire views over the Ligurian Sea, a wonderful setting for weddings and parties. Magic yourself into the natural grotto, an Aladdin's Cave of stalagmites and stalactites. And enjoy dinners on the panoramic terrace where occasional music evenings are held.

Cette élégante villa du XVIIIe siècle fût autrefois une résidence d'été privée. Aujourd'hui c'est un hôtel unique, niché au coeur de son parc. Les hôtes peuvent se promener le long des sentiers ombragés, des oliveraies et admirer les vues sur la mer ligurienne, lieu unique pour des mariages et réceptions. Vivez un moment magique dans la grotte naturelle, une cave d'Aladin constellée de stalagmites et stalactites. Dînez sur la terrasse panoramique qui accueille occasionnellement des soirées musicales.

Esta elegante villa del siglo XVIII, una vez residencia de verano privada, es hoy día un singular hotel enclavado en su propio parque. Los huéspedes pueden pasear por senderos protegidos del sol y por los olivares, así como admirar las vistas al Mar Liguria; un entorno ideal para celebrar bodas y fiestas. Encántese en la cueva natural, una cueva de Aladino con estalagmitas y estalactitas y disfrute de las cenas en la terraza panorámica, donde de vez en cuando se organizan noches con música.

Abbadia San Giorgio - Historical Residence

PIAZZALE SAN GIORGIO, 16030 MONEGLIA (GE), ITALY
Tel: +39 0185 491119 **Fax:** +39 0185 490270
Web: www.johansens.com/abbadiasangiorgio **E-mail:** info@abbadiasangiorgio.com

Inspired by its past as a 15th-century Franciscan monastery, this luxury guest house's rooms are peaceful and stylishly decorated. You'll relish the organic breakfasts and drinks by the fireplace before dinner at nearby Villa Edera Hotel, where a pool, sauna and gym is also at your disposal. Cooking demonstrations and wine tours can be arranged.

Inspirée par son passé de monastère franciscain du XVe siècle, cette maison d'hôte de luxe a des chambres calmes et élégamment décorées. Vous savourerez les petits-déjeuners bio et les apéritifs devant la cheminée avant d'aller dîner à l'hôtel voisin Villa Edera, où une piscine, un sauna et une salle de gym sont également à votre disposition. Des démonstrations de cuisine et des visites de vignobles peuvent être organisées.

Inspirado por su historia, este monasterio franciscano del siglo XV posee habitaciones tranquilas y decoradas con gran estilo. Saboreará desayunos ecológicos y bebidas junto a la chimenea antes de la cena en el cercano Hotel Villa Edera, donde están a su disposición: piscina, sauna y gimnasio. Demostraciones gastronómicas y visitas a los viñedos se pueden organizar.

Our inspector loved: *The atmosphere... a truly magical and romantic retreat.*

Price Guide:
double €170-220
junior suite €190-280
suite €230-320

Awards: Condé Nast Johansens Most Excellent Luxury Guest House 2009

Attractions: Cinque Terre Tour, 15km; Portofino National Park, 30km; Genova and Aquarium, 60km

Nearby Towns: Cinque Terre, 15km; Portofino, 30km; Pisa, 100km; Florence, 180km
Airports: Genova, 60km; Pisa, 100km

Category: Luxury Guest House
Closed: November - 20th December

HOTEL SAN GIORGIO - PORTOFINO HOUSE

VIA DEL FONDACO, 11, 16034 PORTOFINO (GENOVA), ITALY
Tel: +39 0185 26991 **Fax:** +39 0185 267139
Web: www.johansens.com/portofinohouse **E-mail:** info@portofinohsg.it

Our inspector loved: *The hotel's intimate ambience and the emerald-green water of its nearby beach.*

Price Guide:
double standard €300-480
junior suite €440-590
suite €610-810

Attractions: Portofino Natural Park, on-site; Private Sandy Beach, 2km; San Fruttuoso Bay and Abby, 20-min boat ride; Tour of Cinque Terre, 100km

Nearby Towns: Santa Margherita, 5km; Genova, 30km; Milan, 180km; Monte Carlo, Monaco, 215km
Airports: Genova, 35km; Pisa, 150km

Category: Luxury Guest House
Closed: Mid-November - mid-March

Meander a few steps from Portofino's square and harbour and you'll discover this charming peaceful hotel offering an elegant alternative to the usual type of accommodation in the area. Its greatest secret is the lovely garden where you can relax and enjoy your breakfast. Interiors are also serene with local "Ardesia" slate floors in the bathrooms.

Flânez à quelques pas de la place et du port de Portofino et vous découvrirez ce charmant et paisible hôtel qui offre une élégante alternative aux hébergements habituellement proposés dans la région. Son plus grand secret est le charmant jardin où vous pouvez vous détendre et apprécier votre petit-déjeuner. Les intérieurs aussi sont sereins, avec des sols en Ardoise locale dans les salles de bain.

A un corto paseo entre callejuelas desde la plaza y puerto de Portofino se topará con este tranquilo hotel que ofrece una elegante alternativa al tipo de alojamiento convencional que se encuentra en esta zona. Su gran secreto es el maravilloso jardín donde podrá relajarse y disfrutar del desayuno. Los interiores son también relajantes con solería de pizarra "Ardesia" en los cuartos de baño.

Grand Hotel Diana Majestic

VIA OLEANDRI 15, 18013 DIANO MARINA (IM), ITALY
Tel: +39 0183 402 727 **Fax:** +39 0183 403 040
Web: www.johansens.com/dianamajestic **E-mail:** info@dianamajestic.com

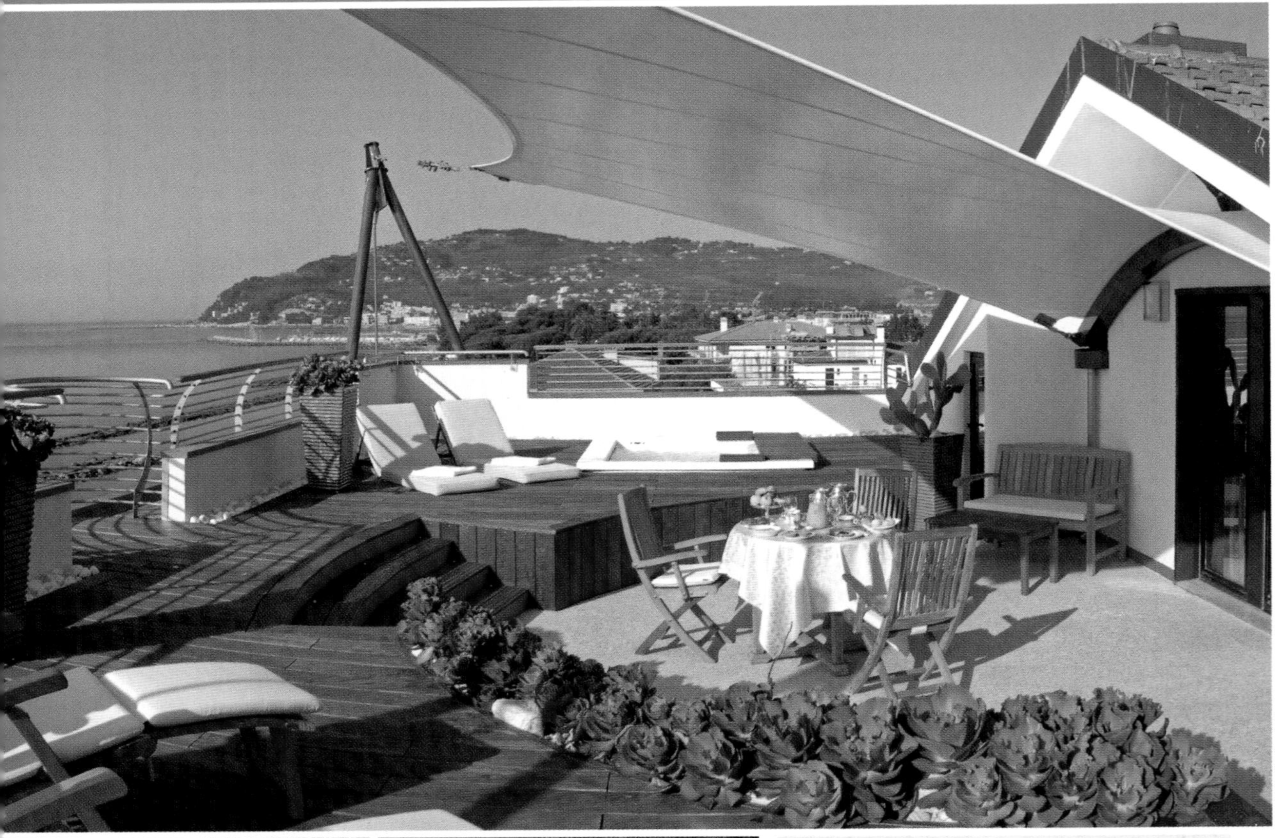

This small resort hotel revels in its great position with private beach and delightful ancient olive groves. Bedrooms have balconies and suites have the added temptation of a large terrace with outdoor Jacuzzi. Dine by candlelight, and sample the bar's 70 brands of whisky, and fine liqueurs and spirits from the 1920s.

Ce petit resort se délecte de son emplacement idéal avec sa plage privée et entouré de ravissantes anciennes oliveraies. Les chambres ont des balcons et les suites ajoutent à la tentation avec leur grande terrasse et leur jacuzzi extérieur. Dînez aux chandelles et dégustez les 70 marques de whisky du bar ou les excellents spiritueux et liqueurs datant des années 20.

Este pequeño hotel turístico se regocija de su singular enclave con playa privada y encantadores olivares centenarios. Sus habitaciones disponen de balcones y las suites del atractivo añadido de una amplia terraza con jacuzzi al aire libre. Cene a la luz de las velas y saboree en su bar las 70 marcas de whisky así como los excelentes licores y otras bebidas alcohólicas de la década de los 20.

Our inspector loved: *Suite N.501's terrace that stretches out over the sea making you feel as if you are in a boat sailing the Mediterranean.*

Price Guide:
single €110-290
double €130-300
suite €350-1,000

Attractions: Medieval Town of Cervo, 3km; Shopping in Alassio, 12km; Sanremo Casino, 30km; Côte d'Azur, 65km

Nearby Towns: Imperia, 6km; Alassio, 12km; Sanremo, 30km; Monte Carlo, Monaco, 78km
Airports: Albenga, 25km; Nice, 90km; Genova, 100km

Category: Hotel
Closed: 15th October - 24th December

Grand Hotel Miramare

VIA MILITE IGNOTO, 30, 16038 SANTA MARGHERITA LIGURE - GENOVA, LIGURIA, ITALY

Tel: +39 0185 287013 **Fax:** +39 0185 284651

Web: www.johansens.com/grandmiramare **E-mail:** miramare@grandhotelmiramare.it

Our inspector loved: *The impeccable wellness centre.*

Price Guide:
single €175-270
double €255-445
suite €410-890

Awards: One of Condé Nast Traveller's Top 100 Southern European Hotels 2009; Condé Nast Johansens Most Excellent Business Venue 2007

Attractions: Portofino Natural Park, 5km; San Fruttuoso Abbey, 10km; Genova's Aquarium, 40km; Cinque Terre Tour and Wine Route, 100km

Nearby Towns: Portofino, 5km; Genova, 40km; Pisa, 120km; Monte Carlo, Monaco, 230km
Airports: Genova, 40km; Pisa, 145km; Milan Linate, 178km

Category: Hotel

Find yourself between lush green hills and deep blue sea in the heart of the Italian Riviera. Overlooking the promenade to the beautiful village of Portofino, this 100-year-old family-owned hotel is one of the region's most exclusive venues that is fantastic for meetings and special events. Join an exclusive clientele drawn to its elegance, impeccable service, traditional style and modern amenities.

Retrouvez-vous entre le vert des collines luxuriantes et le bleu profond de la mer au coeur de la Riviera Italienne. Surplombant la promenade qui mène au superbe village de Portofino, cet hôtel, tenu par la même famille depuis plus de 100 ans, est l'un des plus beaux endroits de la région, fantastique pour l'organisation de réunions ou d'événements spéciaux. Rejoignez une clientèle huppée attirée par son élégance, son service irréprochable, son style traditionnel et ses équipements modernes.

Imagínese entre exuberantes y verdes colinas y el profundo mar azul, en pleno corazón de la Riviera Italiana. Con vistas al paseo marítimo de la bella localidad de Portofino, este centenario hotel de regencia familiar es uno de los establecimientos más selectos de la región y un lugar ideal para reuniones y para celebrar otros eventos. Formará parte de la exclusiva clientela, que es atraída por la elegancia, el servicio impecable, el estilo tradicional y las modernas instalaciones este hotel.

ITALY / LIGURIA (SESTRI LEVANTE)

Hotel Vis à Vis

VIA DELLA CHIUSA 28, 16039 SESTRI LEVANTE (GE), ITALY
Tel: +39 0185 42661 **Fax:** +39 0185 480853
Web: www.johansens.com/visavis **E-mail:** visavis@hotelvisavis.com

Our inspector loved: *Watching the magical sunset from the roof terrace.*

Price Guide:
single€130-160
double €200-290
junior suite €320-410

Attractions: Bay of Silence and Fairytale Bay, 5-min walk; Portofino, 20-min drive; Cinqueterre, 30km; Slate Valley, 40km

Nearby Towns: Chiavari, 5-min train ride; Rapallo-St Margherita, 10-min train ride; Genoa, 30-min train ride; Cinqueterre, 1-hour ferry or train ride
Airports: Genoa, 45km; Pisa, 100km; Milan, 220km

Category: Charming Hotel
Closed: 1st February - 1st April 2010

It's all about the views at this family-run hotel, in a hillside setting that can only be described as idyllic. Be mesmerised by the breathtaking scenery from the hotel's elegant restaurant Olimpo, where the food is also rather special. Enjoy open-air barbecues on the terrace and the glorious roof garden, Ponte Zeus.

Tout est dans les vues de cet hôtel familial, situé à flanc de coteau, dans un cadre véritablement idyllique. Vous serez hypnotisés par le paysage époustouflant depuis l'élégant restaurant de l'hôtel, Olimpo, où la cuisine est également exceptionnelle. Faites vous plaisir en profitant des barbecues en plein air sur la terrasse et du splendide jardin suspendu, Ponte Zeus.

Lo más llamativo son las vistas desde este hotel de gestión familiar, un entorno montañoso que sólo puede describirse como idílico. Quedará hipnotizado por el sobrecogedor paisaje que se contempla desde el elegante restaurante del hotel, Olimpo, cuya carta resulta ser también especial. Disfrute de las barbacoas al aire libre en su terraza y del memorable jardín sobre el ático, Ponte Zeus.

Bagni di Bormio Spa Resort

LOCALITÀ BAGNI NUOVI, 23038 VALDIDENTRO (SONDRIO), ITALY
Tel: +39 0342 910131 **Fax:** +39 0342 918511
Web: www.johansens.com/bagnidibormio **E-mail:** info@bagnidibormio.it

Our inspector loved: *The impressive spa and thermal baths with hot spring water from 9 mountain sources.*

Price Guide:
single €134-196
double €180-334
suite €230-378

Attractions: Stelvio National Park, on-site; Lake Como, 100km

Nearby Towns: Livigno, 35km; St Moritz, Switzerland, 70km; Como, 100km; Milan, 180km
Airports: Milan Orio, 180km; Milan Linate, 180km

Category: Hotel

Opportunities to pamper yourself are endless at this grand old dame, with 7 outdoor thermal water pools, Roman baths and thermal spring caves amid the Belle Epoque architectural splendour. Classical bedrooms have opulent white Carrara marble bathrooms, and elsewhere public rooms are awash with period furnishings, beautiful frescoes and Murano glass chandeliers.

Les possibilités de vous faire dorloter sont infinies dans cet établissement de légende, avec 7 piscines thermales extérieures, des bains romains et des caves de source thermale au milieu de la splendeur architecturale de la Belle Epoque. Les chambres classiques ont d'admirables salles de bains en marbre de Carrara et les salons sont remplis de mobilier d'époque, de superbes fresques et de chandeliers en verre de Murano.

Permítase el lujo de infinitos mimos en esta "gran dama" experimentada con 7 piscinas exteriores termales, baños romanos y cuevas de manantiales termales rodeado todo ello por la espectacular arquitectura de Belle Époque. Sus clásicas habitaciones poseen opulentos baños con mármol de Carrara y sus zonas comunes están repletas de mobiliario de época, bonitos frescos y candelabros de cristal de Murano.

ITALY / LOMBARDY (ERBUSCO)

L'ALBERETA

VIA VITTORIO EMANUELE II, NO 23, 25030 ERBUSCO (BS), ITALY
Tel: +39 030 7760 550 **Fax:** +39 030 7760 573
Web: www.johansens.com/albereta **E-mail:** info@albereta.it

Our inspector loved: *The hotel's vineyards, winery and restaurant.*

Price Guide: (breakfast €30)
double €240-610
suite €650-920
suite bellavista €880-1,100

Awards: Condé Nast Johansens Most Excellent Hotel for Service 2009

Attractions: Franciacorta Wine Region, on the doorstep; Lake Iseo, 10km; Franciacorta Fashion Outlet, 15km; Lake Garda, 60km

Nearby Towns: Bergamo, 35km; Verona, 80km; Milan, 90km; Mantova, 112km
Airports: Bergamo Orio Al Serio, 35km; Verona, 80km; Milan Linate, 80km

Category: Hotel

As you relax at this superb hideaway in the renowned wine region of Franciacorta, with views of Lake Iseo and the Alps, you might almost forget that Milan's shopping is just a whisker away. Rooms have period furnishings and decadent fabrics, and food is sublime. For extra pampering, The Henri Chenot Espace Vitalité spa obliges.

En vous relaxant dans ce magnifique refuge, situé dans la fameuse région vinicole de Franciacorta, profitant des vues sur les Alpes et le lac Iseo, vous oublierez sûrement que Milan et ses boutiques ne sont qu'à quelques kilomètres. Les chambres sont décorées de mobilier d'époque et des tissus décadents. Le menu est sublime et pour vous faire plaisir encore un petit peu plus, vous devez faire une visite à l'Espace Vitalité et spa Henri Chenot.

Mientras se relaja en este magnífico refugio de la renombrada región vinícola de Franciacorta, con vistas al Lago Iseo y a los Alpes, llegará casi a olvidarse de que las compras en Milán están a menos de un paso. Las habitaciones presentan decoración de época y telas decadentes, y la carta es sublime. Si desea Vd. permitirse un lujo más, el spa Henri Chenot Espace Vitalité es de visita obligada.

ITALY / LOMBARDY (LAKE GARDA - GARDONE RIVIERA) 

Grand Hotel Gardone Riviera

VIA ZANARDELLI 84, 25083 GARDONE RIVIERA (BS), LAKE GARDA, ITALY
Tel: +39 0365 20261 **Fax:** +39 0365 22695
Web: www.johansens.com/gardoneriviera **E-mail:** ghg@grangardone.it

Our inspector loved: *The splendid view of Lake Garda and the charm of past years.*

Price Guide:
single €116-148
double €190-254
junior suite €244-308

Attractions: Lake Garda, on the doorstep; Il Vittoriale D'Annunzio House, Gardens and Museum, 900 metres; N. 3 Golf Courses, 12km; Tour of the Dolomites, 100km

Nearby Towns: Brescia, 30km; Mantova, 55km; Verona, 60km; Venice, 175km
Airports: Brescia, 30km; Verona, 55km; Bergamo, 75km

Category: Hotel
Closed: November - March

Stretched along the lakeside, with beautiful views, this handsome hotel has a private lake promenade and beach. In summer soak up the sunshine and enjoy lunch on the garden terrace, then as evening falls, a romantic dinner with stunning backdrop. Winnies Bar has a relaxed ambience with pianist-singer and dancing.

S'étirant le long des bords du lac, avec de splendides vues, ce très bel hôtel bénéficie d'une promenade et d'une plage privées. En été, faites le plein de soleil puis appréciez le déjeuner sur le jardin en terrasse et, enfin, en début de soirée, faites un dîner romantique avec toile de fond époustouflante. Le Winnies Bar, avec son pianiste-chanteur et sa piste de danse, offre une ambiance décontractée.

Bordeando el lago y provisto de bellas vistas, este hermoso hotel dispone de un paseo privado a la vera del lago y playa. En verano podrá empaparse de sol y disfrutar de sus almuerzos en la terraza del jardín, para a continuación, con el atardecer, tomar una cena romántica junto a un maravilloso telón de fondo. Winnies Bar goza de un ambiente relajado con pianista-cantante y música de baile.

ITALY / LOMBARDY (LAKE GARDA - SALÒ)

Hotel Bellerive

VIA PIETRO DA SALÒ 11, 25087 SALÒ (BS), ITALY
Tel: +39 0365 520 410 **Fax:** +39 0365 290 709
Web: www.johansens.com/bellerive **E-mail:** info@hotelbellerive.it

Next to glistening Lake Garda, the warm, inviting ambience of this hotel reflects the mesmerising light and colours of the lake and nearby harbour. Bedrooms have fresh tones and comfortable furnishings, and in the restaurant you can try delicious Gardenese delicacies. Meander the atmospheric narrow streets and gardens of the historical Salò quarter.

Près du scintillant Lac de Garde, l'atmosphère chaleureuse et accueillante de l'hôtel reflète la lumière et les couleurs fascinantes du lac et du port à proximité. Les chambres ont des tons frais, un mobilier confortable et vous pouvez déguster de délicieux mets locaux. Flânez dans les rues étroites et les jardins pleins d'atmosphères du quartier historique de Salò.

Junto al deslumbrante lago Garda, el cálido ambiente de este hotel refleja la fascinante luz y color del lago y del cercano puerto. Las habitaciones decoradas con tonos frescos y cómodos muebles y en el restaurante puede probar deliciosas especialidades de Garda. Pasee por las estrechas calles llenas de ambiente y por los jardines del histórico barrio Salò.

Our inspector loved: *The charming evening atmosphere with the flickering lights of the harbour and moon reflecting in the lake.*

Price Guide: (room only, excluding VAT)
single €150-225
double €175-275
suite €250-400

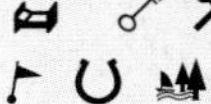    

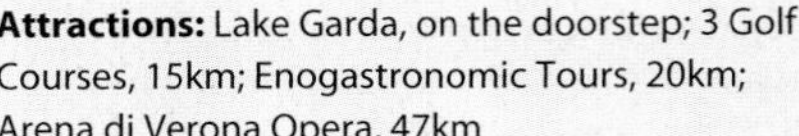

Attractions: Lake Garda, on the doorstep; 3 Golf Courses, 15km; Enogastronomic Tours, 20km; Arena di Verona Opera, 47km

Nearby Towns: Verona, 47km; Mantova, 60km; Venice, 120km; Milan, 120km
Airports: Brescia, 25km; Verona, 47km; Bergamo, 70km

Category: Hotel
Closed: 15th December - 15th January

Hotel Parco San Marco Beach Resort, Golf & SPA

VIALE PRIVATO SAN MARCO 1, 22010 CIMA DI PORLEZZA (CO), ITALY
Tel: +39 0344 629111 **Fax:** +39 0344 629112
Web: www.johansens.com/parcosanmarco **E-mail:** info@parco-san-marco.com

Our inspector loved: *The range of facilities.*

Price Guide: (per person)
junior suite from €98
suite from €115
Villa Olivo upon request

Awards: One of Europe's 50 Most Beautiful Wellness Oases, Wienerin Spa Guide '08/'09; One of the Best 90 Hotels in Europe, Geo Season '07 & '08

Attractions: Golf Courses, 8 km; Tour of Lake Como and Lugano and the 3 Lake Flights, 15km; Lugano and Campione Casino, 15km

Nearby Towns: Lugano, 15km; Como, 45km; Milan, 90km; St Moritz, 110km
Airports: Lugano, 15km; Milan Malpensa, 105km; Milan Linate, 120km

Category: Hotel
Closed: January - mid-March

This friendly, refined resort is set on the beautiful Lake Lugano, with a stunning backdrop of mountains and parkland. An astonishing range of services and facilities is on offer, including the largest private beach on the lake, 2 swimming pools, an impressive wellness centre, 3 restaurants, a botanical garden and Club Bambini for children aged 2 and up.

Ce resort amical et raffiné est situé sur le superbe lac de Lugano, avec un magnifique arrière plan de montagnes et d'espaces verts. Un étonnant choix de services et d'équipements est proposé, dont la plus grande plage du lac, 2 piscines, un impressionnant centre de remise en forme, 3 restaurants, un jardin botanique et un Club Bambini pour les enfants de 2 ans et plus.

Este acogedor y refinado complejo se encuentra situado en el bello lago Lugano, con un espléndido fondo de montañas y zonas de parque. Una impresionante selección de servicios e instalaciones incluyen la playa privada más extensa del lago, 2 piscinas, un impresionante centro de wellness, 3 restaurantes, un jardín botánico y el Club Bambini para niños de 2 años en adelante.

ITALY / LOMBARDY (MONZA, NR MILAN)

HOTEL DE LA VILLE

VIALE REGINA MARGHERITA DI SAVOIA 15, 20052 MONZA (MI), ITALY

Tel: +39 039 39421 **Fax:** +39 039 367 647

Web: www.johansens.com/hoteldelaville **E-mail:** info@hoteldelaville.com

Close to the Formula 1 race track and Milan, this refined and peaceful hotel boasts exquisitely furnished rooms, precious objets d'art and extremely warm and attentive staff. Relax in the American Bar before trying delicious specialities in Derby Grill, considered one of the best restaurants in Italy. Adjacent to the hotel is a recently renovated villa offering additional rooms and suites, a sauna, gym and private garden.

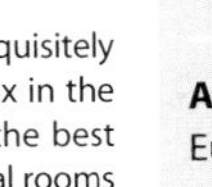

À deux pas du circuit de Formule 1 et de Milan, cet hôtel raffiné et paisible offre des chambres meublées de manière exquise, des objets d'art de valeur, un accueil chaleureux et un personnel attentionné. Relaxez-vous au Bar Américain avant de goûter aux spécialités locales servies dans le fameux Derby Grill, considéré comme l'un des meilleurs restaurants d'Italie. A côté de l'hôtel se trouve, dans une villa récemment rénovée, des chambres et suites supplémentaires, un sauna, une salle de gym et un jardin privé.

Cerca de las pistas de Fórmula 1 y de Milán, este hotel refinado y tranquilo posee habitaciones de exquisito mobiliario, valiosos objetos de arte y un personal de lo mas atento. Tome un aperitivo en el American Bar antes de degustar deliciosos platos especiales de la casa en el Derby Grill, considerado como uno de los mejores restaurantes de Italia. Una villa al lado del hotel, recientemente reformada, proporciona más habitaciones y suites, así como una sauna, un gimnasio y jardin privado.

Our inspector loved: *The professionalism, impeccable service and delicious cuisine.*

Price Guide: (breakfast €27)
superior €227-287
de luxe €297-367
suite €447-547

Awards: Condé Nast Johansens Most Excellent European Service Award 2008

Attractions: Royal Palace and Park, on the doorstep; Duomo and Monza Race Circuit, 1km; Milan and Brianza Areas, 15km; Lake Como, 41km

Nearby Towns: Milan, 16km; Como, 41km; Lecco, 42km; Lugano, 84km
Airports: Milan Linate, 19km; Milan Malpensa, 58km; Bergamo Orio Al Serio, 43km

Category: Hotel
Closed: 24th Dec - 7th Jan and 1st - 26th Aug

Relais Bella Rosina

PARCO REGIONALE LA MANDRIA, VIA AGNELLI, 2, 10070 FIANO (TO), ITALY

Tel: +39 011 9233600 **Fax:** +39 011 9233601

Web: www.johansens.com/bellarosina **E-mail:** info@bellarosina.it

Our inspector loved: *The lovely surroundings and relaxing ambience.*

Price Guide:
double €190-240
junior suite/suite €265-330

Attractions: Turin and Royal Park I Roveri Golf Clubs, 1km; Reggia of Venaria Reale, 8km; Langhe and Roero Wineries and Castles, 80km; Olympic Ski Resorts, 80km

Nearby Towns: Turin, 15km; Alba, 80km; Sestriere Olympic Ski Resort, 95km; Milan, 140km
Airports: Turin Caselle, 15km; Milan Malpensa, 90km; Genova, 190km

Category: Charming Hotel
Closed: 7th - end of January

This 61-acre estate was used by Vittorio Emmanuele II as a hunting ground. A far cry from its origins, the relais is now an eco-friendly, stylish refuge with inviting rooms, a refined restaurant and Beauty Farm. Its philosophy is based on ecologically sound, biologically conscious and energy saving principles proving that sustainable living can also be luxurious living!

Ce domaine de 24 hectares a été utilisé comme lieu de chasse par Victor Emmanuel II. Loin de ses origines, le relais est aujourd'hui un refuge élégant avec des chambres accueillantes, un restaurant raffiné et une Beauty Farm, tout ceci dans le plus grand respect de l'environnement. Sa philosophie est basée sur une écologique saine, une conscience biologique et des principes d'économie d'énergie prouvant qu'écologie peut rimer avec luxe.

Esta propiedad de 24 hectáreas fue utilizada por Vittorio Emmanuele II como coto de caza. Muy distinto de lo que fue en sus orígenes, este relais es ahora un lugar elegante y ecoamigable provisto de encantadoras habitaciones, un refinado restaurante y de Beauty Farm. Su filosofía se basa en sólidos principios ecológicos y el respeto por la biología así como con el ahorro de energía, demostrando con ello que la vida sostenible puede ser compatible con el lujo.

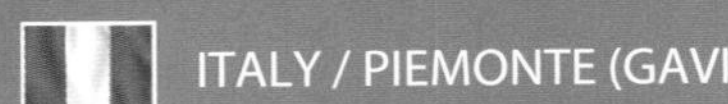

ITALY / PIEMONTE (GAVI)

Albergo L'Ostelliere

FRAZIONE MONTEROTONDO 56, 15065 GAVI (AL), PIEMONTE, ITALY
Tel: +39 0143 607 801 **Fax:** +39 0143 607 811
Web: www.johansens.com/ostelliere **E-mail:** info@ostelliere.it

Wonderfully set within the picturesque Piemontese hills, located between the sea and Milan, this former farmhouse has been transformed into a 21st-century 4-star resort surrounded by well-stocked vineyards. Only the views of the hills outshine the lovely antique furnishings and attractive artworks. You'll find the prestigious restaurant and wines from the 18th-century cellar well worth staying in for.

Superbement située au cœur des pittoresques collines piémontaises entre Milan et la mer, cette ancienne ferme a été transformée en un hôtel 4 étoiles du XXIe siècle, entouré de luxuriantes vignes. Seules les vues sur les collines piémontaises peuvent éclipser le superbe mobilier antique et les oeuvres d'arts. Le prestigieux restaurant et les vins de la cave du XVIIIe siècle qui, à eux seuls, justifient le séjour.

Con una posición magnifica entre Milan y el mar, y ubicada en los bellos montes del Piemonte, esta antigua granja rodeada de frondosos viñedos ha sido transformada en un resort de 4 estrellas del siglo XXI. Sólo las vistas de las colinas eclipsan el maravilloso mobiliario antiguo y las atractivas obras de arte por doquier. Encontrará que el prestigioso restaurante y los vinos de la bodega del siglo XVIII merecen la pena hospedarse aquí.

Our inspector loved: *La Gallina restaurant, the extensive vineyards and impressive wine cellars.*

Price Guide:
double €175-230
suite €240-695

Attractions: Vintage Wineries, on-site; Gavi Wine Region, on the doorstep; Serravalle Design Fashion Outlet, 3km; Castles, Wine Fairs and Historic Buildings, 10km

Nearby Towns: Genova, 40km; Alba, 50km; Portofino, 70km; Torino, 100km
Airports: Genova, 40km; Milan Airports, 95km; Torino, 110km

Category: Charming Hotel
Closed: 1st December - 28th February

ITALY / PIEMONTE (GHIFFA - LAKE MAGGIORE) 

Residenza Dolce Vita Wellness Resort

CORSO RISORGIMENTO 289, 28823 GHIFFA (VB), ITALY

Tel: +39 0323 59658 **Fax:** +39 0323 59373

Web: www.johansens.com/residenzadolcevita **E-mail:** info@residenzadolcevita.com

Our inspector loved: *The location, gorgeous lake view, and the wellness centre, made entirely of local slate, stone and wood.*

Price Guide:
double (single occupancy) €124-175
double €154-194
suite €174-294

Attractions: Music Festivals and Events, on-site; Natural Reserve, 10-min walk; Villa Taranto Botanical Garden, 10km; Tour of Lake Maggiore and Borromean Islands, 40-min boat ride

Nearby Towns: Stresa, 20km; Locarno, 33km; Lugano, 75km; Milan, 110km

Airports: Milan Malpensa, 70km; Milan LInate, 120km; Milan Orio al Serio, 150km

Category: Charming Hotel

Restoring well-being to its guests since the 1920s, this romantic and modish hotel stands in the heart of an unspoilt UNESCO World Heritage site, overlooking Lake Maggiore. Choose from a lake or village facing bedroom or suite, feast on fresh Italian cuisine in Restaurant Convivium and be pampered at Aquavitae Wellness Centre.

Rétablissant le bien-être chez ses hôtes depuis les années 1920, ce romantique hôtel à la mode se trouve au cœur d'un site intact, classé au Patrimoine Mondial de l'UNESCO, surplombant le Lac Majeur. Choisissez entre une chambre face au lac ou au village et une suite, régalez vous de la cuisine italienne du Restaurant Convivium et faites vous choyer au centre de remise en forme Aquavitae.

Comprometido con el bienestar de sus clientes desde la década de los 20, este moderno y romántico hotel se erige en el corazón de un virginal emplazamiento considerado Patrimonio de la Humanidad de la UNESCO, con vistas al Lago Maggiore. Elija entre una habitación con vistas al lago o a la aldea o una suite, disfrute de la cocina casera italiana en el Restaurante Convivium y déjese mimar en el Aquavitae Wellness Centre.

ITALY / PIEMONTE (LAKE MAGGIORE - CANNOBIO)

Hotel Pironi

VIA MARCONI 35, 28822 CANNOBIO, LAKE MAGGIORE (VB), ITALY
Tel: +39 0323 70624 **Fax:** +39 0323 72184
Web: www.johansens.com/pironihotel **E-mail:** info@pironihotel.it

Our inspector loved: *The cosiness of this retreat with an inviting and charming lakeside atmosphere.*

Price Guide:
single €120
double €140-180

Attractions: Trekking and Hiking in the Ticino Valleys, 15km; Ascona Jazz Festival and Locarno International Film Festival, 20km; Botanical Gardens of Villa Taranto, 25km; Borromean Islands, 40-min boat ride

Nearby Towns: Locarno, Switzerland, 20km; Stresa, 35km; Lugano, Switzerland, 80km; Milan, 100km
Airports: Lugano, 50km; Milan Malpensa, 80km; Milan Orio Al Serio, 150km

Category: Charming Hotel
Closed: November - March

Small and intimate, this exquisite house on the shore of Lake Maggiore, is housed in a 15th-century building that was originally a Franciscan monastery. Send quiet thanks for a skilful restoration, combining romantic, cosy rooms, original frescoes, antiques, vaulted ceilings, stone columns and a gentle touch of modern design.

Petite et intime, cette maison exquise au bord du lac Majeur est installée dans un bâtiment du XVe siècle qui fut, à l'origine, un monastère franciscain. Saluons une restauration très réussie qui combine chambres romantiques et confortables, fresques originales, antiquités, plafonds voûtés, colonnes en pierre et une légère touche de décoration contemporaine.

Pequeña y íntimo, esta exquisita casa a la orilla del lago Maggiore se encuentra ubicada en un edificio del siglo XV que en su origen fue monasterio franciscano. Agradecerá en él su artística restauración, en la que se combinan acogedoras y románticas habitaciones, frescos originales, antigüedades, techos abovedados, columnas de piedra y un sutil toque de modernidad en su diseño.

ITALY / PIEMONTE (LANGHE - SANTO STEFANO BELBO) 

Relais San Maurizio

LOCALITÀ SAN MAURIZIO 39, 12058 SANTO STEFANO BELBO (CN), ITALY
Tel: +39 0141 841900 **Fax:** +39 0141 843833
Web: www.johansens.com/relaissanmaurizio **E-mail:** info@relaissanmaurizio.it

Our inspector loved: *The enchanting surroundings, great cuisine, and amazing spa.*

Price Guide: (breakfast €20)
double from €280
junior suite from €330
suite from €380

Awards: 1 Star Michelin

Attractions: Langhe Wine Cellars of Barolo and Barbaresco, 2km; White Truffle Fair, 15km; Historic Towns and Castles, 10km; Egyptian Museum and Royal Residence, Turin, 90km

Nearby Towns: Alba, 25km; Asti, 25km; Torino, 90km; Milan, 120km
Airports: Turin, 90km; Genova, 100km; Milan, 140km

Category: Charming Hotel
Closed: During January and February

After winding up a tiny road, you will reach this exclusive hideaway, perched at the top of a hill overlooking ancient vineyards and castles. Originally a monastery, the antique-filled rooms are stylish and in-keeping with its past. The award-winning cellar restaurant serves outstanding food, and the unique medical and beauty spa, La Via del Sale, is at your disposal.

Après avoir emprunté une petite route sinueuse, vous arriverez dans ce refuge de luxe, perché au sommet d'une colline qui donne sur d'anciens vignobles et des châteaux. Cet ancien monastère propose des chambres élégantes remplies de meubles anciens, en accord avec son passé. Dans le cellier, le restaurant primé sert une cuisine exceptionnelle et le spa medical et de beauté, La Via del Sale, est à votre disposition.

Tras subir por una pequeña carretera llegará a este exclusivo refugio, encaramado en la cima de una colina con vistas a ancestrales viñedos y castillos. Originariamente un monasterio, sus habitaciones repletas de antigüedades son elegantes y respetuosas con su pasado. El galardonado restaurante-bodega proporciona una extraordinaria carta, y el singular spa medico y de belleza, La Via del Sale, se encuentra también a su disposición.

ITALY / PIEMONTE (LANGHE - TREZZO TINELLA)

CASCINA LANGA

VIA CAPPELLETTO 36, 12050 TREZZO TINELLA (CUNEO), ITALY
Tel: +39 0173 630289
Web: www.johansens.com/cascinalanga **E-mail:** info@cascinalanga.it

Tucked away in 148 acres of greenery and woodland, this age-old farmhouse is now a colourful design boutique hotel. Steeped in history, the transformation of this peaceful country retreat has resulted in 5 themed guest rooms, an intimate spa and an excellent restaurant serving a menu based on fresh seasonal ingredients from the Langhe region.

Caché dans 60 hectares de verdure et de forêt, cette ferme séculaire est aujourd'hui un boutique hôtel design et coloré. Chargée d'histoire, la transformation de cette paisible retraite campagnarde a conduit à la réalisation de 5 chambres à thèmes, d'un spa intime et d'un excellent restaurant servant un menu à base d'ingrédients frais de saison de la région de Langhe.

Arropado por 60 hectáreas de zona verde y boscosa, esta antigua granja es en la actualidad un llamativo hotel boutique de diseño. Empapado de historia, la transformación de este tranquilo lugar de retiro rural ha dado pie a 5 habitaciones temáticas, un intimista spa y un excelente restaurante que ofrece una carta basada en ingredientes frescos de temporada procedentes de la región de Langhe.

Our inspector loved: *The joyful blend of colours and design that adhere to enhancing the mind, body and soul philosophy.*

Price Guide:
junior design suite €170-250

5 40

Attractions: Wineries and Enogastronomic Tours, 10km; White Truffles Fair, Music and Film Festivals in Alba, 12km; Castles and Wineries in Langhe and Roero Region, 12km; Torino Sightseeing, Egyptian Museum and Royal House, 90km

Nearby Towns: Alba, 12km; Bra, 32km; Asti, 40km; Torino, 90km
Airports: Turin, 70km; Milan Linate, 170km; Genova, 180km

Category: Charming Hotel
Closed: During January and February

Hotel Principi di Piemonte

VIA PIERO GOBETTI, 15, 10123 TURIN, ITALY
Tel: +39 011 55151 **Fax:** +39 011 5185 870
Web: www.johansens.com/principidipiemonte **E-mail:** booking@principidipiemonte.com

Our inspector loved: *The sumptuous Salone delle Feste with 1930s Venini's Murano chandeliers and mosaics.*

Price Guide: (other suites available on request)
de luxe €210-450
junior suite €240-550
suite €380-5,000

Attractions: Turin with its Egyptian Museum, Mole Antonelliana and National Museum of Cinema, 5-min walk; La Venaria Reale, 12km; Val di Susa Ski Resort, 50km; Langhe and Roero Wine Truffle District and Truffle Fair in Alba, 55km

Nearby Towns: Asti, 57km; Alba, 60km; Sestriere Ski Resort, 60km; Milan, 140km
Airports: Turin Caselle, 12km; Milan Malpensa, 135km; Genova, 165km

Category: Hotel

Built by the Agnelli family in the 1930s, this refined bolthole was recently renovated to further enhance its opulent status along with the latest technology. Bedrooms offer elegant furnishings and views of the town and the Alps. Be sure to dine at the exclusive restaurant, relax in the inviting wellness centre or the Salone delle Feste with Venini's Murano chandeliers and mosaics.

Construit par la famille Agnelli dans les années 1930, ce refuge raffiné a été récemment rénové pour améliorer encore son somptueux standing tout en le dotant des dernières technologies. Les chambres offrent un mobilier élégant et des vues sur la ville et les Alpes. N'oubliez pas de dîner au très sélect restaurant, relaxez-vous dans le centre de bien-être ou dans le Salone delle Feste avec les mosaïques et les lustres Venini de Murano.

Construido por la familia Agnelli en los años 30, este refinado refugio ha sido renovado recientemente para realzar aún más su opulento status junto a los últimos avances en tecnología. Las habitaciones lucen elegantes muebles y ofrecen vistas a la ciudad y a los Alpes. No se olvide de cenar en el distinguido restaurante, descansar en el apetecible centro wellness y no deje de ver el Salone delle Feste con sus mosaicos y lámparas arañas Murano de Venini.

ITALY / PUGLIA (CANOSA)

Country House Cefalicchio

CONTRADA CEFALICCHIO, CANOSA DI PUGLIA (BARI), ITALY

Tel: +39 0883 642123 **Fax:** +39 0883 642123

Web: www.johansens.com/cefalicchio **E-mail:** direzione@cefalicchio.it

In the heart of extensive biodynamic vineyards, the largest in southern Italy, this charming retreat has been restored in an authentic rural style that successfully incorporates modern-day comforts. A relaxing home-from-home feeling pervades throughout each corner, and the shaded garden is a tranquil respite. The imaginative cuisine is created from organic, locally grown produce and prepared in accordance with biodynamic principles.

Au cœur de vignobles biodynamiques étendus, les principaux en Italie du sud, ce refuge de charme a été restauré dans un style authentique rural qui a su intégrer harmonieusement les conforts des temps modernes. Le sentiment relaxant d'être à la maison se retrouve dans chaque coin et le jardin ombragé est un refuge tranquille. La cuisine imaginative est créée à partir de produits organiques locaux et est préparée en conformité avec les principes de la biodynamique.

En el corazón de extensos viñedos biodinámicos, los mayores del sur de Italia, este encantador refugio ha sido restaurado en genuino estilo rural en el que se incorporan las más modernas comodidades. Una relajante sensación hogareña invade cada rincón, y el sombreado jardín es un edén de tranquilidad. La cocina es imaginativa y está elaborada con productos orgánicos del lugar según principios biodinámicos.

Our inspector loved: *The excellent wine produced on the estate, a great added bonus to this lovely property.*

Price Guide:
double €130
suite €195
mini apartment €260

Attractions: Wild Foods Cooking Courses, Natural Wine Tastings, Yoga Classes, Winetherapy Spa, on-site; Food and Wine Tours, 15-min drive, Historical Sites (Frederic II Castle), 15-min drive, Gargano Beach Spots, 50-min drive

Nearby Towns: Canosa Historical City, 3km; Trani, 30km; Altamura, 75km; Matera, 95km

Airports: Bari, 75km; Napoli, 180km; Brindisi 180km

Category: Charming Hotel

MASSERIA ALCHIMIA

CONTRADA FASCIANELLO, 72010 FASANO, BRINDISI, ITALY

Tel: +39 335 6094647

Web: www.johansens.com/masseriaalchimia **E-mail:** info@masseria-alchimia.it

Our inspector loved: *The globe-trotting owner, who has made this luxury guest house a fashionable, charming, relaxed and stylish getaway.*

Price Guide: (room only)
double €53-165
romantic sea view room €90-165
suite €135-245

Attractions: Fasano Zoo, 1km; Beach Clubs, 3km; Polignano Village and Fjord, 15km

Nearby Towns: Fasano, 1km; Alberobello, 15km; Ostuni, 20km; Cisternino, 20km
Airports: Bari, 45km; Brindisi, 50km

Category: Luxury Guest House

On Apulia's Adriatic coast, surrounded by olive trees and countryside as far as the eye can see, is this extraordinarily futuristic oasis of tranquillity. A 17th-century mansion that is now 6 self-catering accommodations, owner and manager Caroline Groszer has successfully created an innovative, inspirational and environmentally conscious escape from the hectic pace of modern life.

Cette extraordinaire oasis futuriste de tranquillité est située sur la côte de l'Adriatique des Pouilles et entourée d'oliviers et de maquis à perte de vue. C'est une ferme du XVIIe siècle qui abrite dorénavant 6 hébergements équipés. La propriétaire et gérante, Caroline Groszer, a réussi à créer avec succès un refuge innovant, inspiré, en respect avec l'environnement et loin du rythme soutenu de la vie moderne.

En la costa adriática de Apulia y rodeado de olivos y paisaje hasta donde alcanza la vista, se encuentra este oasis de paz y de extraordinario futurismo. Se trata de una mansión del siglo XVII convertida ahora en 6 alojamientos equipados con self-catering. Su propietaria y directora, Caroline Groszer, ha conseguido crear un lugar innovador y sugerente, a la vez que respetuoso con el medio ambiente, apartado del bullicio de la vida moderna.

ITALY / SAN MARINO REPUBLIC (SAN MARINO)

Hotel Titano

CONTRADA DEL COLLEGIO 31, 47890 SAN MARINO (RSM), SAN MARINO REPUBLIC
Tel: +378 0549 991007 **Fax:** +378 0549 991375
Web: www.johansens.com/hoteltitano **E-mail:** info@hoteltitano.com

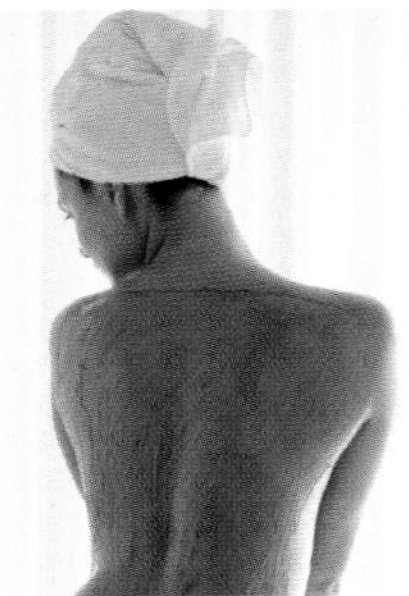

Amid the winding cobbled streets of the ancient independent Republic of San Marino, a UNESCO World Heritage site within the borders of the Emilia Romagna region, Hotel Titano proudly revels in its views of the surrounding countryside. Rooms reflect the building's 19th-century history, and there are 2 restaurants with fantastic outlooks over Contrada or the Apennines. Maurice Messegue Beauty Centre offers consultations and treatments.

Parmi les tortueuses rues pavées de l'ancienne République de Saint-Marin, site classé au Patrimoine Mondial de l'UNESCO aux frontières de la région Emilia Romagna, l'hôtel Titano peut être fier de ses vues sur la campagne environnante. Les chambres se font l'écho de l'histoire de ce bâtiment du XIXe siècle. Vous pouvez choisir entre les 2 restaurants avec leurs vues fantastiques sur le Contrada ou sur les Appenins. L'Institut de Beauté Maurice Messegue prodigue des conseils et des soins.

Ubicado entre las calles adoquinadas y sinuosas de la antigua República de San Marino, Patrimonio de la Humanidad de UNESCO dentro de los confines de la región de Emilia Romagna, el Hotel Titano se deleita orgulloso del panorama rural que le rodea. Las habitaciones reflejan la historia de este edificio del siglo XIX, y los 2 restaurantes, tienen fantásticas vistas a Contrada o a los Apeninos. El Centro de Belleza Maurice Messegue atiende consultas y ofrece tratamientos.

Our inspector loved: *The enchanting view and easy access to the heart of San Marino, one of the oldest and smallest Republics in the world.*

Price Guide:
double (single occupancy) €50-120
double €90-190
junior suite €150-210

Attractions: Ferrari Car Museum, on-site; Tax Free Shopping and Fashion Outlets, on-site; Adriatic Coast, Beaches and Amusement Parks, 25km; Faenza Ceramic Museum, Ravenna Byzantine Heritage and Dante's Grave, 85km

Nearby Towns: Rimini, 25km; Urbino, 50km; Bologna, 140km; Florence, 190km
Airports: Rimini F Fellini, 36km; Forlì , 1-hour drive; Ancona R Sanzio, 120km

Category: Charming Hotel

Villa Las Tronas Hotel & Spa

LUNGOMARE VALENCIA 1, 07041 ALGHERO (SS), ITALY
Tel: +39 079 981 818 **Fax:** +39 079 981 044
Web: www.johansens.com/lastronas **E-mail:** info@hvlt.com

Our inspector loved: *The magical atmosphere, the sea and wonderful spa.*

Price Guide:
single €128-247
double €182-427
suite €386-622

Attractions: Art Exhibitions and Concerts, on-site; Necropolis of Anghelu Ruju, 10km; Antiquarium with Roman Excavations, 40km; Monte d'Accodi with Prehistoric Altar, 40km

Nearby Towns: Portotorres, 36km; Sassari, 37km; Bosa, 45km; Stintino, 45km
Airports: Alghero, 10km; Olbia, 150km

Category: Hotel

A holiday home to Italian royalty until the 1940s, this tranquil 5-star hotel is located on the coastline with piers and terraces leading directly into the sea. Traditionally-styled rooms and suites look out to sea or garden views, and these vistas can also be enjoyed during candle-lit dinners to a background of classical music. The hotel and spa, with its covered pool, sauna, Turkish bath, kneipp walkway, gym and beauty area, are open throughout the year.

Résidence de vacances de la famille royale italienne jusque dans les années 40, cet hôtel tranquille 5 étoiles est situé sur la côte et possède un accès direct à la mer par ses terrasses et pontons. Les chambres et suites de style traditionnel offrent des vues sur la mer ou sur les jardins et ces panoramas peuvent être également admirés lors de dîners aux chandelles sur fond de musique classique. L'hôtel et son spa, avec piscine couverte, sauna, bain turc, thérapie Kneipp, salle de gym et coin beauté, sont ouverts toute l'année.

Residencia de la realeza italiana hasta la década de los 40, este tranquilo hotel de 5 estrellas esta situado en la costa con embarcaderos y terrazas que dan a la mar. Las habitaciones y suites de clásico mobiliario tienen vistas del mar o del jardín, y estas vistas se pueden disfrutar también durante una cena a la luz de las velas con música clásica de fondo. Ambos hotel y Spa, con piscina cubierta, sauna, baño turco, kneipp walkway, gimnasio y zona de belleza, estan abiertos durante todo el año.

ITALY / SARDINIA (COSTA SMERALDA - SAN PANTALEO)

PETRA SEGRETA RESORT & SPA

STRADA BUDDEU, CP 130, 07026 SAN PANTALEO, OLBIA, ITALY
Tel: +39 0789 183 1365 **Fax:** +39 0789 480 310
Web: www.johansens.com/petrasegretaresort **E-mail:** info@petrasegretaresort.com

Our inspector loved: *The magical atmosphere and surroundings of granite caves and rocks.*

Price Guide: (half board rates available)
de luxe €250-600
junior suite €310-660

Attractions: Pevero Golf Course, 7km; Porto Cervo and Costa Smeralda Beaches, 12km; Marine Park of Tavolara and Molara, 50-min boat ride; La Maddalena and Caprera Island, 1-hour ferry ride

Nearby Towns: Cala di Volpe, 10km; Porto Cervo, 12km; Pevero, 12km; Olbia, 15km
Airports: Olbia Ferry Port, 12km; Olbia, 15km; Alghero, 160km

Category: Charming Hotel
Closed: November - March

This unparalleled, exclusive and elegantly furnished resort stands in 12 acres of untouched nature and weather-beaten rock formations, looking down on spectacular views of the Arzachena Gulf and over to Corsica. Consisting of typical local houses, interiors have been transformed into first-class rooms, a superb restaurant and unusual spa where Far Eastern treatments are carried out in granite caves.

Ce resort exclusif, incomparable et élégamment décoré se situe au coeur de 5 hectares de nature intacte et de formations rocheuses battues par les éléments. Il offre des vues spectaculaires sur le Golfe d'Arzachena et sur la Corse. Composés de maisons locales typiques, les intérieurs ont été transformés en somptueuses pièces, un superbe restaurant et un spa atypique où les soins d'Extrême-Orient sont prodigués dans des caves de granite.

Este inigualable complejo, exclusivo y elegantemente amueblado, se erige en medio de 5 hectáreas de naturaleza salvaje y formaciones rocosas curtidas por la intemperie, con vistas espectaculares del golfo de Arzachena y de Córcega en la lejanía. Formado de casas típicas del lugar, sus interiores han sido transformados para crear habitaciones de primera, un restaurante fabuloso y un singular spa, cuyos tratamientos procedentes del lejano oriente se realizan dentro de cuevas de granito.

ITALY / SARDINIA (PORTO CERVO - COSTA SMERALDA) 

Grand Hotel in Porto Cervo

LOCALITÀ CALA GRANU, 07020 PORTO CERVO (OT), ITALY

Tel: +39 0789 91533 **Fax:** +39 0789 91508

Web: www.johansens.com/portocervo **E-mail:** info@grandhotelinportocervo.com

Our inspector loved: *The sea-facing, open-air lounges, and the beach restaurant.*

Price Guide:
double room classic €180-440
double room superior €250-560

Attractions: La Maddalena Archipelago, 30km; Santa Teresa di Gallura Bay, 45km; Supramonte and Barbagia, 90km; Alghero, 170km

Nearby Towns: Olbia, 30km; Porto Rotondo, 25km; Sassari, 130km; Nuoro, 130km
Airports: Olbia, 35km; Alghero, 170km

Category: Hotel
Closed: October - April

It's blue as far as the eye can see from the charming bay of Cala Granu. Most of the rooms and suites at this welcoming hotel have sea views, balconies or terraces and modern amenities. There are 2 restaurants, including the exclusive Orange restaurant. This hotel is justly proud of its panoramic pool.

Du bleu à perte de vue depuis la ravissante baie de Cala Granu. La plupart des chambres et des suites de cet hôtel accueillant ont des vues sur la mer, des balcons ou terrasses et tout le confort moderne. Il y a 2 restaurants, dont l'exclusif restaurant Orange. La piscine panoramique est la fierté de l'hôtel.

Tan azul como puede percibir el ojo humano resulta el paisaje que se contempla desde la encantadora bahía de Cala Granu. La mayoría de las habitaciones y suites de este acogedor hotel disponen de vistas al mar, balcones o terrazas y modernas instalaciones. Cuenta con 2 restaurantes, entre los que se incluye el exclusivo restaurante Orange. Este hotel tiene motivos para estar orgulloso de su panorámica piscina.

ITALY / SICILY (AEOLIAN ISLANDS - SALINA)

HOTEL SIGNUM

VIA SCALO 15, 98050 SALINA~MALFA, ITALY
Tel: +39 090 9844222 **Fax:** +39 090 9844102
Web: www.johansens.com/signum **E-mail:** salina@hotelsignum.it

A favourite with the rich and famous due to its extreme privacy, magical atmosphere, amazing food and open-air spa, this intimate hotel enjoys a hillside location where fragranced pathways lead to a small rocky beach. Each room is beautifully decorated with a unique personal touch that is simply charming, and the staff provide the utmost in hospitality.

Lieu privilégié des personnes riches et connues du fait de sa situation loin des regards indiscrets, de son atmosphère magique, de la délicieuse cuisine et de son spa à ciel ouvert, cet hôtel intime jouit d'un emplacement sur une colline où des sentiers parfumés mènent à une petite plage rocheuse. Chacune des chambres est magnifiquement décorée avec une touche personnelle unique, qui est tout simplement délicieuse et le personnel offre le meilleur de l'hospitalité.

Un lugar favorito de los ricos y de los famosos debido a su extrema privacidad, su ambiente mágico, su fabulosa carta y spa al aire libre. Este hotel intimista se ubica sobre una colina en las que los senderos plenos de fragancias conducen a una pequeña playa rocosa. Cada habitación está decorada con suma belleza y con un toque propio simplemente encantador. Su personal proporciona el no va en hospitalidad.

Our inspector loved: *The new spa, which is a stylish and magical place, especially on starry nights!*

Price Guide:
classic/superior €130-320
de luxe double €210-360

Attractions: Vineyards and Trekking on Salina, 15-min drive; Monte Fosse Volcano on Salina, 2-hour walk; Panarea Diving and Night-life, 30-min boat ride; Volcano Trekking and Thermal Springs, 40-min boat ride

Nearby Towns: Vulcano Island, 40-min boat ride; Lipari Island, 30-min boat ride; Stromboli Island, 1-hour boat ride; Milazzo, 90-min boat ride
Airports: Milazzo Catania, 2-hour drive; Milazzo Palermo, 3-hour drive

Category: Charming Hotel
Closed: November - February

Palazzo Failla Hotel

VIA BLANDINI 5, 97010 MODICA (RG), ITALY
Tel: +39 0932 941059 **Fax:** +39 0932 941059
Web: www.johansens.com/palazzofailla **E-mail:** info@palazzofailla.it

Our inspector loved: *The dining options, from the 1 Michelin-Starred restaurant to the traditional "Locanda."*

Price Guide:
single €110
double €150-195
junior suite €210

 10      60 

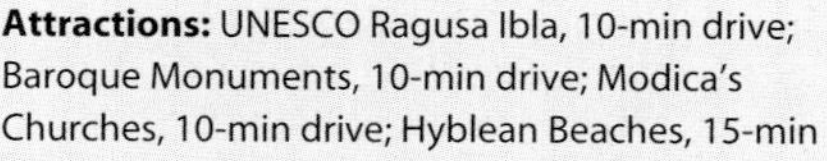

Attractions: UNESCO Ragusa Ibla, 10-min drive; Baroque Monuments, 10-min drive; Modica's Churches, 10-min drive; Hyblean Beaches, 15-min drive

Nearby Towns: UNESCO Ragusa Ibla, 10-min drive; Noto, 45-min drive; Siracusa, 1-hour drive
Airports: Comiso, 30km; Catania, 85km

Category: Charming Hotel

Live the life of an aristocrat and stay in the former Failla family home. Hand-made tiles, frescoes and antique furniture uphold its grand character, and for truly romantic stays reserve the Green Room. For total privacy retreat to one of the stunning suites. Michelin Star-awarded Chef Accursio Craparo offers an innovative menu at La Gazza Ladra Restaurant whilst a traditional trattoria is also available.

Vivez la vie d'un aristocrate et résidez dans l'ancienne maison de famille des Failla. Les carrelages faits main, les fresques et les meubles anciens sont les traces de son caractère grandiose et pour un séjour particulièrement romantique, réservez la chambre Verte. Retirez-vous dans l'une des magnifiques suites pour une intimité totale. Le Chef étoilé Michelin, Accursio Craparo, propose une cuisine inventive au restaurant Gazza Ladra et une trattoria traditionnelle est également disponible.

Viva la vida de un aristócrata en el antiguo hogar de la familia Failla. Azulejos artesanales, frescos y muebles de época mantienen el carácter grandioso de esta casa, y si desea una estancia verdaderamente romántica, reserve la Sala Verde. Para total intimidad escoja una de las impresionantes suites. El Chef Accursio Craparo, galardonado por la guía Michelin, le ofrece una innovadora carta en el restaurante La Gazza Ladra y en la trattoria se sirve comida tradicional.

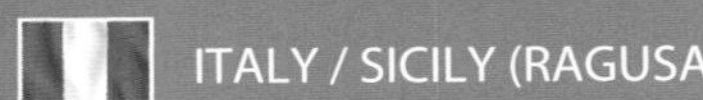

ITALY / SICILY (RAGUSA)

Locanda Don Serafino

VIA XI FEBBRAIO, 15 RAGUSA IBLA, ITALY
Tel: +39 0932 220065 **Fax:** +39 0932 663186
Web: www.johansens.com/serafino **E-mail:** info@locandadonserafino.it

Our inspector loved: *Its location, in the atmospheric old part of Ragusa Ibla.*

Price Guide:
standard/superior/de luxe €148-195

10    

Awards: 1 Star Michelin

Attractions: Hyblean Beaches, 15-min drive; UNESCO Baroque City of Modica, 15-min drive; Islands of Pozzallo and Malta, 90-min boat ride

Nearby Towns: Ragusa, 5-min drive; Modica, 15-min drive; Scicli, 20-min drive
Airports: Comiso, 21km; Catania, 101km

Category: Charming Hotel

Baroque Ragusa Ibla unravels to reveal this 19th-century mansion. Rooms feature hand-made wooden furniture, luxurious mattresses and a choice of pillows to suit the most discerning sleeper! The Michelin-Starred restaurant, with an excellent menu and wine list of over 1,000 labels, is located in the old church nearby. The hotel's private beach and additional seaside restaurant are a short drive away in Marina di Ragusa.

Baroque ville de Ragusa Ibla se dévoile pour révéler cette demeure du XIXe siècle. Les chambres sont équipées de meubles en bois faits main, de luxueux matelas et d'un choix d'oreillers destinés à satisfaire le dormeur le plus délicat ! Le restaurant étoilé Michelin, avec un excellent menu et une liste de plus de 1000 vins, est situé dans une ancienne église à proximité. La plage privée de l'hôtel et un autre restaurant en bord de mer sont à quelques minutes en voiture, à Marina di Ragusa.

Barroca Ragusa Ibla se abre para descubrir esta mansión del siglo XIX. Las habitaciones disponen de mobiliario realizado en madera artesanal, colchones de lujo y una selección de almohadas que complacerá al más delicado de los durmientes. El restaurante, poseedor de una estrella Michelin y una carta de vinos de más de 1,000 marcas, esta ubicado en una antigua iglesia cercana. La playa privada del hotel y su otro restaurante al lado del mar se encuentran a corta distancia en Marina di Ragusa.

Grand Hotel Atlantis Bay

VIA NAZIONALE 161, TAORMINA MARE (ME), ITALY
Tel: +39 0942 618011 **Fax:** +39 0942 23194
Web: www.johansens.com/atlantis **E-mail:** info@atlantisbay.it

Our inspector loved: *The brand new spa and its range of treatments.*

Price Guide:
single €300-480
double €365-560
suite €570-1,050

Awards: Condé Nast Johansens Most Excellent European Meeting Venue 2008

Attractions: Isolabella, 1km; Taormina Greek Theatre, 5km; Mount Etna, 40km

Nearby Towns: Taormina, 4km; Catania, 50km
Airports: Catania, 50km

Category: Hotel
Closed: December - January

Prepare to be swept away by the exotic Grand Hotel, home to many celebrities and international guests. Walking inside is like entering an enchanted cave; each bedroom has cool, white-washed walls and elegant fabrics, and the indulgent Presidential Suite, with 2 bathrooms, dining and living rooms, even has it very own tropical fish aquarium! The candle-lit restaurant, terraces and panoramic views are truly romantic.

Laissez-vous transporter par l'exotique du Grand Hotel, le résidence de nombreuses célébrités et d'hôtes internationaux. Y entrer est comme pénétrer dans une caverne enchantée : chaque chambre est décorée de murs blancs peints à la chaux et d'élégantes étoffes et la Presidential Suite avec ses 2 salles de bain, ses salons et salle à manger possède son propre aquarium de poissons tropicaux. Le restaurant éclairé aux chandelles, les terrasses et les vues panoramiques garantissent un véritable séjour romantique.

Déjese deslumbrar por el exótico del Grand Hotel, el hogar de muchas celebridades y clientes internacionales. Entrar en el hotel es como meterse en una cueva encantada. Todas las habitaciones combinan frescas paredes blancas con elegantes telas, y la lujosa Presidential Suite posee 2 cuartos de baño, comedor, salón y un acuario lleno de peces tropicales. El restaurante iluminado con velas, las terrazas y las vistas panorámicas crean un ambiente verdaderamente romántico.

ITALY / SICILY (TAORMINA RIVIERA - GIARDINI NAXOS)

Grand Hotel Mazzarò Sea Palace

VIA NAZIONALE 147, 98030 TAORMINA (ME), SICILY, ITALY

Tel: +39 0942 612111 **Fax:** +39 0942 626237

Web: www.johansens.com/mazzaroseapalace **E-mail:** info@mazzaroseapalace.it

Grand by name and by nature, the hotel presides over one of Taormina Riviera's loveliest spots right on the beach of a small bay, and offers breathtaking views. The bedrooms are exquisitely furnished and have amazing terraces; some even have private pools. Soak up the sun on the private beach, explore the beauties of Taormina and nearby coastal villages and treat yourself with a visit to the new wellness centre.

Grand par son nom et par nature, l'hôtel domine l'un des plus ravissants sites de Taormina, sur la plage d'une petite baie et offre des vues à couper le souffle. Les chambres sont meublées avec raffinement et possèdent de magnifiques terrasses; certaines ont même une piscine privée. Faites le plein de soleil sur la plage privée ou découvrez les splendeurs de Taormina et des villages côtiers situés à proximité et offrez-vous une visite au nouveau centre de bien-être.

Grandioso por nombre y por naturaleza, este hotel con impresionantes vistas, se erige en la playa de una pequeña cala en uno de los lugares más encantadores de Taormina. Las habitaciones están decoradas con exquisitez y disponen de increíbles terrazas; algunas con piscinas privadas. Empápese del sol en la playa privada, descubra las beldades de Taormina y otros pueblos cercanos a la costa y disfrute de una placentera visita al nuevo centro Wellness.

Our inspector loved: *The ideal location, perfect for a well-deserved break away, special event or celebration.*

Price Guide:
single €220-440
double €320-530
suite €560-980

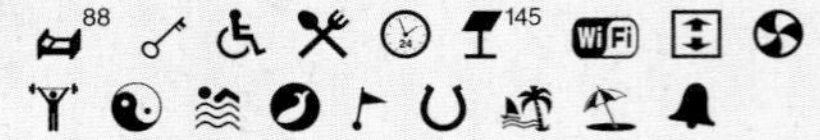

Awards: Condé Nast Johansens Most Excellent Business Venue Award 2008

Attractions: Isolabella, 1km; Taormina Greek Theatre, 5km; Mount Etna, 40km; Taormina, 10-min cable car or private chauffeur

Nearby Towns: Taormina, 4km; Catania, 50km; Messina, 80km
Airports: Catania, 50km

Category: Hotel

Baia Taormina Grand Palace Hotels & Spa

VIA NAZIONALE, KM 39, 98030 MARINA D'AGRO, TAORMINA RIVIERA (ME), ITALY
Tel: +39 0942 756292 **Fax:** +39 0942 756603
Web: www.johansens.com/baiataormina **E-mail:** sales@baiataormina.com

Our inspector loved: *The superb view, and the relaxing, rejuvenating atmosphere.*

Price Guide: (per person, half board available)
executive €125-188
junior suite €155-218

Attractions: Isolabella, 6km; Forza d'Agrò, 5km; Taormina Greek Theatre, 10km; Mount Etna Volcano, 30-min drive

Nearby Towns: Taormina, 6km; Messina, 40km; Catania, 50km; Siracusa 120km
Airports: Catania, 50km

Category: Hotel
Closed: November - March

Recently unveiled alongside the existing hotel, the Grand Palace wing blends into its surroundings thanks to inspired use of natural stone, Sicilian, and traditional Caltagirone ceramics. Gaze across the Ionian Sea from several terraces, and explore interiors reflecting local style with designer touches. When reserving rooms in the Grand Palace wing, quote Condé Nast Johansens.

Récemment inaugurée à côté de l'hôtel existant, l'aile du Grand Palace se fond dans son environnement grâce à la très belle utilisation de pierre naturelle et de céramiques siciliennes et traditionnelles de Caltagirone. Vous pourrez contempler la mer ionienne depuis les multiples terrasses et découvrir les intérieurs reflétant le style local mêlé de notes contemporaines. Citez Condé Nast Johansens quand vous réservez dans la Grand Palace aile.

Recientemente inaugurada y revelada al público, al mismo tiempo que el hotel ya existente, el ala del Grand Palace forma parte integral del paisaje gracias al inspirado uso de la roca natural y de la cerámica siciliana y tradicional de Caltagirone. Dirija su mirada contemplativa hacia el mar Jónico desde sus variadas terrazas y explore sus interiores rebosantes de estilo local y toques de diseño. Cuando reserve habitaciones en su Grand Palace ala, no olvide mencionar Condé Nast Johansens.

Hotel Villa Ducale

VIA LEONARDO DA VINCI 60, 98039 TAORMINA (ME), SICILY, ITALY
Tel: +39 0942 28153 **Fax:** +39 0942 28710
Web: www.johansens.com/villaducale **E-mail:** info@villaducale.com

Our inspector loved: *The incredible view over the Taormina Gulf and amazing Etna Volcano.*

Price Guide:
double €120-280
suite €250-450

Attractions: Beaches, 5km; Taormina Greek Theatre, 5-min drive; Mount Etna, 30-min drive; Siracusa, 110km

Nearby Towns: Taormina, 5-min drive; Catania, 50km; Siracusa, 110km
Airports: Catania, 50km

Category: Luxury Guest House

Feel like a VIP at this pretty villa overlooking Mount Etna and the bay of Taormina. With the charm and warm atmosphere of a private residence, you would be forgiven for thinking you were staying with friends. Owners, Andrea and Rosaria Quartucci and their amazing staff will totally take care of you, so relax and enjoy your surroundings and head to the town centre and beach via the free shuttle service.

Vous vous sentirez comme un VIP dans cette jolie villa qui donne sur l'Etna et la baie de Taormina. Grâce au charme et à l'atmosphère chaleureuse d'une résidence privée, vous oublierez où vous vous trouvez et aurez l'impression d'être accueillis chez des amis. Les propriétaires, Andrea et Rosaria Quartucci, et leur merveilleuse équipe prendront complètement soin de vous. Alors relaxez-vous et profitez des environs ou utilisez la navette gratuite pour vous rendre en centre ville ou à la plage.

Se sentirá como un VIP en esta preciosa villa con vistas al monte Etna y a la bahía de Taormina. Gracias al encanto y al cálido ambiente propios de una residencia particular, se le perdonará que piense que se hospeda en casa de unos amigos. Los dueños Andrea y Rosaria Quartucci y su admirable personal le cuidarán totalmente, así que usted podrá relajarse, disfrutar del entorno, y hacer viajes a la ciudad y a la playa a través del servicio de transporte gratuito que ofrece el hotel.

VILLA CARLOTTA

VIA PIRANDELLO 81, 98039 TAORMINA (ME), ITALY
Tel: +39 0942 626058 **Fax:** +39 0942 23732
Web: www.johansens.com/villacarlotta **E-mail:** info@villacarlotta.net

Our inspector loved: *The privacy and exclusivity. This is the perfect setting for a truly relaxing break.*

Price Guide:
double €130-320
junior suite €160-380
de luxe suite €200-500

Attractions: Beaches, 3km; Taormina Greek Theatre, 5-min walk; Mount Etna, 25km

Nearby Towns: Taormina Centre, 5-min walk; Catania, 50km; Siracusa, 100km
Airports: Catania, 50km

Category: Charming Hotel

This beautiful villa was built by an aristocratic family at the end of the 19th century, and is a wonderful example of sophisticated décor with pieces of art in every corner. Its warm, luxurious setting is sleek and elegant, reflecting the refined taste of the proprietors. And outside, the bougainvillea-filled garden is a secluded and colourful sanctuary. The view from the villa is superb and the service is outstanding.

Cette splendide villa, construite par une famille d'aristocrates à la fin du XIXe siècle, est l'exemple même d'une décoration sophistiquée avec des oeuvres d'art disposées à chaque coin. Son intérieur chaleureux et luxueux, harmonieux et élégant, est à l'image du goût raffiné des propriétaires. A l'extérieur, le jardin rempli de bougainvillées est un havre de paix et de couleurs. Les vues depuis la villa sont magnifiques et le service est de premier ordre.

Esta bella villa fue construida por una familia noble a finales del siglo XIX y es un magnifico ejemplo de decoración sofisticada con piezas de arte en cada rincón. Su cálido, lujoso interior es pulcro y elegante, lo cual refleja el refinado gusto de sus propietarios. En el exterior, el colorido de su buganvilla engalana el tranquilo y encantador jardín. Las vistas desde la villa son maravillosas y el servicio es estupendo.

ITALY / TRENTINO - ALTO ADIGE / DOLOMITES (AVELENGO/HAFLING - MERANO/MERAN)

GranPanorama Hotel Miramonti

St. Kathrein Str., Santa Catharina 14, 39010 Avelengo/Hafling - Merano/Meran, Italy

Tel: +39 0473 27 93 35 **Fax:** +39 0473 27 93 37

Web: www.johansens.com/hotelmiramonti **E-mail:** info@hotel-miramonti.com

Utterly revamped, this sleek hotel is a great illustration of modern design that incorporates its historic roots: the façade has not been altered and its Tyrolean origins are evident throughout. Guest rooms are extremely large and soothing resting places, whilst the spectacular panoramic views of Merano and surrounding mountains are sure to take your breath away.

Complètement remis en état, cet hôtel reluisant est une superbe illustration du design moderne qui prend en compte ses racines historiques: la façade n'a jamais été modifiée et ses origines tyroliennes sont manifestes à travers tout le batiment. Les chambres sont extrêmement spacieuses tout en étant de parfaits lieux de repos et les vues panoramiques spectaculaires de Mérano et de ses environs sont à couper le souffle.

Tras una completa modernización, este radiante hotel se constituye en un excepcional ejemplo del diseño moderno que incorpora sus raíces históricas: la fachada no ha sido modificada y sus orígenes tiroleses se hacen evidentes por doquier. Las habitaciones, lugares para el relajamiento y el descanso, son sumamente amplias a la vez que las espectaculares vistas panorámicas de Merano y las montañas de los alrededores conseguirán con toda seguridad sobrecogerle gratamente.

Our inspector loved: *The romantic atmosphere in the restaurant with view of the mountains and twinkling lights of Merano.*

Price Guide: (discounts available for stays of more than 7 days)
double €160-300
suite/junior suite €196-400

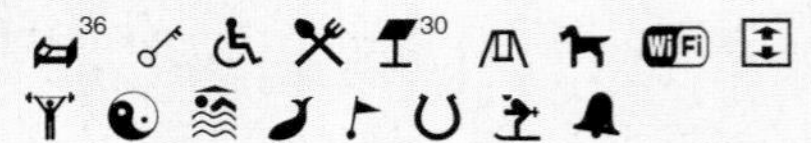

Attractions: St Caterina Church, 50 metres; Castel Trauttmandorff Gardens, 10km; Maia Horse Racecourse, 10km; Merano Town, 15-min drive

Nearby Towns: Merano, 15-min drive; Bolzano, 40-min drive; Innsbruck, 2-hour drive
Airports: Bolzano, 40-min drive; Innsbruck, 2-hour drive; Verona, 2-hour drive

Category: Hotel

Castel Fragsburg

VIA FRAGSBURG 3, 39012 MERANO, ITALY
Tel: +39 0473 244071 **Fax:** +39 0473 244493
Web: www.johansens.com/fragsburg **E-mail:** info@fragsburg.com

Our inspector loved: *The chef's creations that have reached incredible new heights.*

Price Guide: (including 7-course gourmet dinner)
single €185-200
double €330-370
suite €350-410

Awards: 15/20 Gault Millau

Attractions: Castel Trauttmansdorff Gardens, 3km; Interactive Museum, 3km; Golf Passeier, 15km; Glacier Man Museum, 25km

Nearby Towns: Merano, 5km; Bolzano, 25km
Airports: Bolzano, 25km; Innsbruck, 140km; Verona, 170km

Category: Hotel
Closed: November - April

This exclusive hotel was originally built for noble shooting parties and guests of local feudal lords. Today, it provides excellent accommodation, attentive service and an award-winning restaurant. Every room is individually decorated with unique period pieces and the L-shaped suites offer additional space and comfort. The Ortner family is happy to organise extra special excursions such as a helicopter ride over the Dolomites.

Cet hôtel unique fût construit à l'origine pour les parties de chasse nobles et pour les invités des seigneurs féodaux locaux. Il offre aujourd'hui un hébergement de premier ordre, un service attentif et un restaurant réputé. Chaque chambre est décorée de manière individuelle avec des meubles d'époque uniques et les suites en L offrent un espace et un confort supplémentaire. La famille Ortner se fait un plaisir d'organiser des excursions originales telles qu'un vol en hélicoptère au-dessus des Dolomites.

Este exclusivo hotel se construyó originalmente para las cacerías de la nobleza y los invitados de los señores feudales del lugar. Hoy en día ofrece un excelente alojamiento, atento servicio y un restaurante premiado. Cada habitación está decorada individualmente con piezas únicas de época, y las suites, en forma de "L", ofrecen más espacio y confort. La familia Ortner estará encantada de organizar excursiones especiales adicionales tales como un paseo en helicóptero por las Dolomitas.

ITALY / TRENTINO - ALTO ADIGE / DOLOMITES (NOVA PONENTE)

GANISCHGERHOF MOUNTAIN RESORT & SPA

RIO NERO 22, I-39050 NOVA PONENTE (BZ) ALTO ADIGE/DOLOMITES, ITALY
Tel: +39 0471 616504 **Fax:** +39 0471 616444
Web: www.johansens.com/ganischgerhof **E-mail:** office@ganischgerhof.com

Embrace the freedom of choice at this South Tyrolian hotel where a flexible service with unregimented schedule allows you to take control of your holiday. Choose from 3 dining venues, 4 bars, a plethora of activities year-round and treatments at the extensive spa. But be sure to enjoy your surroundings in the heart of the Dolomites.

Adoptez la liberté de choix dans cet hôtel du sud Tyrol où un service flexible sans aucun impératif d'horaire vous permet d'être en contrôle de vos vacances. Choisissez parmi 3 restaurants, 4 bars, de nombreuses activités tout au long de l'année et la multitude de soins au vaste spa. Mais pensez à profiter des environs, dans le cœur des Dolomites.

Disfrute de su libre elección en este hotel del sur del Tirol en el que un servicio flexible y sin horarios fijos le permitirá dirigir personalmente sus vacaciones. Elija entre los 3 comedores, 4 bares, entre una plétora de actividades disponibles durante todo el año o entre los distintos tratamientos de su amplio spa. Pero no se olvide de disfrutar de los alrededores en pleno corazón de las Dolomitas.

Our inspector loved: *The carefree lifestyle. You can eat, sleep and play wherever and whenever you wish! And each area has its own mood music!*

Price Guide:
double €120-234
suite €186-266

Attractions: Dolomites, 1km; Hiking Trails, 10-min walk; Obereggen Ski Area, 10-min drive

Nearby Towns: Nova Ponente, 4km; Obereggen, 10-min drive; Bolzano, 26km; Verona, 150km
Airports: Bolzano, 26km; Innsbruck, 139km; Verona, 168km; Munich, Germany, 300km

Category: Hotel
Closed: Early November - Early December and after Easter - mid-May

Parkhotel Holzner

39059 OBERBOZEN RITTEN/SOPRABOLZANO RENON, SÜDTIROL/ALTO ADIGE, ITALY
Tel: +39 0471 345 231 **Fax:** +39 0471 345 593
Web: www.johansens.com/parkhotelholzner **E-mail:** info@parkhotel-holzner.com

Our inspector loved: *The love of family life that fills every corner of this historic house.*

Price Guide: (including gourmet dinner)
double €186-350 suite €246-360

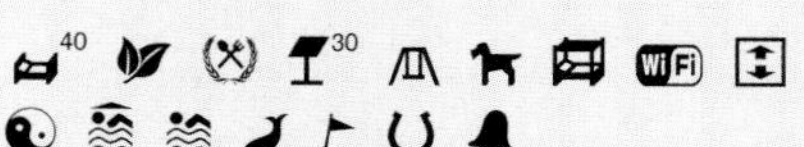

Awards: 14/20 Gault Millau; Historical Licensed House of the Year in South Tyrol 2008, South Tyrolean Hotel Association

Attractions: Historic Rittner Railway, 1-min walk; Earth Pyramids, 15-min walk; Glacial Man Museum, 12-min funicular ride; Dolomites, 30-min walk

Nearby Towns: Bolzano, 12-min funicular ride; Merano, 40km; Innsbruck, 129km; Verona, 170km
Airports: Bolzano, 45-min drive; Innsbruck, 129km; Verona, 170km

Category: Hotel
Closed: 9th-27th November, 20th-24th December and 7th January - 3rd April

Ideal for families, historic Parkhotel Holzner provides a crèche that operates all afternoon with daily programmes, special menus and mealtimes for children. Further adventures are found in fairy-tale surroundings that include the park, pool and a children's zoo. A tram connects Oberbozen to nearby villages and many walking trails meander from the hotel.

Idéal pour les familles, l'historique Parkhotel Holzner propose une garderie qui accueille les enfants tous les après-midi avec des programmes différents chaque jour et des menus adaptés. D'autres aventures se trouvent dans les environs dignes d'un conte de fée qui comprennent un parc, une piscine et un zoo où les enfants peuvent caresser les animaux. Un tramway relie Oberbozen aux villages voisins et de nombreuses randonnées partent de l'hôtel.

El histórico Parkhotel Holzner, ideal para familias, ofrece servicio de guardería abierto durante toda la tarde con programas diarios y menús y horarios de comidas especiales para niños. Más aventuras podrán seguir encontrándose en los mágicos alrededores entre los que se incluyen parque, piscina y una granja escuela. Un tranvía conecta Oberbozen con los pueblos cercanos y son muchos los senderos para caminar que serpentean desde el hotel.

ITALY / TRENTINO - ALTO ADIGE / DOLOMITES (ORTISEI - VAL GARDENA)

Hotel Gardena Grödnerhof

STR. VIDALONG 3, 39046 ORTISEI, ITALY
Tel: +39 0471 796 315 **Fax:** +39 0471 796 513
Web: www.johansens.com/gardena **E-mail:** info@gardena.it

This hotel's open, airy style drifts from the lobby into the large bedrooms and suites, all with balconies overlooking the grounds. Find out about your surroundings in the daily newspaper such as guided mountain excursions. Alternatively, head to the unique spa for relaxing Ayurvedic treatments and yoga classes before a romantic Michelin-Starred meal accompanied by fine wine.

Le style aéré de cet hôtel, se retrouve dans le lobby et dans les chambres et suites spacieuses, toutes ayant un balcon surplombant le parc. Renseignez-vous sur les environs dans le journal et qui liste les activités locales disponibles telles que des excursions guidées en montagne. Vous pouvez également vous rendre au spa unique et profiter des soins ayurvédiques relaxants et des cours de yoga avant un dîner étoilé Michelin romantique et accompagné de bons vins.

El estilo abierto y fresco de este hotel comienza en el vestíbulo y se desplaza a las amplias habitaciones y suites, todas provistas de balcones con vistas a la finca. A través del periódico se enterará de lo que ocurre en la zona y de las actividades en las que puede participar, como excursiones guiadas por la montaña. También puede relajarse en el singular Spa con un tratamiento ayurvédico o clases de yoga para luego disfrutar de una romántica cena con buen vino en el restaurante galardonado con una estrella Michelin.

Our inspector loved: *The guided trek, and incredible Michelin-Starred meal.*

Price Guide: (including dinner)
double (single occupancy) €165-720
double €254-640
suite €328-800

Awards: 1 Star Michelin; 17/20 Gault Millau; Best Mountain Hotel 2008, Gambero Rosso Guide

Attractions: Cable Gondola to Alpe di Siusi, 3-min walk; Mountain Hiking Trails, 5-min walk; Visits to Local Wineries, 30-50-min drive

Nearby Towns: Castelrotto, 11km; Bressanone 30km; Bolzano, 36km; Cortina, 77km
Airports: Bolzano, 36km; Innsbruck, 100km; Verona, 206km

Category: Hotel
Closed: 6th April-20th May and 11th Oct-3rd Dec

Du Lac et Du Parc Grand Resort

VIALE ROVERETO 44, 38066 RIVA DEL GARDA (TN), ITALY
Tel: +39 0464 566600 **Fax:** +39 0464 566566
Web: www.johansens.com/dulacetduparc **E-mail:** info@dulacetduparc.com

Our inspector loved: *The green park, the secluded pool, the thrill of windsurfing on the lake, and watching the sunset while enjoying an apéritif.*

Price Guide:
double €170-330
junior suite/suite €330-810

Attractions: Sailing School, on-site; Monte Baldo, 18km; Mart Museum Rovereto, 19km; Parco Sigurtà Gardens, 84km

Nearby Towns: Malcesine, 18km; Trento, 41km; Verona, 80km; Brescia, 81km
Airports: Brescia "Gabriele D'Annunzio," 77km; Verona Valerio Catullo, 85km; Bergamo "Orio al Serio," 89km

Category: Hotel
Closed: November - Easter

Mountains and a lake surround this lush and relaxing hideaway. Its garden setting is stunning, as are the Murialdo Suites with adjacent pool. Family-style bungalows and contemporary villa suites with a classic 1950s twist are also available. Massages can be enjoyed in a canopied tent within the grounds or in the well-equipped Wellness and Beauty Centre ArmoniA where a variety of treatments and packages are on offer.

Des montagnes et un lac entourent ce refuge luxueux et relaxant. Son parc est magnifique, comme le sont les Suites Murialdo et la piscine adjacente. Des bungalows, adaptés aux familles, et des suites contemporaines dans la villa, aux accents des années 50, sont également disponibles. Des massages sont pratiqués sous une tente privée au milieu du parc ou dans le superbe et bien équipé centre de beauté et de bien-être ArmoniA, où de nombreux soins et packages sont proposés.

Este hermoso refugio de vegetación exuberante y relajante, está envuelto por montañas y por el lago. Los jardines son impresionantes y también lo son las Suites Murialdo con su piscina al lado. Unos bungaloes, ideales para familias, y las villa suites, contemporáneas con un toque clásico de los años 50 completan el conjunto. Podrá disfrutar de un masaje al aire libre bajo una carpa, o en ArmoniA, el perfectamente equipado centro de Wellness y de belleza donde se ofrecen una gran variedad de tratamientos y paquetes.

ITALY / TRENTINO - ALTO ADIGE / DOLOMITES (SAN GIOVANNI IN VALLE AURINA)

Alpenpalace Deluxe Hotel & Spa Resort

I-39030 ST. JOHANN IM AHRNTAL, SAN GIOVANNI IN VALLE AURINA, SOUTH TYROL, ITALY
Tel: +39 0474 670230 **Fax:** +39 0474 671156
Web: www.johansens.com/alpenpalace **E-mail:** info@alpenpalace.com

Our inspector loved: *The new spa suite, perfect for incurable romantics.*

Price Guide:
single €150-220
double €280-450
junior suite and suite €330-680

Attractions: Castel Tures, 2km; Predoi Mine, 5km; Dolomites, 30km; Ice Man Museum, 90km

Nearby Towns: Brunico, 25km; Corvara, 60km; Cortina, 80km; Bolzano, 90km
Airports: Innsbruck, 90km; Bolzano, 90km; Munich, Germany, 300km

Category: Hotel

This is a great choice for a holiday dedicated to comfort, recreation and well-being. Grand yet unfussy, and luxurious but not ostentatious, its spa and beauty centre and fantastic food aim to enhance your relaxation and enjoyment. Warm and inviting, this is also a wonderful honeymoon destination and location for a plethora of outdoor pursuits and activities.

C'est un excellent choix pour des vacances dédiées au confort, aux loisirs et au bien-être. Imposant mais simple, luxueux sans être ostentatoire, son centre de beauté et spa et sa cuisine fantastique visent à améliorer votre plaisir et votre relaxation. Chaleureux et accueillant, c'est également une parfaite destination de voyages de noces et lieu pour grand nombre d'activités en plein air et de loisirs.

Es una excelente elección para quien busque confort, esparcimiento y bienestar en sus vacaciones. Se trata de un complejo grandioso y lujoso, pero no por ello recargado y ostentoso. Tanto el spa como el salón de belleza y su fantástica carta pretenden aumentar su capacidad de relax y disfrute. Sumamente sugerente y acogedor, este complejo constituye un inmejorable destino de luna de miel así como de una gran variedad de entretenimientos y actividades al aire libre.

Piemonte
Parma
Fornovo di Taro
Modena
Reggio nell'Emilia
Cento
Portomaggiore
Comacchio
Bardi
Borgo Val di Taro
Berceto
Vignola
Bologna
Ravenna
Lugo
Castelnovo ne'Monti
Pianoro
Imola
Varese Ligure
Pontremoli
Pavullo nel Frignano
Emilia~Romagna
Forlì
Chiavari
Liguria
Aulla
Fivizzano
Castelnuovo di Garfagnana
Levanto
La Spezia
Firenzuola
Marradi
Rimini
Carrara
Massa
Bagni di Lucca
SAN MARINO REPUBLIC
Novafeltria
Pietrasanta
Forte dei Marmi
Camaiore
Pistoia
Pescia
Prato
Massarosa
Viareggio
Lucca
Pontassieve
Bagno di Romagna
Urbino
Pisa
Empoli
Florence
Scandicci
Pontedera
San Miniato
Poppi
Marche
LIGURIAN SEA
Sansepolcro
Castelfiorentino
S. Giovanni Valdarno
Livorno
Collesalvetti
Poggibonsi
Montevarchi
Arezzo
Voltena
S. Gimignano
Gorgona
Umbertide
Castiglion Fiorentino
Rosignano Marittimo
Tuscany
Cortona
Siena
Asciano
Sinalunga
Cecina
Perugia
Montepulciano
Magione
Pienza
Montalcino
Chianciano Terme
Campiglia Marittima
Chiusi
Umbria
Massa Marittima
Capraia
Marsciano
Roccastrada
Follonica
Piombino
Arcidosso
Todi
Elba
Portoferraio
Grosseto
Orvieto
Castiglione della Pescaia
Scansano
Pitigliano
Pianosa
Manciano
Montefiascone
Lazio
Porto Ercole
Viterbo
Corsica
Montalto di Castro
Montecristo
Giglio
Tarquinia
Bracciano
Rome
187
189
197
188
177
172
191
174
195
193
194
190
173
192
196
175
176

ITALY / TUSCANY (AREZZO - LORO CIUFFENNA)

Relais Villa Belpoggio (Historical House)

VIA SETTEPONTI PONENTE 40, 52024 LORO CIUFFENNA, AREZZO, ITALY
Tel: +39 055 9694411 **Fax:** +39 055 9694411
Web: www.johansens.com/villabelpoggio **E-mail:** info@villabelpoggio.it

Our inspector loved: *The homely hospitality, and the easy access to the major places of interest in Tuscany.*

Price Guide:
double (single occupancy) €100-130
double €135-230
junior suite €175-250

Attractions: Il Borro Medieval Village, 15km; Prada Outlet, 14km; Chianti Wineries, 20km; Arezzo Antique Fairs and Medieval Tournaments, 35km

Nearby Towns: Arezzo, 35km; Florence, 35km; Siena, 45km; Cortona, 60km
Airports: Florence, 55km; Pisa, 120km; Bologna, 120km

Category: Luxury Guest House
Closed: 8th January - mid-March

Warm Tuscan hospitality and classic country living await you at this 17th-century home-from-home. Locally carved furnishings adorn bedrooms and 2 self-catering apartments, and if you don't feel like cooking for yourself, you will enjoy the traditional buffet breakfasts in the old cellars. Views of the Arno Valley and Chianti mountains are spectacular.

La chaleur de l'hospitalité toscane et un mode de vie campagnard classique vous attendent dans ce second chez-soi du XVIIe siècle. Du mobilier régional sculpté orne les chambres ainsi que 2 appartements avec cuisine équipée et, si vous n'avez pas envie de cuisiner vous-même, vous apprécierez le traditionnel buffet du petit-déjeuner dans les anciennes caves. Les vues sur la vallée de l'Arno et les montagnes du Chianti sont impressionnantes.

Le espera la cálida hospitalidad y la clásica vida campestre característica de la Toscana en esta hogareña mansión del siglo XVII. Un mobiliario de confección local decoran las habitaciones y 2 apartamentos self-catering, y si no le apetece a Vd. cocinar, podrá disfrutar de los tradicionales desayunos buffet en los viejos sótanos. Las vistas al Valle de Arno y los montes Chianti son espectaculares.

ITALY / TUSCANY (BIBBONA - BOLGHERI WINE AREA)

Relais Sant'Elena

VIA CAMPO DI SASSO , 57020 BIBBONA (LIVORNO), ITALY

Tel: +39 0586 671071 **Fax:** +39 0586 671882

Web: www.johansens.com/relaisantelena **E-mail:** info@relaisantelena.it

Our inspector loved: *The warm homely atmosphere, and the enchanting surrounding landscape.*

Price Guide:
double €140-280
suite €250-340

Attractions: Medieval Villages Including Bibbona and Bolgheri, nearby; Bolgheri Wineries of Sassicaia and Ornellaia and Gastronomic Tours, 7km; Parco WWF Oasi di Bolgheri, 7km; Etruscan Riviera Beaches, 8km

Nearby Towns: Livorno, 40km; Volterra, 40km; Pisa, 70km; Siena, 80km
Airports: Pisa, 70km; Florence, 120km; Rome, 250km

Category: Luxury Guest House
Closed: 1st January - Easter

Peacefully positioned in the Tuscan countryside, this warm, intimate and romantic relais has been restored to its former glory. The interior is elegantly decorated in natural tones with antique furniture and terracotta flooring, while outside is a lush rose garden leading to a pool; the perfect spot from which to admire the magical sunset.

Tranquillement situé dans la campagne toscane, ce relais chaleureux, intime et romantique a retrouvé son éclat d'antan. L'intérieur est élégamment décoré dans des tons naturels avec des sols en terracota et des meubles anciens, tandis que l'extérieur est un jardin luxuriant de roses qui mène à une piscine, endroit idéal d'où admirer le sublime coucher de soleil.

Situado en un lugar tranquilo dentro del paisaje toscano, este acogedor, íntimo y romántico relais ha sido restaurado hasta recuperar su antiguo esplendor. El interior, elegantemente decorado a base de tonos naturales, cuenta con muebles antiguos y suelo embaldosado de terracota, mientras que en su exterior encontrará un exuberante jardín de rosas que conduce a una piscina: el lugar perfecto desde el cual podrá admirar la mágica puesta de sol.

ITALY / TUSCANY (CASTELNUOVO BERARDENGA - SIENA)

HOTEL BORGO SAN FELICE

LOCALITÀ SAN FELICE, 53019 CASTELNUOVO BERARDENGA (SI), TUSCANY, ITALY

Tel: +39 0577 3964 **Fax:** +39 0577 3590 89

Web: www.johansens.com/borgosanfelice **E-mail:** info@borgosanfelice.it

Within a medieval hamlet's main square, nestled amidst vineyards and olive groves, is this relaxing, authentic Tuscan hotel. Furnished with antiques, bedrooms look out to the Chianti hills or the stone-built hamlet where time has stood still. The first-class local wine and olive oil can be savoured in Poggio Rosso restaurant where traditional dishes feature on the menu.

Au centre de la place principale d'un hameau médiéval, niché au coeur de vignobles et d'oliviers, se trouve cet agréable et authentique hotel toscan. Meublées d'antiquités, les chambres donnent sur les collines de Chianti ou sur le hameau en pierre où le temps semble s'être arrêté. L'huile d'olive et les vins locaux de premier ordre peuvent être dégustés au Poggio Rosso restaurant qui propose des plats traditionnels au menu.

Dentro de la plaza principal de una aldea medieval y rodeado de viñedos y olivares, se encuentra este relajante y genuino hotel toscano. Amueblado a base de piezas de anticuario, las habitaciones dan a las colinas de Chianti o a la aldea de piedra en la que el tiempo parece haberse detenido. El excelente vino y aceite de oliva del lugar pueden saborearse en el Poggio Rosso restaurante cuya carta ofrece platos tradicionales.

***Our inspector loved:** The authentic hamlet setting, the service and estate's wine and oil.*

Price Guide: (including tennis, access to pitching and putting green and bicycle hire)
double €265-385
junior suite/suite €460-650

Awards: Condè Nast Traveller Gold List 2009; One of The Top 25 Europe Resorts and Top 50 World Restaurants, Condé Nast Traveller 2008

Attractions: Chianti Wine District, on-site; Enogastronomic Tours, 10km; Medieval Hamlets and Villages, 10km; Palio of Siena, 25km

Nearby Towns: Siena, 25km; Cortona, 57km; Florence, 75km; Perugia, 90km

Airports: Siena, 30km; Florence, 90km; Pisa, 190km

Category: Hotel

Closed: November - March

ITALY / TUSCANY (CASTIGLIONE DELLA PESCAIA - MAREMMA) 

L'ANDANA

TENUTA LA BADIOLA, LOCALITÁ BADIOLA, 58043 CASTIGLIONE DELLA PESCAIA (GROSSETO), ITALY
Tel: +39 0564 944 800 **Fax:** +39 0564 944 577
Web: www.johansens.com/andana **E-mail:** info@andana.it

Our inspector loved: *The amazingly picturesque setting, colours and atmosphere.*

Price Guide:
room €350-900
suite €700-1,800

Awards: 1 Star Michelin

Attractions: Wine Tasting & Cookery Classes, on-site; Archaeological Sites and Maremma Natural Park, 20km; Daily Cruises to Elba Island, 100km

Nearby Towns: Castiglione, 9km; Grosseto, 11km; Siena, 60km; Pisa, 160km
Airports: Pisa, 160km; Florence, 180km; Rome, 190km

Category: Hotel
Closed: Beginning of Jan - beginning of March

Quintessentially Italian: olive groves, vineyards and scented gardens, with the sea nearby as an added bonus! Once the 16th-century summer palace of Duke Leopold, L'Andana is now memorable for many reasons, including its luxurious interiors and superb Alain Ducasse-inspired cuisine such as the excellent buffet brunch. Try your own hand at some classic, regional dishes during a cookery class or relax in the exquisite Espa.

La quintessence de l'Italie: champs d'oliviers, vignobles et jardins parfumés, avec la mer à côté en bonus ! Cet endroit fût, au XVIe siècle, le palais d'été du duc Léopold. L'Andana est aujourd'hui incontournable pour de nombreuses raisons, notamment pour ses intérieurs luxueux et pour la délicieuse cuisine inspirée par Alain Ducasse, comme le buffet servi pour le brunch. Essayez-vous à la réalisation de quelques plats régionaux typiques pendant un cours de cuisine ou détendez-vous dans le merveilleux spa Espa.

Un lugar eminentemente italiano: olivares, viñedos y aromáticos jardines, con el mar cercano como premio añadido. Antaño el palacio veraniego del duque Leopoldo, L'Andana es en la actualidad memorable por muchas razones, entre las que se incluyen sus lujosos interiores y su exquisita cocina, como el excelente buffet brunch, de inspiración Alain Ducasse. Pruebe a cocinar algunos platos regionales clásicos que aprendera con las clases de cocina o relájese en el maravilloso Espa.

Hotel Villa Ottone

LOC. OTTONE, 57037 PORTOFERRAIO (LI), ISOLA D'ELBA, ITALY
Tel: +39 0565 933 042 **Fax:** +39 0565 933 257
Web: www.johansens.com/ottone **E-mail:** hotel@villaottone.com

Our inspector loved: *Watching the sunset from the terrace bar whilst listening to gentle piano music.*

Price Guide: (per person, half board)
double de luxe €131-335
double prestige €195-315
suite €195-450

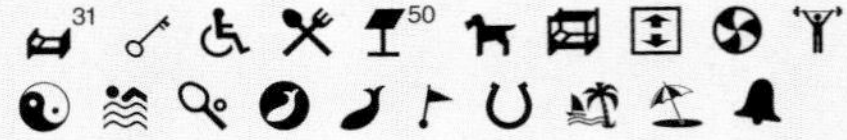

This outstanding 19th-century villa, with authentic frescoes and true Italian charm, is located in a most picturesque setting on Elba Island; a pearl of the Mediterranean. Lie and listen to the sea on the private beach, relax in one of the suites or cottages that blend into quiet gardens and enjoy apéritifs at sunset. Pure bliss.

Cette incroyable villa du XIXe siècle, avec ses fresques authentiques et son véritable charme italien, est située dans un endroit très pittoresque de l'île d'Elbe; une perle de la Méditerranée. Allongez-vous et écoutez le bruit de la mer sur la plage privée, détendez-vous dans l'une des suites ou l'un des cottages qui se fondent dans des jardins tranquilles et profitez d'un apéritif au crépuscule. C'est un pur bonheur.

Esta extraordinaria villa del siglo XIX, con frescos auténticos y verdadero encanto italiano esta ubicada en un marco de lo mas atractivo, en la isla de Elba; una perla del Mediterraneo. Túmbese a escuchar el mar en su playa privada, relájese en una de las suites o cottages que se funden con los pacíficos jardines y disfrute de aperitivos a la puesta del sol. Pura felicidad.

Attractions: Diving and Sailing, on-site; Golf Club, 2km; International Music Festival Yuri Bashment, 5km; Napoleon Bonaparte's Villa and Museums, 7km

Nearby Towns: Lucca, 95km; Pisa, 130km; Florence, 170km; Rome, 180km
Airports: Marina di Campo, 12km; Piombino, 50-min ferry ride; Pisa, 135km

Category: Charming Hotel
Closed: 11th October - end of April

porto
rigo
ucci
ANDRO GUIDONI
VIA REGINALDO GIULIANI
VIA GIOVANI FILIPO MARITI
VIA FAENTINA
Giardino del
Museo Stibbert
Giardino
Orticoltura
VIA F. PUCCINOTTI
VILLA G. MILTON
VILLA ALESSANDRO VOLTA
186
Stazione
Centrale
Palazzo dei
Congressi
VIALE G. MATTEOTTI
Campo
di Marte
dromo
ascine
VIALE F. ROSSELLI
Santa Maria
Novella
San Lorenzo
Giardino dei
Semplici
Giardino della
Gherardesca
Piazza del
Duomo
Piazza Massimo
d'Azeglio
178
Galleria
Corsini
183
Piazza Della
Signora
181
VIA DE AMICUS
Monte
Oliverto
VIALE A. ALEARDI
184
182
Palazzo
Vecchio
180
Biblioteca
Nazionale
Giardino
Torrigiani
Palazzo
Pitti
LUNO C. COLOMBO
Villa del
Ombrellino
Giardino
di Boboli
VIALE DEL POGGIO IMPERIALE
VIALE EURO
VIA SENESE
A-1
GHERARDO SILVANI
185

Casa Howard Guest Houses - Rome and Florence

18 VIA DELLA SCALA, PIAZZA SANTA MARIA NOVELLA, FLORENCE, ITALY
Tel: +39 066 992 4555 **Fax:** +39 066 794 644
Web: www.johansens.com/casahoward **E-mail:** info@casahoward.it

Intimate and homely, Casa Howard makes you feel that you're really living Florence as it's just a walk from the Uffizi and the Duomo. Themed guest rooms and a small apartment mix antiques with modern style and special touches. Breakfast includes home-made jams and honey, while dinner reservations can be arranged by helpful housekeepers. If visiting Rome, then stay at Casa Howard, Rome too.

Intime et accueillant, Casa Howard vous fait vous sentir comme vivant Florence de l'intérieur puisqu'il n'est situé qu'à quelques minutes de l'Uffizi et du Duomo. Les chambres à thèmes et le petit appartement mélangent ancien et moderne avec des touches spéciales. Confitures et miel faits maison sont servis au petit-déjeuner et les gouvernantes seront ravies d'organiser vos réservations pour le dîner. Si visitant Rome, réservez alors à la Casa Howard, Rome aussi.

Íntima y hogareña, Casa Howard le hace sentirse como si estuviera viviendo Florencia, ya que está a sólo un paso de Uffizi y del Duomo. Sus habitaciones temáticas y un pequeño apartamento fusionan las antigüedades con el estilo moderno y toques especiales. El desayuno incluye miel y mermeladas caseras, y se pueden hacer reservas para cenar a través de los serviciales caseros. Si visita Roma, entonces reserve en Casa Howard, Roma también.

Our inspector loved: *The children's room with climbing wall, and the feeling of being at home.*

Price Guide: (breakfast €15)
single €110-200
double €170-260
suite €500-600

Awards: Condé Nast Johansens Readers' Award 2009

Attractions: Museums, Churches and Duomo, 5-min walk; Shopping in Forte dei Marmi, 60km; Spa in Bagno Vignoni, 80km; Spa in San Casciano dei Bagni, 95km

Nearby Towns: Siena, 60km; Pisa, 100km; Arezzo, 120km; Rome, 280km
Airports: Florence, 8km; Pisa, 100km; Rome, 280km

Category: Luxury Guest House

Marignolle Relais & Charme

VIA DI S QUIRICHINO A MARIGNOLLE 16, 50124 FLORENCE, ITALY
Tel: +39 055 228 6910 **Fax:** +39 055 204 7396
Web: www.johansens.com/marignolle **E-mail:** info@marignolle.com

Our inspector loved: *The elegance, tranquil ambience, and easy access to the city centre.*

Price Guide:
double (single occupancy) €115-235
double €130-255
suite €235-375

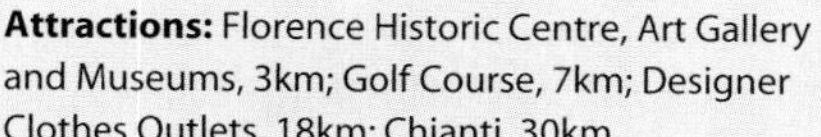

Attractions: Florence Historic Centre, Art Gallery and Museums, 3km; Golf Course, 7km; Designer Clothes Outlets, 18km; Chianti, 30km

Nearby Towns: San Gimignano, 40km; Siena, 65km; Arezzo, 75km; Lucca, 80km
Airports: Florence, 10km; Pisa, 100km; Bologna, 110km

Category: Luxury Guest House

This little gem overlooks the beautiful hillsides around Florence. Situated in the Certosa Convent area you would expect it to be peaceful, so the panoramic terrace is perfect for a quiet drink and light meals on request. 9 spacious rooms are immaculately styled thanks to the owners' impeccable taste.

Ce petit joyau d'hôtel offre des vues sur les magnifiques collines qui entourent Florence. Situé dans le quartier calme du Couvent de Certosa vous pouvez profiter d'un verre ou d'un repas léger, sur demande, sur les tranquilles terrasses panoramiques. Les 9 chambres spacieuses meublées avec soin sont le reflet du goût impeccable des propriétaires.

Esta pequeña joya de hotel dispone de vistas a las hermosas laderas que rodean Florencia. Situado en la zona del Convento Certosa, no podría tratarse sino de un lugar apacible, por lo tanto su terraza panorámica es ideal para disfrutar tranquilamente de una copa o de una comida ligera a demanda. Tiene 9 amplias habitaciones de estilo impecable gracias al gusto exquisito de sus propietarios.

ITALY / TUSCANY (FLORENCE)

Palazzo Magnani Feroni - All-Suites Florence

BORGO SAN FREDIANO 5, 50124 FLORENCE, ITALY
Tel: +39 055 2399544 **Fax:** +39 055 2608908
Web: www.johansens.com/florencepalace **E-mail:** cj@florencepalace.it

Our inspector loved: *The Palazzo's rooftop terrace with beautiful 360° views of Florence.*

Price Guide:
suite €200-1,300

Attractions: Medici's Villas, 7km; Chianti Wine District, 10km; Designer Fashion Outlet, 30km; Colle Val d'Elsa Crystal Production, 55km

Nearby Towns: San Gimignano, 60km; Siena, 75km; Lucca, 75km; Versilia Coast, 100km
Airports: Florence, 5km; Pisa, 80km, Bologna, 80km

Category: Luxury Guest House

"Live like the noble Florentines used to live" is the motto at this beautiful property, and you certainly will! Characterised by frescoes, vaulted ceilings and antique furnishings, the 12 luxury suites subtly combine comfort and modern technology. Just steps away are the city museums, galleries and shopping streets; all viewed from the glorious rooftop terrace where dinner by prior arrangement can be enjoyed.

"Vivre comme vivait la noblesse Florentine" est la devise de cette jolie propriété et c'est certainement ce que vous ferez ! Caractérisées par des fresques, des plafonds voûtés et des meubles antiques, les 12 suites de luxe associent subtilement confort et technologie moderne. A quelques pas de là, se trouvent les musées, les galeries et les rues commerçantes de la ville; que l'on voit depuis la merveilleuse terrasse sur le toit, et où l'on peut dîner sur demande.

El lema de este bello lugar es "Viva como lo hacían los nobles de Florencia". Pruebe y verá que es absolutamente cierto. Las 12 suites de lujo, caracterizadas por sus frescos, techos abovedados y antiguo mobiliario, combinan de forma sutil el confort y la moderna tecnología. A sólo unos pasos se encuentran los museos, las galerías y la zona comercial de la ciudad, todo lo cual podrá contemplar desde la magnífica azotea, donde puede cenar con aviso previo.

PALAZZO VECCHIETTI

VIA DEGLI STROZZI 4, 50123 FLORENCE, ITALY
Tel: +39 055 2302802 **Fax:** +39 055 215142
Web: www.johansens.com/palazzovecchietti **E-mail:** info@palazzovecchietti.com

Our inspector loved: *The home-away-from-home ambience, and the butler service.*

Price Guide:
superior €375
de luxe €425
junior suite €800

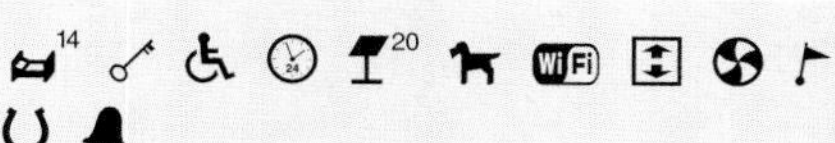

Attractions: Art Galleries and Museums, 2-min walk; Impruneta Traditional Terracotta Production and Chianti Wine Area, 20km; Designer Shopping Outlets, 30km

Nearby Towns: San Gimignano, 60km; Siena, 70km; Lucca, 75km; Pisa, 80km
Airports: Florence, 4km; Pisa, 80km; Bologna, 120km

Category: Luxury Guest House

Think of this 16th-century palace as your second home! An exclusive city town house, it provides 2 superior, 5 de luxe, 3 junior suites, 2 suites and 2 apartments complete with personal butler service. Each accommodation opens out to the central lobby and elegant lounge, the former palace courtyard. The sophistication of the rooms is enhanced by fine furnishings and paintings created by contemporary Florentine artisans.

Imaginez ce palais du XVIe siècle comme si c'était votre résidence secondaire! Une maison de ville unique qui propose 2 chambres supèrieures, 5 de luxe, 3 junior suites, 2 suites et 2 appartements, complétés par un service de majordome. Chacun des hébergements donne sur le salon central et élégant, anciennement la cour du palais. La sophistication des chambres est mise en valeur par de magnifiques meubles et tableaux créés par des artisans florentins contemporains.

¡Considere este palacio del siglo XVI como su segundo hogar! Se trata de una exclusiva casa de ciudad que dispone de 2 suites superiores, 5 de lujo, 3 suites junior, 2 suites y 2 apartamentos con servicio personalizado de mayordomo. Cada alojamiento cuenta con acceso al vestíbulo central y al elegante salón, el antiguo patio del palacio. Los magníficos muebles y cuadros creados por artesanos florentinos contemporáneos realzan el toque sofisticado de sus habitaciones.

Relais Piazza Signoria

VIA VACCHERECCIA 3, 50122 FLORENCE, ITALY
Tel: +39 055 3987239 **Fax:** +39 055 286306
Web: www.johansens.com/piazzasignoria **E-mail:** info@relaispiazzasignoria.com

You're right in Florence's hub here in the exclusive Piazza della Signoria guest house, home to Palazzo Vecchio and the Uffizi. Each private suite-apartment is well-equipped, with a cooking area in a fresh, modern style. You can enjoy fabulous views, and some suites have terraces, ideal for a romantic evening meal!

Vous êtes en plein centre de Florence, dans la très sélecte maison d'hôtes Piazza della Signoria, à côté du Palazzo Vecchio et des Offices. Ici, vous pouvez profiter de vues fabuleuses. Chaque suite-appartement privée est parfaitement équipée, avec un coin cuisine inclus, dans un style original et moderne. Certaines suites ont des terrasses, ce qui est idéal pour un dîner romantique !

Sepa que está en pleno centro neurálgico de Florencia, en la exclusiva casa de huéspedes de Piazza della Signoria, emplazamiento del Palazzo Vecchio y de Uffizi. Todos y cada uno de los suite-apartamentos están bien equipados, cocina incluida, siguiendo un estilo moderno y desenfadado. Puede disfrutar de vistas fabulosas y algunas de las suites disponen de terraza, ideales para una cena romántica.

Our inspector loved: *The view over Piazza della Signoria, right in the centre of Florence.*

Price Guide: (room only)
double €130-230
suite €250-390

Attractions: Art Galleries and Museums, on the doorstep; 18-hole Golf Course, 5km; Chianti Wineries and Vineyards, 20km; High Fashion Outlet, 25km

Nearby Towns: San Gimignano, 45km; Greve in Chianti, 20km; Siena, 60km; Lucca, 70km
Airports: Florence, 10km; Pisa, 90km; Bologna, 90km

Category: Luxury Guest House

Residenza del Moro

VIA DEL MORO 15, 50123 FLORENCE, ITALY
Tel: +39 055 290884 **Fax:** +39 055 2648494
Web: www.johansens.com/delmoro **E-mail:** info@residenzadelmoro.com

Our inspector loved: *The historical setting, and the precious collection of contemporary artworks.*

Price Guide:
double €263
suite €900

Attractions: Historic Centre of Florence, 2-min walk; Museums and Art Galleries, 2-min walk; Haute Couture Outlets, 15km; Wine Tasting Tours, 40km

Nearby Towns: Arezzo, 60km; Pisa, 70km; Siena, 70km; Lucca, 70km
Airports: Florence, 10km; Pisa, 80km

Category: Luxury Guest House

This 11-suite small luxury hotel sits on the noble floor of a 16th-century Florentine palace. You'll discover mind-blowing furnishings, including contemporary artwork and precious ornaments spanning the centuries. Each suite unfolds with original period details, stucco and frescoes, brocades and silks. Excellent breakfasts are served on the private roof garden.

Cet petit hôtel de luxe composé de 11 suites se situe à l'étage d'un palais florentin du XVIe siècle. Vous découvrirez un mobilier somptueux, de superbes œuvres d'arts contemporains et des ornements précieux couvrant plusieurs époques. Chaque suite possède des détails d'origine, des décorations en stuc, des fresques, des brocarts et soies. De délicieux petits-déjeuners sont servis dans le jardin privé sur le toit.

Este pequerio hotel de lujo de 11 suites se asienta en el noble emplazamiento de un palacio florentino del siglo XVI. Descubrirá en él mobiliario de ensueño, que incluye obras de arte contemporáneo y valiosos elementos decorativos que se remontan a varios siglos. Cada suite está provista de detalles originales de época, estuco y frescos, brocados y sedas. Sus excelentes desayunos se sirven en su jardín privado en el ático.

TORNABUONI SUITES

VIA TORNABUONI 9, 50123 FLORENCE, ITALY
Tel: +39 055 234 6865 **Fax:** +39 055 247 6322
Web: www.johansens.com/tornabuonisuites **E-mail:** info@tornabuonisuites.com

The Tornabuoni Suites Collection is an inspired concept of elegant apartment-suite accommodation. It is the ability to deliver additional privileges and personalised service that a hotel may not be able to offer that sets it apart. These intimate and exclusive suites are located on Florence's most fashionable and chic street, with city views that will take your breath away.

Le Tornabuoni Suites Collection est un concept inspiré d'hébergements en appartement élégants. Sa capacité à obtenir des privilèges supplémentaires et un service personnalisé, différent de celui que peut offrir un hôtel, fait véritablement la différence. Les suites intimes et exclusives sont situées sur l'une des rues les plus chics de Florence et les vues sur la ville sont à couper le souffle.

El Tornabuoni Suites Collection es un concepto de alojamiento inspirado en elegantes apartamentos-suites. Es su capacidad para dar mayores ventajas y un servicio personalizado, lo que otros hoteles pueden no llegar a ofrecer, lo que lo distingue. Estas íntimas y exclusivas suites se encuentran en la calle más elegante y refinada de Florencia, y tienen unas vistas a la ciudad que le dejarán sin respiración.

***Our inspector loved:** The great location, privacy and total peace and quiet.*

Price Guide: (room only)
suite €150-330

Attractions: Historic Centre of Florence, on the doorstep; Museums, Art Galleries and Shopping, on the doorstep; Golf Club, 14km; Chianti Wine Area, 20km

Nearby Towns: Arezzo, 60km; Siena, 70km; Lucca, 70km; Pisa, 81km
Airports: Amerigo Vespucci Florence, 10km; Galileo Galilei Pisa, 81km

Category: Luxury Guest House

Relais Villa il Sasso

VIA DI BELMONTE 27, 50012 BAGNO A RIPOLI - FLORENCE, ITALY
Tel: +39 055 643845 **Fax:** +39 055 6466004
Web: www.johansens.com/villailsasso **E-mail:** info@relaisvillailsasso.com

Our inspector loved: *Enjoying a fantastic breakfast in the typically Tuscan kitchen, and Suite Ciampolini with its original frescoes, fireplace c.1700 and direct access to the pool.*

Price Guide:
single €100-150
double €120-200
suite €170-280

Attractions: Ugolino Golf Course, 5km; Chianti Wine Area, 5km; Historical Centre of Florence, 7km; Upscale Shopping Outlets, 15km

Nearby Towns: Florence, 7km; Fiesole, 10km; Siena, 30km; Lucca, 60km
Airports: Florence, 20km; Pisa, 50km; Bologna, 116km

Category: Luxury Guest House
Closed: 25th January - 1st March

A countryside setting with easy city access is offered at this enchanting 14th-century villa. Set on the verdant Tuscan hills, just a short drive from Florence, this modernised villa is an elegantly furnished hideaway filled with period furniture, precious paintings, frescoes and coffered ceilings. Guest rooms are spacious and sophisticated. Restaurant service is available upon request.

Un décor de campagne et un accès rapide à la ville sont proposés dans cette villa enchanteresse du XIVe siècle. Nichée sur les collines toscanes verdoyantes, à quelques minutes de Florence, cette villa modernisée est un refuge élégamment meublé, rempli de meubles anciens, de peintures uniques, de fresques et de plafonds à caissons. Les chambres sont spacieuses et sophistiquées. Le service du restaurant est disponible sur demande.

Esta encantadora villa del siglo XIV ofrece un paisaje rural provisto de fácil acceso a la ciudad. Emplazada en las frondosas colinas de la Toscana, a un corto trayecto en coche de Florencia, esta modernizada villa resulta ser un lugar de retiro repleto de elegante mobiliario de época, valiosos lienzos, frescos y techos con artesonado. Las habitaciones son amplias y sofisticadas. El servicio de restaurante está disponible a petición expresa del cliente.

Monsignor Della Casa Country Resort

VIA DI MUCCIANO 16, 50032 BORGO SAN LORENZO, FLORENCE, ITALY
Tel: +39 055 840 821 **Fax:** +39 055 840 8240
Web: www.johansens.com/monsignor **E-mail:** booking@monsignore.com

Our inspector loved: *The lovely welcome and the utmost attention to guests' requirements.*

Price Guide:
single from €145
double from €160
suite from €225

Rural, relaxed and romantic, this ancient hamlet, next to the 15th-century home of Monsignor della Casa, has blossomed into beautiful villas and suites. Instantly calming, rooms are in an elegant country style with trussed ceilings, cotto floors, fireplaces and wrought-iron canopied beds. Flit between the welcoming restaurant/wine bar and the wellness centre.

Rural, relaxant et romantique, cet ancien hameau, proche de la demeure du XVe siècle de Monsignor della Casa, s'est transformé en splendides suites et villas. Particulièrement reposantes, les chambres sont d'un élégant style champêtre avec leurs plafonds à caissons, leurs sols en carreaux de terre cuite, leurs cheminées et leurs lits à baldaquin en fer forgé. Passez tranquillement de l'accueillant restaurant/bar à vins au centre de remise en forme.

Esta antigua aldea, rural, relajante y romántica, situada junto a la casa de Monsignor della Casa del siglo XV ha florecido hasta convertirse en una aldea de bellas villas y suites. De inmediato efecto tranquilizador, sus habitaciones son de elegante estilo rural y disponen de techos apuntalados, suelos cotto, chimeneas y camas de hierro forjado con baldaquín. Le agradará combinar la acogedora taberna/restaurante con el centro de wellness.

Attractions: Golf Course and Mugello Car and Motorbike Circuit, 7km; Chianti Wine Tasting, 15km; Fashion Outlets, 20km; Museums and Art Galleries, Florence, 27km

Nearby Towns: Florence, 27km; Bologna, 80km; Lucca, 90km; Siena, 100km
Airports: Florence, 30km; Bologna, 90km; Pisa, 105km

Category: Charming Hotel
Closed: 7th January - 5th March

Hotel Byron

VIALE A MORIN 46, 55042 FORTE DEI MARMI (LU), ITALY
Tel: +39 0584 787 052 **Fax:** +39 0584 787 152
Web: www.johansens.com/byron **E-mail:** info@hotelbyron.net

Our inspector loved: *The refined and charming ambience.*

Price Guide:
classic €260-600
double de luxe €270-750
suite €350-1,200

Awards: Condé Nast Johansens European Reader Award 2008

Attractions: Puccini Opera Festival, 5km; Tour of Carrara Marble Caves, 30km; Historical Tuscan Sites, 30km; Tour of Cinque Terre, 70km

Nearby Towns: Lucca, 20km; Pisa, 40km; Florence, 95km; Portofino, 125km
Airports: Pisa, 45km; Florence, 95km; Genova, 190km

Category: Hotel
Closed: Restaurant closed during November

The name evokes romance, as does the place, made up of 2 Liberty-style seafront villas in an exclusive spot on the Versilian coast. Restored to its original elegance, the ambience is of a private home, and interiors are fresh and crisp, bursting with plants and flowers. La Magnolia restaurant has an excellent reputation.

L'endroit, évocateur de romance, au même titre que le nom, est composé de 2 villas de style Liberty, en front de mer sur un site unique de la côte versilienne. Rénové pour redécouvrir son élégance d'origine, l'atmosphère est celle d'une maison privée dont l'impeccable intérieur regorge de plantes et de fleurs. Le restaurant La Magnolia jouit d'une excellente réputation.

Su nombre evoca romance; el lugar también. Este hotel está compuesto de 2 villas de estilo Liberty en plena línea de playa en un emplazamiento exclusivo de la costa versiliana. Restaurado para recobrar su elegancia original, el ambiente es el propio de una casa particular: los interiores son refrescantes y pulcros, rebosantes de plantas y flores. El restaurante La Magnolia goza de excelente fama.

VILLA LE BARONE

VIA SAN LEOLINO 19, 50022 PANZANO IN CHIANTI (FI), TUSCANY, ITALY
Tel: +39 055 852621 **Fax:** +39 055 852277
Web: www.johansens.com/villalebarone **E-mail:** info@villalebarone.com

Refined, picturesque, serene and charming. The Della Robbia family residence since the 16th century, this inviting boutique hotel is a beautifully furnished home adorned with antique furniture, paintings, books and a touch of romance. Guest rooms are located in the main house or in renovated cottages and barns, whilst the former winery is now the restaurant.

Raffiné, pittoresque, tranquille et charmant. Résidence de la famille Della Robbia depuis le XVIe siècle, cet accueillant boutique hôtel est une maison magnifiquement meublée et remplie d'antiquités, de tableaux anciens, de livres et d'une touche de poésie. Les chambres sont situées dans la maison principale ou dans les cottages et granges rénovés et l'ancien cellier est devenu un restaurant.

Refinado, pintoresco, tranquilo y encantador. Residencia de la familia Della Robbia desde el siglo XVI, este encantador hotel boutique se erige como un hogar de excelente decoración gracias a su mobiliario de anticuario, lienzos, libros y un toque de romance. Las habitaciones se encuentran en el edificio principal o en sus renovados cottages y establos, a la vez que su antigua bodega es ahora el restaurante.

Our inspector loved: *The enchanting gardens with heart-shaped hedges!*

Price Guide:
double (single occupancy) €145-250
double €180-315
junior suite €285-345

Attractions: Cooking Classes, on-site, Vino al Vino Wine Festival, Sunday Markets and Concerts in the Pieve of San Leolino, 5-min walk; Concerts and Markets of Greve in Chianti, 6km; Impruneta, 23km

Nearby Towns: Florence, 29km; Siena, 30km; San Gimignano, 40km; Volterra, 62km
Airports: Florence, 29km; Pisa, 97km

Category: Charming Hotel
Closed: 1st January - 8th April

Albergo Pietrasanta - Palazzo Barsanti Bonetti

VIA GARIBALDI 35, 55045 PIETRASANTA (LUCCA), ITALY
Tel: +39 0584 793 727 **Fax:** +39 0584 793 728
Web: www.johansens.com/pietrasanta **E-mail:** info@albergopietrasanta.com

Our inspector loved: *The romantic ambience, and outstanding collection of modern art.*

Price Guide: (room only)
single €115-200
double €185-380
suite from €550

Awards: Condé Nast Johansens European Reader Award 2007

Attractions: The Most Exclusive Beach in Marina di Pietrasanta, 3km; Antro Del Corchia Caves, 8km; Carrara Marble Tour, 10km; Puccini Opera Festival, 11km

Nearby Towns: Carrara, 15km; Pisa, 19km; Lucca, 26km; Cinque Terre, 50km
Airports: Pisa, 19km; Florence, 90km

Category: Charming Hotel
Closed: During December, January and February

An authentic 17th-century Renaissance palace, this is an excellent location for special events and small gatherings. The hotel's main hall cleverly mixes contemporary paintings with antique furniture, marble tile floors and beautiful moulded stucco and fresco ceilings. And a covered courtyard has been transformed into a breakfast area complete with pretty waterfall. You can walk to some good restaurants nearby.

Cet authentique palais renaissance du XVIIe siècle est un endroit parfait pour des événements particuliers et intimes. Le hall principal de l'hôtel mélange subtilement peintures modernes avec meubles antiques, sols en marbre, magnifiques stucs moulés et fresques aux plafonds. Une cour couverte a été transformée en une salle de petit-déjeuner avec de ravissantes fontaines. Vous pouvez également vous rendre à pied dans les délicieux restaurants situés à proximité.

Un auténtico palacio renacentista del siglo XVII, este es un lugar excelente para celebrar eventos intimos y especiales. El vestíbulo principal mezcla inteligentemente pinturas contemporáneas con mobiliario antiguo, suelos de mármol y hermosos techos con frescos y molduras en estuco.. Un patio cubierto, con bonita cascada, ha sido transformado en zona de desayuno. Hay buenos restaurantes a corta distancia a pie.

ITALY / TUSCANY (MONTALCINO)

Castello Banfi - Il Borgo

CASTELLO DI POGGIO ALLE MURA, 53024 MONTALCINO (SI), ITALY

Tel: +39 0577 877 700 **Fax:** +39 0577 877 701

Web: www.johansens.com/castellobanfi **E-mail:** borgo@castellobanfi.it

This picturesque Tuscan retreat is ideal for tired urbanites looking to unwind in the Italian wine country. Within this 18th-century hamlet, next to a medieval fortress, are the luxurious rooms of Il Borgo. Taste the estate's wines in the Enoteca shop and sample the delights of the casual dining La Taverna in the vaulted cellars. There is also the Giovanni F Mariani Museum of Glass to visit where a private collection from the 4th-5th centuries to the present day are displayed.

Ce pittoresque refuge toscan est idéal pour les citadins fatigués cherchant à se détendre dans la région du vin italien. Le hameau du XVIIIe siècle, à côté d'une forteresse médiévale, abrite les chambres luxueuses d'Il Borgo. Dégustez les vins du domaine dans la boutique Enoteca et goûtez les délices du restaurant La Taverna situé dans les caves voûtées. Le musée de Verre Giovanni F Mariani, où est présenté une collection privée allant du IV-V siècle à nos jours, est également à visiter.

Este pintoresco refugio toscano es el lugar ideal para los que viven en la ciudad y buscan el descanso y relax en el campo vinícolo italiano. En esta aldea del siglo XVIII, al lado de una fortaleza medieval, se encuentran las lujosas habitaciones de Il Borgo. Deguste los vinos de la finca en la Enoteca y pruebe las delicias de la casa, en un ambiente informal, que ofrece la abovedada La Taverna. También puede visitar la colección privada que data desde los siglos IV y V hasta el presente, en el Museo de Cristal Giovanni F Mariani.

Our inspector loved: *The spectacular Tuscan setting and the splendid rose garden.*

Price Guide:
dus €286-1,000
double €341-650
suite €605-1,001

Awards: Wine Spectator Award of Excellence 2007-2009; Condé Nast Traveller Hot List 2008

Attractions: Enoteca Wine Bar, Winery Tour and Glass Museum, on-site; Sant'Antimo Abbey, 30-min drive

Nearby Towns: Montalcino, 20km; Pienza, 40km; Montepulciano, 57km; Siena, 60km
Airports: Florence, 150km; Pisa, 190km; Rome, 220km

Category: Charming Hotel
Closed: 1st Jan - 28th Feb and 1st Nov - 31st Dec

ITALY / TUSCANY (MONTEBENICHI - CHIANTI REGION) 

Country House Casa Cornacchi

LOC. MONTEBENICHI, 52021 AREZZO, TUSCANY, ITALY
Tel: +39 055 998229 **Fax:** +39 055 9983863
Web: www.johansens.com/cornacchi **E-mail:** info@cornacchi.com

Our inspector loved: *The picturesque surroundings and the feeling of freedom and complete relaxation.*

Price Guide: (minimum 3-night stay)
suite €160-220
apartment from €200
villa from €440

Attractions: Chianti Wineries, 20-min walk; Chianti Castles, 20-min drive; Hot Spring Spa and Resort, 20-min drive; High Fashion Outlets, 30-min drive

Nearby Towns: Siena, 25-min drive; Arezzo, 30-min drive; Florence, 1-hour drive
Airports: Florence, 1-hour drive; Perugia, 1-hour drive; Pisa, 2-hour drive

Category: Charming Hotel
Closed: Beginning of January - end of March

After an exhilarating drive through the breathtaking Chianti countryside, you'll receive a warm welcome at this tranquil country house. Stone buildings date back to the 16th century, and bedrooms can only be described as exquisite. Good Tuscan wines offer refreshment, and there is plenty to explore in this exciting region.

Après une promenade grisante en voiture à travers la somptueuse campagne du Chianti, vous recevrez un accueil chaleureux dans cette résidence de campagne tranquille. Les bâtiments en pierre datent du XVIe siècle et les chambres sont tout simplement exquises. Les délicieux vins toscans étanchent la soif et il y a beaucoup d'endroits à visiter dans cette région unique.

Tras un estimulante trayecto por el impresionante paisaje rural de la región Chianti, recibirá una calurosa bienvenida nada más llegar a esta tranquila casa de campo. Los edificios de piedra datan del siglo XVI y sus habitaciones pueden describirse como sencillamente exquisitas. Los buenos vinos toscanos proporcionan solaz y hay mucho que explorar en esta encantadora región.

ITALY / TUSCANY (SAN VINCENZO - ETRUSCAN RIVIERA)

Relais Poggio ai Santi

VIA SAN BARTOLO 100, 57027 SAN VINCENZO - LIVORNO, ITALY
Tel: +39 0565 798032 **Fax:** +39 0565 798090
Web: www.johansens.com/poggioaisanti **E-mail:** poggioaisanti@toscana.com

Surrounded by organic farmland overlooking the sea, the stylish rooms of this picturesque relais are scattered within a magnificent park and lush garden. Sample fine cuisine prepared from the estate's fresh produce at Il Sale, enjoy daily cruises around Elba Island and the Tuscan Archipelagos and experience diving lessons, cooking classes, wine, oil and cheese tasting and wellness treatments.

Entouré de ferme organique surplombant la mer, les chambres élégantes de ce relais pittoresque sont dispersées dans le magnifique parc et dans le jardin luxuriant. Dégustez à Il Sale une délicieuse cuisine préparée à partir des produits frais du jardin, profitez des excursions quotidiennes autour de l'île d'Elbe et de l'archipel toscan et expérimentez les leçons de plongée, les cours de cuisine, les dégustations de vins, d'huile et de fromages et les soins de bien-être.

Rodeado de cultivos ecológicos con vistas al mar, las elegantes habitaciones de este pintoresco relais se encuentran repartidas en el interior de un magnífico parque y exuberante jardín. Pruebe su excelente cocina preparada a partir de productos frescos de la propia finca de Il Sale, disfrute de los cruceros diarios por la isla de Elba y los archipiélagos toscanos y pruebe a recibir lecciones de buceo, clases de cocina, degustación de vinos, aceites y quesos y los tratamientos wellness.

Our inspector loved: *The open space concept and respect for the surrounding environment.*

Price Guide:
suite €145-420

Attractions: Beaches, 5km; Bolgheri Wineries, 15km; Elba Island, 1-hour ferry ride; San Gimignano, 87km

Nearby Towns: Livorno, 60km; Pisa, 75km; Siena, 110km; Florence, 141km
Airports: Pisa, 75km; Florence, 145km; Rome Fiumicino, 245km

Category: Charming Hotel
Closed: 11th January - 11th February

Borgo La Bagnaia Resort, Spa and Events Venue

STRADA STATALE 223, KM 56, 53016 LOCALITA BAGNAIA - SIENA, ITALY
Tel: +39 0577 813000 **Fax:** +39 0577 817464
Web: www.johansens.com/labagnaia **E-mail:** info@borgolabagnaia.com

Our inspector loved: *The unique combination of space, peace and abundance of facilities.*

Price Guide:
single €200-300
double €300-455
suite €455-1,575

Attractions: Palio of Siena - Annual Horse Race, 15-min drive; Medieval Festival in Certaldo, 35-min drive; Montalcino and Montepulciano Wineries, 40-min drive; Florentine May Music Festival, 1-hour drive

Nearby Towns: Siena, 15-min drive; Montalcino, 40-min drive; Pienza, 45-min drive; Florence, 1-hour drive
Airports: Florence, 1-hour drive; Pisa, 2-hour drive; Siena Aerotaxi Service, 10-min drive

Category: Hotel
Closed: End of November - beginning of March

Deer, leverets and pheasants wander freely in the grounds of this ancient borgo, complete with beautiful medieval church and Buddha Spa. Visit the spa with its enticing treatments or head to the Bagnaia Golf Academy's indoor teeing areas and putting green. The professional 18-hole course will be open soon. This is the ideal location for meetings and special events thanks to the superb conference centre.

Cerfs, levrauts et faisans se promènent en liberté sur les terres de cet ancien bourg qui comprend également une superbe église médiévale et le Spa Bouddha. Visiter le Spa et profiter de ses soins attrayants ou aller directement sur les aires de tee couvertes ou sur le green de la Golf Academy La Bagnaia. Le parcours professionnel de 18 trous devrait ouvrir prochainement. L'endroit est idéal pour des réunions ou des événements particuliers grâce au centre de conférence superbe.

Ciervos, lebratos y faisanes campean con total libertad por las fincas de este antiguo borgo transformado en resort con bella iglesia medieval y el estupendo Spa Buddah. Visitar el spa con sus seductores tratamientos o de unos golpes en la zona interior de tee y pruebe el putting green de la Academia de Golf Bagnaia. El campo de golf profesional de 18 agujeros se inaugurara dentro de poco. Este lugar también es ideal para reuniones y otros eventos gracias el magnífico centro de conferencias.

ITALY / TUSCANY (SIENA - LUCIGNANO D'ASSO)

LUCIGNANELLO BANDINI (BORGO STORICO)

LOC. LUCIGNANO D'ASSO, 53020 SAN GIOVANNI D'ASSO (SI), ITALY
Tel: +39 0577 803 068 **Fax:** +39 0577 803 082
Web: www.johansens.com/lucignanello **E-mail:** info@borgolucignanello.com

The perfect base from which to explore Tuscany, the Piccolomini family have owned these 5, 2-bedroomed houses and 4-bedroomed villa since the 15th century, located within the heart of the region in the idyllic hamlet of Lucignano d'Asso. Today, the restoration of the original architectural features has helped to create this authentic and picturesque setting overlooking the amazing Tuscan rolling hills.

Un endroit parfait pour partir à la découverte de la Toscane ! La famille Piccolomini est propriétaire de 5 maisons de 2 chambres et d'une villa de 4 chambres, depuis le XVe siècle, au cœur de la région, dans le hameau idyllique de Lucignano d'Asso. De nos jours, la restauration des éléments d'architecture d'origine a contribué à créer cet authentique et pittoresque cadre surplombant les extraordinaires collines toscanes.

La base ideal para descubrir la Toscana, esta villa de 4 habitaciones y 5 casas de 2 habitaciones pertenecen a la familia Piccolomini desde el siglo XV y estan ubicadas en el centro de esta region, en el idílico pueblo de Lucignano d'Asso. La restauración de los rasgos arquitectónicos originales ha ayudado a crear hoy dia este marco auténtico y típico con vistas a las impresionantes colinas onduladas toscanas.

Our inspector loved: *This enchanting hamlet with its traditional little food shop.*

Price Guide:
guest house for 2-4 people
2-night stay €200-290 per night
7-night stay €1,400-1,900 per week
guest house for 7 people
2-night stay €590-700 per night
7-night stay €4,100-4,600 per week

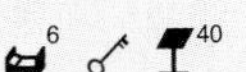

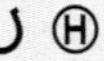

Attractions: Gastronomic Fairs and Events, on the doorstep; Medieval Festivals and Events, 15km; Montalcino and Montepulciano Wineries, 16km; Palio and Musical Festivals in Siena, 45km

Nearby Towns: Montalcino, 16km; Pienza, 25km; Siena, 45km; Florence, 120km
Airports: Perugia, 85km; Florence, 120km; Pisa, 180km

Category: Luxury Guest House
Closed: 8th - 31st January

Relais La Suvera (Dimora Storica)

53030 PIEVESCOLA – SIENA, ITALY
Tel: +39 0577 960 300 **Fax:** +39 0577 960 220
Web: www.johansens.com/relaislasuvera **E-mail:** lasuvera@lasuvera.it

Our inspector loved: *The magical atmosphere, historic and cultural heritage, and precious antiques and furnishings.*

Price Guide:
double/twin €330-680
suite €480-1,500

Awards: Condé Nast Johansens Most Excellent Hotel 2009; Trip Advisor's Travellers' Choice 2008

Attractions: The UNESCO Family Museum, on-site; Crystal Production in Colle Val d'Elsa, 15-min drive; Monteriggioni Medieval Town 20-min drive; Chianti Wineries, 1-hour drive

Nearby Towns: San Gimignano, 22km; Siena, 26km; Volterra, 30km; Florence, 60km
Airports: Florence, 65km; Pisa, 110km

Category: Hotel
Closed: During November - 25th March

Created in 1989 by the Marchess Ricci and Principessa Eleonora Massimo, this luxurious hotel comprises 4 houses surrounding a romantic courtyard. Exquisite rooms and suites are packed with antiques and the family art collection, whilst in the hotel's museum and library, documents and furnishings significant to the Ricci and Massimo family histories are on display. Tuscan dishes are available in the restaurant, and relaxation in the spa.

Créé en 1989 par le Marquis Ricci et la Princesse Eleonora Massimo, cet hôtel luxueux est composé de 4 maisons qui entourent une cour romantique. Les chambres ravissantes et les suites sont décorées avec des objets anciens et la collection d'oeuvres d'art familiale. Dans le musée et la bibliothèque de l'hôtel, des documents, meubles et tissus relatant l'histoire des familles Ricci et Massimo sont exposés. Des plats toscans sont servis au restaurant et vous pouvez vous relaxer au spa.

Creado en 1989 por el Marqués Ricci y Princesa Eleonora Massimo, este hotel de lujo consta de 4 edificios alrededor de un romántico patio. Las magníficas habitaciones y suites están decoradas con antigüedades y la colección de arte de la familia. Otros interesantes documentos y mobiliario pertenecientes a la historia de las familias Ricci y Massimo están expuestos en el museo del hotel, así como en la biblioteca. Podrá probar platos toscanos en el restaurante y relajarse en el Spa.

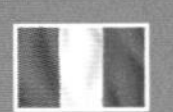

ITALY / TUSCANY (TERME DI PETRIOLO - MAREMMA)

Petriolo Spa & Resort

LOC. GRAND HOTEL TERME - (S.S. 223 SI > GR, KM 40,600) 58045 PARI, CIVITELLA PAGANICO (GR), ITALY
Tel: +39 0564 9091 **Fax:** +39 0564 9090 64
Web: www.johansens.com/petriolo **E-mail:** info@petriolosparesort.com

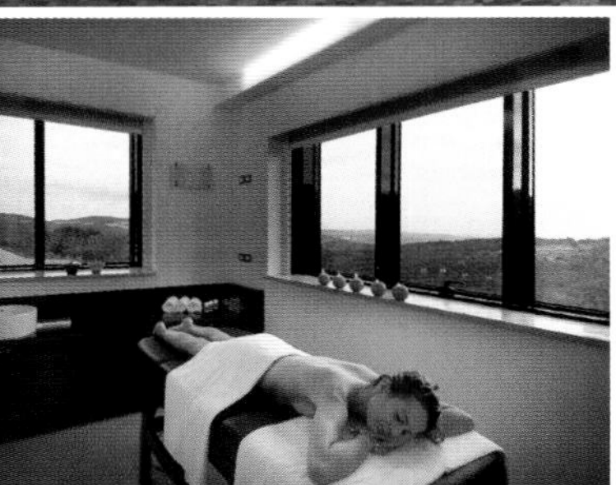

Our inspector loved: *The amazing spa, and the beautiful surroundings.*

Price Guide:
single €330-400
double €390-550
suite €650-2,200

Awards: Condé Nast Johansens Most Excellent Spa Hotel 2009

Attractions: San Galgano Romantic Cathedral, Roman Ruins and Wine Tasting, on-site; Medieval Towns, 10km; Montalcino Wine District, 35km

Nearby Towns: Siena, 28km; Grosseto, 40km; Florence, 90km
Airports: Siena, 12km; Florence, 90km; Pisa, 241km

Category: Hotel

Set in the tranquil Tuscan hills, next to the ancient thermal baths of Petriolo, this exclusive spa resort offers the utmost in relaxation, stunning views over an unspoilt natural park and 3 restaurants serving Tuscan and Mediterranean cuisine. The impressive and innovative spa includes a gym, indoor and outdoor pools and medical studios for personalised anti-ageing treatments, healthy nutritional advice and natural medicinal prescriptions.

Niché sur les collines tranquilles de Toscane, proche des thermes antiques de Petriolo, ce spa resort unique offre le meilleur en relaxation, de somptueuses vues sur un parc naturel intact et 3 restaurants qui servent une cuisine toscane et méditerranéenne raffinée. Le spa innovant et impressionnant comprend une salle de gym, des piscines intérieures et extérieures et des studios médicaux de traitements anti-âge personnalisés, de conseils nutritionnels et de prescriptions médicales naturelles.

Sito en las tranquilas colinas de la Toscana, junto a los antiguos baños termales de Petriolo, este exclusivo complejo-spa pone a su disposición lo último en relajamiento, impresionantes vistas a un virginal parque natural y 3 restaurantes de refinada cocina toscana y mediterránea. El impresionante e innovador spa incluye gimnasio, piscina cubierta y piscina exterior, consultas medicas para tratamientos personalizados de anti-envejecimiento, asesoramiento de nutrición saludable y recetas de medicina natural.

Hotel Plaza e de Russie

PIAZZA D'AZEGLIO 1, 55049 VIAREGGIO (LU), ITALY
Tel: +39 0584 44449 **Fax:** +39 0584 44031
Web: www.johansens.com/russie **E-mail:** info@plazaederussie.com

Our inspector loved: *The hotel's well-preserved Liberty style.*

Price Guide:
single €133-228
double €158-286
junior suite €294-396

Attractions: Puccini Opera Festival, 5km; Tuscan Historic Sites, 30km; Tour of Carrara Marble Cave, 35km; Tour of Cinque Terre, 55km

Nearby Towns: Lucca, 20km; Pisa, 30km; Florence, 90km; Portofino, 150km
Airports: Pisa, 30km; Florence, 85km; Genova, 150km

Category: Charming Hotel

The first hotel built in Viareggio in 1871, the Plaza e de Russie wears its stately magnificence well. Tall, elegantly proportioned rooms are lavished with rich antiques, marble, and Murano chandeliers. For a taste of the Mediterranean head to La Terrazza restaurant, and enjoy the outstanding views of the Versilia coastline from the terrace.

Premier hôtel construit à Viareggio en 1871, le Plaza e de Russie porte à merveille son imposante magnificence. Les chambres élégamment proportionnées et avec hautes plafonds sont remplies de meubles antiques, de marbre et de chandeliers de Murano. Pour une dégustation méditerranéenne, rendez-vous au restaurant La Terrazza et profitez des magnifiques vues de la côte versilienne depuis la terrasse.

El Plaza e de Russie, el primer hotel construido en Viareggio en 1871, conserva aún su majestuosa prestancia. Sus habitaciones de techo alto y de elegantes proporciones están repletas de valiosas antigüedades, mármoles y candelabros de cristal de Murano. Si desea gozar de un toque mediterráneo, diríjase al restaurante La Terrazza y disfrute de las sobrecogedoras vistas de la costa de Versilia desde la terraza.

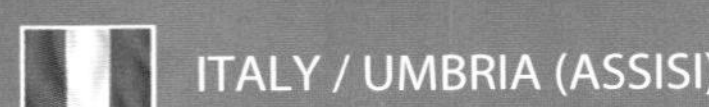

RESIDENZA D'EPOCA SAN CRISPINO

VIA SANT' AGNESE 11, 06081 ASSISI (PG), ITALY
Tel: +39 075 8155124 **Fax:** +39 075 8155124
Web: www.johansens.com/sancrispino **E-mail:** info@assisiwellness.com

Step back in time and marvel at the medieval splendour of ancient times. Let your mind absorb the evocative atmosphere of this beautiful historical mansion situated in the heart of Assisi, a remarkable city and the birthplace of St Frances. The café boasts a partly visible Roman Domus!

Retournez dans le temps et émerveillez-vous devant cette splendeur médiévale des temps passés. Laissez votre esprit s'imprégner de l'atmosphère unique de cette magnifique demeure historique située au cœur d'Assise, une cité remarquable et lieu de naissance de St Francis. Une Domus gallo-romaine est partiellement visible dans le café.

Retroceda en el tiempo y maravíllese del esplendor medieval de tiempos remotos. Deje que la mente se impregne del ambiente evocador de esta bella e histórica mansión situada en pleno corazón de Asís, extraordinaria ciudad cuna de San Francisco. Su cafetería incluso presume de permitir la vista parcial de una Domus romana.

Our inspector loved: *The intimate atmosphere, and Villa Salus' anti-ageing medical spa treatments.*

Price Guide: (including daily cleaning and linen charges)
suite per night €130-300
suite 2-night stay €250-580
suite 3-night stay €360-840

Attractions: Basilica di San Francesco, Churches, Monasteries and Shrines, on the doorstep; Monte Subasio Natural Park, 7km; Medieval Towns of Art, 15km; Umbria Jazz Festival, 27km

Nearby Towns: Spello, 14km; Perugia, 27km; Spoleto, 47km; Gubbio, 48km
Airports: Perugia, 15km; Rome, 190km; Florence, 170km

Category: Charming Hotel

Romantik Hotel le Silve di Armenzano

06081 LOC. ARMENZANO, ASSISI (PG), ITALY
Tel: +39 075 801 9000 **Fax:** +39 075 801 9005
Web: www.johansens.com/lesilve **E-mail:** info@lesilve.it

Our inspector loved: *The stunning Umbrian surroundings, and protected wildlife.*

Price Guide:
double (single occupancy) €120-150
double/twin €160-220
junior suite €400-500

Attractions: Monte Subasio Natural Park, on the doorstep; Assisi's Churches and Monuments, 15km; Sagrantino Wine Cellars, 18km; Umbria Jazz Festival, 40km

Nearby Towns: Assisi, 15km; Perugia, 40km; Gubbio, 60km; Spoleto, 60km
Airports: Perugia, 25km; Rome, 150km

Category: Charming Hotel
Closed: 31st October - Easter

At the foot of the Subasio mountains, this small hotel pre-dates the birth of St Francis of Assisi. Air is scented by olive groves, and deer and horses ramble through the countryside. Umbrian cooking is delicious, with bread traditionally baked in the fireplace. Swim in the salt-water pool and soak up the unspoilt rural simplicity.

Situé au pied du mont Subasio, ce petit hôtel date d'avant la naissance de Saint-François d'Assise. L'air est parfumé par les oliveraies; les cerfs et les chevaux se promènent tranquillement dans la campagne. La cuisine ombrienne est délicieuse, avec son pain traditionnel cuit dans la cheminée. Nagez dans la piscine d'eau salée et imprégnez-vous de la simplicité rurale, et naturelle.

Este hotel, situado al pie de las montañas de Subasio, es anterior al nacimiento de San Francisco de Asís. El aire está perfumado por los olivares, y los ciervos y los caballos pasean libremente por el campo. La cocina de Umbría, acompañada de pan cocido tradicionalmente en chimenea, resulta deliciosa. Disfrute de un baño en la piscina de agua salada y empápese de incólume sencillez rural.

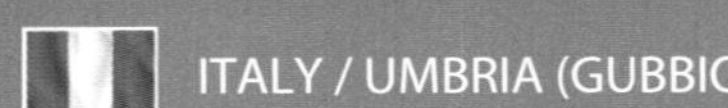

Castello di Petroia

LOCALITÀ SCRITTO DI GUBBIO, PETROIA, 06020 GUBBIO (PG), ITALY
Tel: +39 075 92 02 87 **Fax:** +39 075 92 01 08
Web: www.johansens.com/castellodipetroia **E-mail:** info@petroia.it

Steeped in Italian history, the hotel is a beautiful collection of buildings within castle walls, and was birthplace of the Duke of Urbino. Today, restored in complete sympathy with its medieval origins, it offers tastefully decorated bedrooms and a suite with its very own indoor pool. This magical place promises you a unique experience and the occasional medieval play and music festival.

Imprégné d'histoire italienne, l'hôtel se compose de magnifiques bâtiments dans l'enceinte du château et fût le lieu de naissance du Duc d'Urbino. Aujourd'hui restauré, en accord avec ses origines médiévales, il offre des chambres décorées avec goût et une suite qui possède sa propre piscine intérieure. Cet endroit magique vous garantira une expérience unique, notamment grâce aux jeux médiévaux et au festival de musique qui ont lieu de temps en temps.

Saturado de la historia de Italia, este hotel es una colección de bellos edificios rodeados de los muros de un castillo donde nació el Duque de Urbino. Hoy en día, restaurado en absoluta armonía con sus orígenes renacentistas, el hotel dispone de habitaciones decoradas con sumo gusto y una suite con su propia piscina cubierta. Este mágico lugar le promete una experiencia única y también, de vez en cuando, una obra medieval o un festival de música.

Our inspector loved: *The apéritifs, dinner with the Lord, and the medieval music festival.*

Price Guide:
double (single occupancy) €90-120
double €140-170
suite €170-240

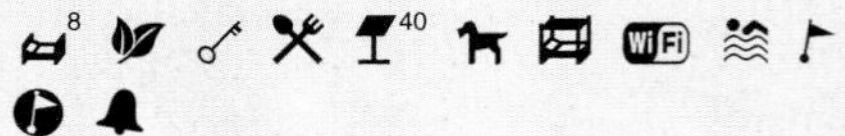

Attractions: Traditional Events and Enogastronomic Tours, 10km; Surrounding Medieval Towns, 20km; Umbria Jazz Festival and Eurochocolate in Perugia, 25km; Spoleto Festival, 79km

Nearby Towns: Gubbio, 13km; Perugia, 25km; Assisi, 28km; Siena, 120km
Airports: Perugia, 25km; Ancona, 85km; Rome, 225km

Category: Charming Hotel
Closed: Mid-January - mid-March

Relais L'Oliveta Spa Resort

LOC. I GIORGI, 06061 PETRIGNANO DEL LAGO (PG), ITALY
Tel: +39 075 9689015 **Fax:** +39 075 9689105
Web: www.johansens.com/relaisloliveta **E-mail:** info@wellcomresort.com

Our inspector loved: *The art deco style of the interiors, and the colourful little spa.*

Price Guide:
double €180-240
suite €300-360

Attractions: Cortona Music Festival and Trasimeno Blues, 12km; Montepulciano and Montalcino Wineries, 20km; Pienza, Bagno Vignoni and Numerous Medieval Hamlets and Cities of Art, 22km; Umbria Jazz Festival, 40km

Nearby Towns: Montepulciano, 12km; Cortona, 14km; Assisi, 72km; Siena, 80km
Airports: Perugia S. Egidio, 40km; Florence, 90km; Rome Fiumicino, 220km

Category: Charming Hotel
Closed: 1st November - mid-December

This former 15th-century convent is the perfect retreat for complete relaxation. A homely and refined art deco interior creates an inviting ambience and the excellent restaurant serves home-made dishes. There is also a great little spa offering wine therapy. The resort's hidden jewel is a tiny church, which is a popular venue for more intimate weddings.

Cet ancien couvent du XVe siècle est le refuge idéal pour une relaxation totale. L'intérieur chaleureux et art déco chic crée une atmosphère accueillante et le délicieux restaurant sert des plats faits maison. Il y a également un sublime petit spa qui propose des soins à base de vin. Le joyau caché de cet hôtel est une petite église, très prisée pour les mariages intimes.

Este antiguo convento del siglo XV es el emplazamiento perfecto para el relax absoluto. Su hogareño y refinado interior art-deco le proporciona un ambiente de lo más acogedor, y su excelente restaurante sirve platos caseros. Dispone también de un magnífico pequeño spa que ofrece vinoterapia. La joya oculta del complejo lo constituye su pequeña iglesia, lugar solicitado para bodas más íntimas.

ITALY / UMBRIA (MASSA MARTANA - TODI)

Castello di Montignano Relais & Spa

LOC. MONTIGNANO 6, 06056 MASSA MARTANA (PG), ITALY
Tel: +39 075 8856113 **Fax:** +39 075 63062268
Web: www.johansens.com/montignano **E-mail:** info@montignano.com

Set in a medieval hamlet surrounded by countryside, this stylish castello is incomparable. Avant-garde design and modern hotel and spa amenities have turned this majestic 10th-century castle into an inspired getaway. An impressive events venue, this is also a great spa break destination. Guests will enjoy sampling the local dishes, and wine and oil in the Materiaprima wine bar.

Situé dans un hameau médiéval et encerclé par la campagne, le style de ce castello est incomparable. Un design avant-gardiste et le modernisme des équipements de l'hôtel et du spa ont transformé ce majestueux château du Xe siècle en un refuge inspiré. C'est un somptueux lieu pour les événements ainsi qu'une magnifique destination spa. Les hôtes adoreront découvrir les plats locaux, le vin et l'huile dans le bar à vin Materiaprima.

Instalado en una aldea medieval en pleno campo, este elegante castello resulta incomparable. Su diseño vanguardista y sus modernas instalaciones propias de hoteles y spas han convertido este majestuoso castillo del siglo X en un inspirado lugar donde alejarse del mundanal ruido. Además de ser un impresionante centro de eventos, resulta también ideal como destino de spa. Sus clientes podrán disfrutar saboreando la gastronomía, el vino y el aceite del lugar en el Materiaprima wine-bar.

Our inspector loved: *The wonderful façade and entrance that is so magical at night when lit up!*

Price Guide:
classic €250-300
de luxe €300-350
suite €350-450

Attractions: Cascata delle Marmore Waterfall, 30km; Medieval Villages and Towns, 15km; Enogastronomic Tours, Oil and Wine Tastings, 30km; Umbria Jazz and Medieval Festivals and Tournaments, 40km

Nearby Towns: Todi, 15km; Spoleto, 40km; Perugia, 50km; Assisi, 55km
Airports: Perugia S. Egidio, 50km; Rome Fiumicino, 150km; Ancona, 160km

Category: Hotel
Closed: Mid-January - mid-February

I CASALI DI MONTICCHIO

VOCABOLO MONTICCHIO 34, 05011 ALLERONA, ORVIETO (TR), ITALY
Tel: +39 0763 62 83 65 **Fax:** +39 0763 62 83 65
Web: www.johansens.com/monticchio **E-mail:** info@monticchio.com

Our inspector loved: *The setting, which speaks for itself. The spa is not to be missed either!*

Price Guide:
de luxe €300-380
suite €380-1,700
villa 2-4 capacity €550-1,900

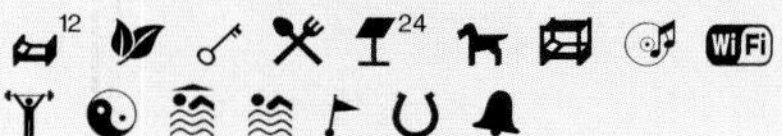

Attractions: Vineyards and Wine Tasting, 20km; Umbria Jazz Festivals and Medieval Towns of Art, 20km; Designer Shopping, 15km; Golf Course, 50km

Nearby Towns: Orvieto, 20km; Montepulciano, 45km; Rome, 100km; Florence, 130km
Airports: Perugia, 75km; Florence, 130km; Rome Fiumicino, 150km

Category: Charming Hotel

Retreat to this beautiful farmhouse in the rolling foothills of the Apennines bordering Umbria, Tuscany and Lazio, bursting with original style and charm. The old stables are now the restaurant serving home-made organic produce such as honey, olive oil and wine. The grand vaulted salon leads to the suites. The guest rooms in the converted outhouses are designed with Italian furnishings reflecting the farmhouse's heritage.

Retirez-vous dans ce magnifique corps de ferme plein de charme, situé aux pieds des collines de l'Apennin, jouxtant l'Ombrie, la Toscane et le Lazio. Le restaurant, construit dans les anciennes écuries, sert des produits biologiques faits maison tels que miel, huile d'olive et vin. Le grand salon voûté conduit directement aux suites. Les chambres qui sont dans les remises aménagées sont décorées de meubles italiens qui rappellent l'ambiance de la ferme.

Refúgiese en esta bella granja rebosante de original estilo y encanto sita en las onduladas estribaciones de los Apeninos que lindan Umbria, Toscana y Lazio. Los viejos establos constituyen en la actualidad el restaurante, que sirve productos orgánicos caseros tales como miel, aceite de oliva y vino. El grandioso salón abovedado conduce a las suites. Las habitaciones de los remodelados edificios anexos están diseñadas con mobiliario italiano, fiel copia del patrimonio de la granja.

ITALY / UMBRIA (PERUGIA - DERUTA)

L'Antico Forziere Restaurant & Country Inn

VIA DELLA ROCCA 2, 06051 CASALINA DERUTA (PG), ITALY
Tel: +39 075 972 4314 **Fax:** +39 075 972 9392
Web: www.johansens.com/anticoforziere **E-mail:** info@anticoforziere.it

This country house hotel is near Deruta, famous for its artworks and majolica. The owners welcome you into this antique rural building that exudes a typical Umbrian country atmosphere. There's a real family ethos here with the owners' twin sons creating culinary masterpieces from local ingredients, whilst their third son - an experienced wedding planner - can suggest the perfect wine to accompany your meal.

Ce hôtel de campagne est proche de Deruta, réputé pour ses oeuvres d'art et ses céramiques. Les propriétaires vous accueillent dans l'ancien bâtiment rural qui respire l'atmosphère typique de la campagne Ombrienne. C'est une véritable affaire de famille puisque les jumeaux des propriétaires créent des chefs d'oeuvres culinaires à partir d'ingrédients locaux tandis que leur troisième fils – un organisateur de mariage expérimenté- propose les meilleurs vins pour accompagner votre repas.

Este hotel-casa de campo se encuentra cerca de Deruta, famosa por su artesanía y mayólica. Sus propietarios le dan la bienvenida a este antiguo edificio rural que rezuma el típico ambiente campestre de la Umbría. Es de carácter realmente familiar, pues los hijos mellizos de los dueños crean obras de arte culinarias utilizando productos del lugar, mientras que el tercer hijo - experto en la organización de bodas - se encarga de sugerir el vino perfecto para acompañar cada comida.

Our inspector loved: *The mouth-watering dishes, so artistically presented.*

Price Guide:
single/double €70-120
suite €130-180

Awards: Italy's Restaurant Quality Award '06-'09

Attractions: Gastronomic and Wine Tastings, on the doorstep; Deruta Ceramic Museum and School, 5-min drive; Umbria Jazz Festival and and Eurochocolate, 15-min drive; Medieval Towns and Traditional Festivals, 25-min drive

Nearby Towns: Perugia, 15-min drive; Todi, 20-min drive; Assisi, 25-min drive; Spoleto, 35-min drive
Airports: Perugia, S. Egidio, 20km; Ancona - Falconara, 134km; Rome, 200km

Category: Charming Hotel

LE TORRI DI BAGNARA (MEDIEVAL HISTORICAL RESIDENCES)

STRADA DELLA BRUNA 8, 06134 PIEVE SAN QUIRICO, PERUGIA, ITALY
Tel: +39 075 579 2001 and +39 335 6408 549 **Fax:** +39 075 579 3001
Web: www.johansens.com/bagnara **E-mail:** info@letorridibagnara.it

Our inspector loved: *The building's heritage that includes 5 castles dating from the 8th-13th centuries.*

Price Guide: (room per night, apartment per week)
abbey rooms double €80-205
abbey rooms junior suite €140-250
tower apartments (2-5 beds) €460-1,500

Attractions: Festivals and Fairs in Medieval Towns, 15km; Umbria Jazz Festival, 18km; Thermal Baths, 30km; Lake Trasimeno, 35km

Nearby Towns: Perugia, 18km; Assisi, 35km; Todi, 60km; Cortona, 70km
Airports: Perugia, 20km; Florence, 159km; Rome, 204km

Category: Charming Hotel
Closed: 7th January - 20th March

Owned by the Tremi-Giunta family since 1901, descendants of Emperor Napoleon I, this historic complex offers refuge high on a hill overlooking the Tiber Valley. The 1,500-acre estate includes a nature reserve, salt-water pool and botanical gardens. Stay in the 12th-century Tower or 11th-century Abbey with meeting room and restaurant serving traditional dishes based on the estate's produce.

Propriété de la famille Tremi-Giunta depuis 1901, descendants de l'Empereur Napoleon 1er, ce complexe historique vous offre un refuge haut perché sur une colline surplombant la vallée du Tibre. Le domaine de plus de 600 hectares comprend une réserve naturelle, une piscine d'eau salée et des jardins botaniques. Séjournez dans la Tour du XIIe siècle ou dans l'Abbaye du XIe siècle qui abrite notamment une salle de réunion et un restaurant qui sert des plats traditionnels à partir de produits cultivés sur place.

Regentado desde 1901 por la familia Tremi-Giunta, descendientes del Emperador Napoleon I, este complejo histórico le proporcionará refugio en la cima de una colina con vistas al valle del Tíber. La finca de 600 hectáreas con una reserva natural, piscina de agua salada y jardines botánicos, le sorprenderá. Puede alojarse en la Torre del siglo XII, o en la Abadía del siglo XI con su sala de reuniones y restaurante donde se sirven platos tradicionales elaborados con productos de la finca.

Abbazia San Faustino - Luxury Country House

LOCALITÀ SAN FAUSTINO DI BAGNOLO, 06026 PIETRALUNGA (PG), ITALY
Tel: +39 075 9462097 **Fax:** +39 075 9462097
Web: www.johansens.com/sanfaustino **E-mail:** info@sanfaustinoresort.com

Set among the Umbrian hills, this gorgeous former abbey is furnished with antiques, wrought-iron accessories, 16th-century frescoes, hand-made pottery and refined fabrics. You will enjoy the restaurant's regional dishes, the beautiful scenery and hunting for truffles in the estate's woodlands. By special agreement, a nearby spa is also at your disposal.

Situé parmi les collines d'Ombrie, cette splendide ancienne abbaye est meublée d'antiquités, d'accessoires en fer forgé, de fresques du XVIe siècle, de poteries artisanales et de tissus raffinés. Vous aimerez les plats régionaux du restaurant, les paysages splendides et la recherche des truffes dans la forêt de la propriété. Grâce à un accord spécial, un spa est aussi à votre disposition à proximité.

Situada entre los montes de la Umbría, esta preciosa antigua abadía contiene antigüedades, diferentes accesorios de hierro forjado, frescos del siglo XVI, cerámica artesanal y refinadas telas. Disfrutará de los platos regionales del restaurante, del bello paisaje o saliendo a buscar trufas en los bosques pertenecientes a la finca. Por especial acuerdo, un spa cercano se encuentra también a su disposición.

Our inspector loved: *The atmosphere and scenery, but above all, the room with the church bell.*

Price Guide:
single €100-130
double €170-230
junior suite/suite €200-350

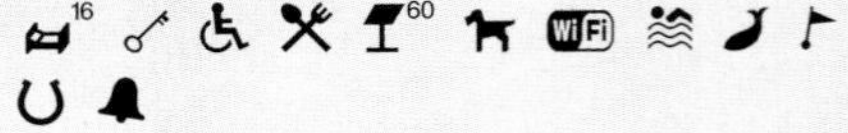

Attractions: Thermal Swimming Pool and Spa, 5-min drive; Medieval Hill Towns and Festivals, 25-min drive; Umbria Jazz, 30-min drive; Lake Trasimeno, 1-hour drive

Nearby Towns: Perugia, 30-min drive; Gubbio, 30-min drive; Assisi, 30-min drive; Cortona, 45-min drive
Airports: Perugia, 40-min drive; Florence, 90-min drive; Rome, 2-hour drive

Category: Charming Hotel
Closed: 7th January - 1st March

ITALY / VALLE D'AOSTA (GRESSONEY~LA~TRINITÉ) 

Romantik Hotel Jolanda Sport

LOC. EDELBODEN 31, GRESSONEY~LA~TRINITÉ, 11020 GRESSONEY~LA~TRINITÉ (AOSTA), ITALY

Tel: +39 0125 366 140 **Fax:** +39 0125 366 202

Web: www.johansens.com/jolandasport **E-mail:** info@hoteljolandasport.com

Our inspector loved: *The wooden furnishings.*

Price Guide: (half board, per person)
comfort €85-135
romantic €95-145
junior suite €105-160

Awards: Condé Nast Johansens Most Excellent Value for Money 2009

Attractions: Monterosa Ski Resorts and Regina Margherita Alpine Refuge, on-site; Heli-Ski, Climbing and Tracking, 1-min walk; Free Green Fee at Golf Course, 4km

Nearby Towns: Aosta, 85km; Torino, 99km; Chamonix, France, 140km; Milan, 170km
Airports: Torino, 90km; Aosta, 80km; Milan Malpensa, 165km

Category: Charming Hotel
Closed: During May, October and November

At this cosy bolthole nestling in the Monterosa ski resort you can be out on 130km of ski runs in the morning and back at the spa unwinding by the afternoon. If you're not a winter sports' enthusiast, just sit back, relax and savour the restaurant's traditional dishes and excellent wines.

Dans ce douillet refuge niché dans la station de ski de Monterosa, vous pouvez profiter des 130km de pistes de ski dès le matin et être de retour pour vous détendre au spa le soir. Si vous n'êtes pas adeptes des sports d'hiver, installez-vous confortablement, reposez-vous et savourez les plats traditionnels et les excellents vins du restaurant.

En este acogedor refugio enclavado en las instalaciones de ski de Monterosa podrá hacer uso de 130 kms de pistas por la mañana y regresar al spa para relajarse en él por la tarde. Si no es Vd. un empedernido practicante de los deportes invernales, limítese a tomar asiento, relajarse y saborear los platos tradicionales y los excelentes vinos de su restaurante.

ITALY / VENETO (BARDOLINO - VERONA)

Color Hotel

VIA SANTA CRISTINA 5, 37011 BARDOLINO (VR), ITALY
Tel: +39 045 621 0857 **Fax:** +39 045 621 2697
Web: www.johansens.com/colorhotel **E-mail:** info@colorhotel.it

Inspired by colour, the essence of life and well-being, the hotel features innovative design and furnishings. Experience the relaxing effects of chromatherapy and chill out by the pool with its unique waterfall and ambient lounge area. The spacious suites have lovely views, and the restaurant offers an exciting menu accompanied by delicious Bardolino wines.

Inspiré par les couleurs, l'essence de la vie et le bien être, cet hôtel propose un design et un ameublement innovants. Essayez les effets relaxants de la chromothérapie et détendez-vous au bord de la piscine avec sa cascade unique et son coin lounge ambiant. Les suites spacieuses ont des vues ravissantes et le restaurant propose des menus innovants accompagnés de délicieux vins de Bardolino.

El hotel cuenta con un diseño y un mobiliario innovador inspirado en el color, el bienestar y la esencia de la vida. Experimente los efectos relajantes de la cromoterapia y refrésquese junto a la piscina con su excepcional cascada y su ambientada sala de estar. Las espaciosas suites ofrecen bellas vistas y al restaurante ofrece una innovadora carta acompañada de deliciosos vinos Bardolino.

Our inspector loved: *How the use of imagination adds colour to this resort, from the food to the ambience and the bright and happy team!*

Price Guide:
single €80-175
double/twin €130-230
junior suite/suite €170-400

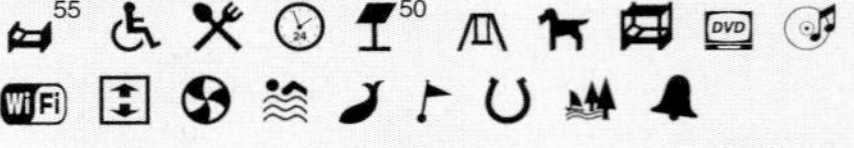

Attractions: Lake Garda, 5-min walk; Opera, 30km; Romeo and Juliet's Balcony, 30km

Nearby Towns: Bardolino Centre, 5-min walk; Verona, 30km; Venice, 120km
Airports: Verona 30km; Brescia Montichiari, 60km; Bergamo 100km; Venice, 150km

Category: Charming Hotel
Closed: 22nd October - 22nd March

Locanda San Vigilio

LOCALITÀ SAN VIGILIO, 37016 GARDA (VR), ITALY
Tel: +39 045 725 66 88 **Fax:** +39 045 627 81 82
Web: www.johansens.com/sanvigilio **E-mail:** info@punta-sanvigilio.it

Our inspector loved: *The stillness when the sun goes down.*

Price Guide: (excluding VAT)
double (single occupancy) €250-380
double €270-400
suite €450-890

Attractions: Mermaid Beach, 1-min walk; Lake Garda, 1-min walk; Monte Baldo, 36km

Nearby Towns: Torri del Benaco, 4km; Lazise, 9km; Sirmione, 38km; Verona, 39km
Airports: Verona, 39km; Brescia, 73km; Bergamo, 117km

Category: Charming Hotel
Closed: November - March

This 16th-century villa is reached via a beautiful lane, lined with cypress and olive trees. Rooms in the villa are rich in antiques and have a magical view of the lake, whilst the suites in the adjacent building have private access and lovely gardens with a new pool. Be sure to book a table on the balcony for a truly romantic dinner, and peruse the new gift shop filled with hand chosen items by the owners.

Il faut cheminer le long d'une allée de cyprès et d'oliviers pour atteindre cette villa du XVIe siècle. Les chambres dans la villa sont riches en meubles anciens et bénéficient de vues magique sur le lac, tandis que les suites, dans le bâtiment adjacent, ont un accès privé, de ravissants jardins avec une nouvelle piscine. N'oubliez pas de réserver une table sur le balcon pour un véritable dîner romantique et découvrez la nouvelle boutique remplie d'objets sélectionnés par les propriétaires.

Un bello camino bordeado de cipreses y olivos conduce hasta esta villa del siglo XVI. Las habitaciones de la villa están repletas de antigüedades y ostentan mágica vistas al lago, mientras que las suites en el edificio anexo tienen acceso privado y bonitos jardines con una nueva piscina. Reserve una mesa en la terraza para disfrutar de una cena verdaderamente romántica y visite la nueva tienda de regalos, repleta de artículos elegidos meticulosamente por los propietarios.

Park Hotel Brasilia

VIA LEVANTINA, 2ND ACC. AL MARE 3, 30016 LIDO DI JESOLO, ITALY

Tel: +39 0421 380851 **Fax:** +39 0421 92244

Web: www.johansens.com/parkhotelbrasilia **E-mail:** info@parkhotelbrasilia.com

Our inspector loved: *The smiling staff that make you feel so welcome.*

Price Guide: (including free WiFi access. Sky Vision Gold Package Pay TV available.)
double (single occupancy) €110-200
double €130-280
suite €180-300

Attractions: Adriatic Sea and Beach, 10 metres; Acqualandia, 5-min drive; Golf, 5-min drive; Punta Sabbioni, 20-min drive

Nearby Towns: Treviso, 45km; Venice, 30-min boat ride
Airports: Venice, 30km; Treviso, 45km

Category: Hotel
Closed: October - Easter

Set on the eastern side of Lido di Jesolo, this hotel lies in a quiet position with private sandy beach and 2 pools. Explore your surroundings and hire one of the hotel's bicycles before retiring to your room where soft, elegant shades enhance their soothing ambience. Each has a marble bathroom and terrace that looks out to the Adriatic. The restaurant's creative chef offers a delightful array of seafood specialities.

Situé coté est du Lido di Jesolo, cet hôtel se trouve dans un endroit calme avec une plage de sable privée et 2 piscines. Explorez les environs et louez l'un des vélos de l'hôtel avant de profiter de votre chambre où l'ambiance relaxante est mise en valeur par les tons doux et élégants. Chacune des chambres possède une salle de bain en marbre et une terrasse surplombant l'Adriatique. L'inventif chef du restaurant propose un délicieux assortiment de spécialités de fruits de mer.

Este hotel situado al este del Lido di Jesolo goza de tranquilidad con playa privada arenosa y 2 piscinas. Descubra los alrededores y alquile una bicicleta del hotel, para luego descansar en su habitación donde los tonos suaves y elegantes ayudan a crear un ambiente tranquilo. Todas disponen de cuartos de baño de mármol y terrazas con vistas al Adriático. El creativo chef del restaurante ofrece una deliciosa variedad de especialidades de mariscos.

Relais la Magioca

VIA MORON 3, 37024 NEGRAR - VALPOLICELLA (VR), ITALY
Tel: +39 045 600 0167 **Fax:** +39 045 600 0840
Web: www.johansens.com/lamagioca **E-mail:** info@magioca.it

Our inspector loved: *The romance that permeates the atmosphere, and Marisa's warm welcome.*

Price Guide:
double de luxe €230-270
junior suite €250-300

Attractions: Wineries, 12km; Arena Opera, 13km; Juliet's Balcony, 13km; Lazise, Lake Garda, 27km

Nearby Towns: Valpolicella, 12km; Verona, 13km; Sirmione, 56km; Brescia, 85km
Airports: Verona, 35km; Brescia, 80km; Venice, 150km

Category: Luxury Guest House

Owner, Marisa Merighi welcomes you to her romantic relais; a lovingly furnished ancient stone-built farmhouse with spacious bedrooms. Sample the home-made cakes and chocolates in the kitchen, and admire the breathtaking views of the surrounding countryside. Its little chapel is perfect for weddings and the vaulted cellar is ideal for private dinners. It's no wonder guests return year on year.

La propriétaire, Marisa Merighi, vous accueille dans son relais romantique ; une ancienne ferme en pierres meublée avec soin avec des chambres spacieuses. Dégustez les gâteaux et chocolats faits maison dans la cuisine et admirez les magnifiques vues sur la campagne environnante. La petite chapelle est idéale pour les mariages et la cave voûtée est parfaite pour des dîners privés. Il n'est pas étonnant que les clients reviennent année après année.

La propietaria, Marisa Merighi les acoge en su romántica demora; una antigua granja construida en piedra, con amplias habitaciones y amueblada con cariño. Pruebe los pasteles y bombones caseros que encontrará en la cocina y admire las espectaculares vistas de la campiña que le rodea. La pequeña capilla es perfecta para celebrar bodas y la bodega con techo abovedado, un lugar ideal para cenas privadas. Se comprende porqué los huéspedes regresan año tras año.

ITALY / VENETO (ROLLE DI CISON DI VALMARINO)

Relais Duca di Dolle

VIA PIAI ORIENTALI 5, 31030 ROLLE DI CISON DI VALMARINO (TV), ITALY
Tel: +39 0438 975 809 **Fax:** +39 0438 975 792
Web: www.johansens.com/ducadidolle **E-mail:** info@ducadidolle.it

The property's lovely setting means that you have only a short distance between the Bisol winery and your bed! Enjoying stunning uninterrupted views, stylish accommodation comprises 5 double rooms and 2 apartments with hi-tech kitchens. 2 great restaurants are within walking distance, and Bisol wine and snacks are served pool-side.

Le charmant emplacement de cet établissement vous permet de n'avoir qu'une courte distance entre le vignoble de Bisol et votre lit! Profitant en permanence de vues exceptionnelles, les élégants logements comprennent 5 chambres doubles et 2 appartements équipés de cuisines hi-tech. 2 très bons restaurants sont accessibles à pied; du vin de Bisol et des encas sont servis au bord de la piscine.

La ubicación encantadora del este establecimiento significa que entre la bodega Bisol y su habitación. ¡sólo hay un paso! Disfrute de las fascinantes vistas ininterrumpidas, el alojamiento de gran estilo consta de 5 habitacións doble y 2 apartamentos con cocinas de alta tecnología. Encontrará 2 famosos restaurantes a corta distancia a pie y junto a la piscina se sirven vino Bisol y tapas.

***Our inspector loved:** Sipping a glass of Prosecco while relaxing in the infinity pool.*

Price Guide:
double €120-150
suite €200-300

     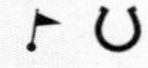

Attractions: Follina Abbey, 5-min drive; Castelbrando, 5-min drive; Croda Mill, 5-min drive; Santa Maria Lake, 10-min drive

Nearby Towns: Follina, 3km; Asolo, 41km; Cortina, 97km; Venice, 1-hour train ride
Airports: Treviso, 73km; Venice, 82km

Category: Luxury Guest House
Closed: Mid-November - 20th December and 8th January - 20th March

Relais Corte Guastalla

VIA GUASTALLA VECCHIA 11, 37060 SONA (VR), ITALY
Tel: +39 045 6095614 **Fax:** +39 045 6099175
Web: www.johansens.com/corteguastalla **E-mail:** info@corteguastalla.it

Our inspector loved: *The most relaxing of pool areas.*

Price Guide:
double €175-220
suite €220-275

Attractions: Verona's Arena Theatre, 15-min drive; Valpolicella, 20-min drive

Nearby Towns: Verona, 15-min drive
Airports: Verona, 10-min drive

Category: Luxury Guest House
Closed: During January

Unfussy yet perfectly restored, this country house is surrounded by green landscape everywhere you look. Grapevines adorn its walls outside, while original art and carefully placed antiques dress the inside. Rooms are warmly furnished with terracotta tiles, wooden beams and stylish bathrooms, and the typical Veronese atmosphere ensures a comfortable, relaxing stay.

Parfaitement restaurée tout en simplicité, cette maison de campagne est entourée de verdure, partout où vous regardez. De la vigne habille les murs extérieurs, des œuvres d'arts originales et des pièces antiques placées avec attention décorent l'intérieur. Les chambres sont chaleureusement décorées avec des carreaux en terracota, des poutres en bois et de ravissantes salles de bains. L'atmosphère typiquement véronaise vous garantit un séjour confortable et reposant.

Sencilla aunque perfectamente reformada, esta casa solariega está por donde alcanza la vista rodeada por un verde paisaje. Las vides adornan sus muros exteriores, sus originales obras de arte y sus antigüedades, colocadas con esmero, engalanan su interior. Las habitaciones muestran un toque acogedor gracias a sus losas de terracota, vigas de madera y elegantes cuartos de baño. El ambiente típicamente veronés le garantiza una cómoda y relajante estancia.

Murano
Sacca della
Misericordia
San Michele
Canale delle Navi
Cannaregio
218
Tronchetto
Stazione
Ferroviaria
S. Lucia
Canal Grande
San Croce
216
Isola le Vignole
Ponte di Rialto
Arsenale
San Croce
San Polo
Bacino
Stazione
Marittima
Canal Grande
S. Marco
220
San Pietro
Castello
Dorsoduro
221
217
Basilica di
San Marco
La Certosa
Canale di San Marco
215
Canale di Fusina
San Giorgio
Maggiore
Sacca Fisola
Canale di Giudecca
La Giudecca
Giardini
Pubblici
Sant' Elena
219
San Clemente
Lido di
Venezia
222
Sacca
Sessola

Ca Maria Adele

DORSODURO 111, 30123 VENICE, ITALY
Tel: +39 041 52 03 078 **Fax:** +39 041 52 89 013
Web: www.johansens.com/camariaadele **E-mail:** info@camariaadele.it

Our inspector loved: *The Campa brothers and their staff who know how to seduce you! They make you feel very, very special.*

Price Guide:
room €341-715
suite €506-770

Attractions: Gondola Ride, on the doorstep; Punta dalla Dogana Museum, 1-min walk; St Mark's Square, 5-min boat ride

Airports: Treviso, 20km; Venice Marco Polo, 30-min drive or 35-min by water taxi

Category: Luxury Guest House

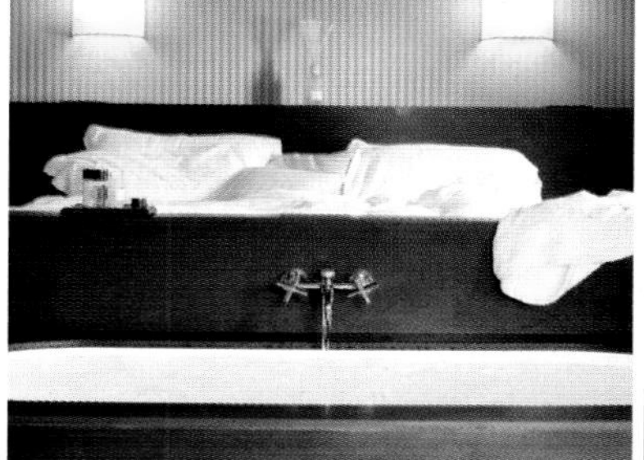

Once a 16th-century palazzo, now a stylish little hotel across the water from St. Mark's Square. The salons are a feast for the senses; from rich brocades to Oriental touches. Guests will love the 5 themed bedrooms, each one beautifully opulent. Breakfasts are truly unique, enjoyed in the breakfast room, by the fireplace in the lounge, on the terrace or in the privacy of your own suite.

Autrefois un palais du XVIe siècle, c'est aujourd'hui un petit hôtel de style situé de l'autre côté de l'eau, en face de la Place Saint-Marc. Les salons, garnis de somptueux brocarts et de touches orientales, sont un régal pour les sens. Les hôtes vont adorer les 5 chambres à thème, toutes magnifiquement opulentes. Les petits-déjeuners sont uniques; à déguster dans la salle de petit-déjeuner, près de la cheminée dans le salon, sur la terrasse ou dans le confort de votre propre suite.

Antaño un palazzo del siglo XVI, ahora es un pequeño hotel elegante situado al otro lado del río de la Plaza de San Marcos. Sus salones, provistos de suntuosos bordados y detalles orientales, son un festín para los sentidos. A los clientes les encantarán las 5 habitaciones temáticas, cada una de ellas de una opulencia maravillosa. Los desayunos son realmente inigualables y los puede degustar en la sala de desayunos, al lado de la chimenea del salon, en la terraza, o en la intimidad de su propia suite.

ITALY / VENETO (VENICE)

Ca' Sagredo Hotel

CAMPO SANTA SOFIA 4198/99, 30121 VENICE, ITALY
Tel: +39 041 2413111 **Fax:** +39 041 2413521
Web: www.johansens.com/casagredo **E-mail:** info@casagredohotel.com

This is city centre, 5-star luxury and splendour at its best. Rich and opulent, yet not too ostentatious, a careful restoration has resulted in a classic Venetian style with impressive stucco work alongside breathtaking pieces of art, including a priceless fresco. Enjoy dining with views over the Grand Canal, and venture out with a private tour organised by the hotel.

Cet hôtel en centre ville incarne le luxe 5 étoiles et le summum de la splendeur. Riche et opulente, sans être trop tape-à-l'oeil, une restauration soigneuse l'a transformé dans un style vénitien classique avec d'impressionnantes décorations en stuc parmi de magnifiques oeuvres d'arts, dont une fresque inestimable. Profitez des dîners avec vues sur le Grand Canal et aventurez-vous lors des visites privées organisées par l'hôtel.

El hotel, situado en el centro de la ciudad, es un magnífico exponente del esplendor y del lujo de 5 estrellas. Es opulento y suntuoso, aunque no demasiado ostentoso. Una esmerada restauración le ha conferido un estilo clásico veneciano dotado de impresionantes estucos junto a sobrecogedoras obras de arte, entre las que se incluye un fresco de incalculable valor. Disfrute de las cenas con vistas al Gran Canal y salga a conocer la ciudad con visíta guiada organizada por el hotel.

Our inspector loved: *The sincere and friendly staff at this Venetian hotel gem.*

Price Guide:
double €400-800
suite €820-2,000

Awards: Condé Nast Traveller Hot List 2008

Attractions: Rialto Market, on the doorstep; Rialto Bridge, 5-min walk; St Mark's Square, 10-min walk

Nearby Towns: Padova, 30-min train/metro
Airports: Venice Marco Polo, 20-min water taxi ride; Treviso, 30-min drive

Category: Hotel

Hotel Flora

SAN MARCO 2283/A, 30124 VENICE, ITALY
Tel: +39 041 52 05 844 **Fax:** +39 041 52 28 217
Web: www.johansens.com/hotelflora **E-mail:** info@hotelflora.it

Our inspector loved: *The barman in the American bar who will serve your favourite cocktail just the way you like it!*

Price Guide:
single €160-210
double €210-300
superior €200-350

 43  15   

Attractions: St Mark's Square, 5-min walk; Accademia Bridge, 5-min walk

Nearby Towns: Mestre, 10-min train/metro; Treviso, 20-min train/metro; Padova, 30-min train/metro
Airports: Venice Marco Polo, 15-min drive; Treviso Canova, 30-min drive

Category: Luxury Guest House

Footsteps from St Mark's Square, Hotel Flora began life as a notable 17th-century painting school. Thankfully, the warmth of an intimate guest house remains, and you can sense a passion for culture in the elegant rooms and Venetian-style period furniture. The courtyard is a haven of green in the middle of the city, which beckons exploration; just ask a member of staff for a special guided tour.

A quelques mètres de la Place Saint-Marc, l'hôtel Flora fut en premier lieu une remarquable école de peinture au XVIIe siècle. Heureusement, il a conservé l'atmosphère chaleureuse d'une intime maison d'hôte, et l'on peut ressentir la passion de la culture dans les pièces élégantes et à travers les meubles d'époque de style vénitien. La cour intérieure est un havre verdoyant au coeur de la ville qui appelle à l'exploration ; demandez simplement une visite guidée spéciale à un membre du personnel.

A unos pasos de la Plaza de San Marcos, el Hotel Flora comenzó como una notable escuela de pintura del siglo XVII. Por fortuna, perdura el calor de una intima casa de huéspedes y se percibe un apasionado interés por la cultura en sus elegantes habitaciones y en el mobiliario de época de estilo veneciano. El patio es un remanso de vegetación en el centro de esta ciudad que quiere ser descubierta y el personal del hotel le puede organizar una visita guiada.

ITALY / VENETO (VENICE)

Hotel Giorgione

SS APOSTOLI 4587, 30121 VENICE, ITALY
Tel: +39 041 522 5810 **Fax:** +39 041 523 9092
Web: www.johansens.com/giorgione **E-mail:** giorgione@hotelgiorgione.com

A stone's throw from the Rialto Bridge and St Mark's Square, this hotel's quiet central location provides all modern comforts yet retains the original charm of its 15th-century beginnings. Rooms are romantic, as is the pretty patio garden. Next door at Osteria-Enoteca Giorgione, you can enjoy great wines and local dishes.

A deux pas du Pont Rialto et de la Place Saint-Marc, cet hôtel à l'emplacement central et tranquille, offre tout le confort moderne en gardant son charme d'origine du XVe siècle. Les chambres sont romantiques, de même que le ravissant jardin dans le patio. Sur le palier voisin, à l'Osteria-Enoteca Giorgione, vous pourrez déguster d'excellents vins et des mets locaux.

A tiro de una piedra desde el Puente de Rialto y la Plaza de San Marcos, el emplazamiento céntrico del hotel proporciona todo tipo de comodidades modernas sin perder el encanto original de sus inicios en el siglo XV. Las habitaciones son románticas, como también lo es su precioso jardín del patio. En la puerta de al lado, en Osteria-Enoteca Giorgione, podrá Vd. disfrutar de excelentes vinos y platos locales.

Our inspector loved: *The unbeatable prices!*

Price Guide:
single €80-200
double €100-500

Attractions: Cannaregio Shopping Area, 1-min walk; St Mark's Square, 10-min walk; Rialto Fish Market, 10-min walk

Nearby Towns: Mestre, 10-min train/metro; Padova, 30-min train/metro
Airports: Venice, 10-min drive; Treviso, 35-min drive

Category: Charming Hotel

Hotel Sant' Elena Venezia

CALLE BUCCARI 10, SANT' ELENA, 30132 VENICE, ITALY
Tel: +39 041 27 17 811 **Fax:** +39 041 27 71 569
Web: www.johansens.com/santelena **E-mail:** info@hotelsantelena.com

Our inspector loved: *The Japanese influence, and the vicinity to the Giardini, the greenest part of Venice.*

Price Guide: (including free internet access in the hall and bedrooms, excluding VAT)
double €112-324
triple €146-423
junior suite € 140-425

Attractions: La Biennale, 2-min walk; Sant' Elena Gardens, 2-min walk; San Marco, 20-25-min walk; Certosa Island and Marina, 5-min boat ride

Nearby Towns: Venice, 15-min walk; Mestre, 20-min water taxi ride and 10-min train ride; Treviso, 20-min water taxi ride and 20-min train ride; Padova, 20-min water taxi ride and 15-min train ride
Airports: Venice Marco Polo, 10km; Treviso, 20km

Category: Hotel

A former convent that still breathes serenity, the hotel is a walk from the centre of Venice, next to Biennale Art Exhibition and Olivetani Monastery, and steps from the marina. Bedrooms and suites are modern and comfortable with a Japanese influence, and guests may dine in Valentine's Restaurant & Bar to sample true Venetian cuisine. A private garden and conservatory are also available for guests to enjoy breakfast or simply relax within.

Cet hôtel fut autrefois un couvent et respire toujours la sérénité. Situé à deux pas du centre de Venise, tout près de la Biennale d'art, du Monastère Olivetani et proche de la marina. Les chambres et les suites sont modernes et confortables avec une touche Japonaise. Les hôtes peuvent dîner dans le restaurant et bar Valentine pour déguster une véritable cuisine vénitienne. Le jardin privatif et la véranda sont parfaits pour prendre son petit-déjeuner ou se relaxer.

Este antiguo convento donde aún se respira serenidad, está a un paso del centro de Venecia, al lado de la exposición de arte Biennale, del monasterio Olivetani y a unos pasos del puerto deportivo. Las habitaciones y suites son modernas y cómodas de inspiración japonesa, y los huéspedes pueden cenar en Valentine's Restaurant & Bar para degustar autentica cocina veneciana. El hotel dispone de un jardín privado e invernadero donde se puede desayunar o simplemente descansar.

Londra Palace

RIVA DEGLI SCHIAVONI, 4171, 30122 VENICE, ITALY
Tel: +39 041 5200533 **Fax:** +39 041 5225032
Web: www.johansens.com/londra **E-mail:** info@londrapalace.com

This boutique hotel, close to St Mark's Square, offers a taste of romance and glamour that you will find irresistible. Most of the richly decorated rooms and suites have stunning views of the lagoon. The restaurant, Do Leoni, serves sophistication on a plate. On sunny days you can people-watch while enjoying lunch, dinner or drinks on the veranda.

Ce boutique hôtel, proche de la Place Saint-Marc, possède un parfum de romance et un éclat que vous trouverez irrésistibles. Les chambres et les suites, somptueusement décorées ont, pour la plupart, des vues sensationnelles sur la lagune. Le restaurant, Do Leoni, sert une cuisine très raffinée. Les jours ensoleillés vous pouvez vous installer dans la véranda pour prendre un repas ou boire un verre en regardant passer les badauds.

Este hotel boutique próximo a la Plaza de San Marco ofrece un sabor a romance y glamour irresistible. La mayoría de las habitaciones y suites profusamente decoradas tienen impresionantes vistas a la laguna. En el restaurante Do Leoni, la sofisticación esta servida y en los días soleados podrá observar a la gente mientras se toma una copa, almuerza o cena en la terraza.

Our inspector loved: *The newly decorated guest rooms with beds featuring exceptionally fluffy pillows!*

Price Guide:
standard €265-525
de luxe €365-625
junior suite €465-825

Awards: Condé Nast Traveller Gold List 2008; Condé Nast Traveller No 33 Best of the Best Hotels 2006-2007

Attractions: Grand Canal, 1-min walk; Opera, 2-min walk; St Mark's Square, 5-min walk

Airports: Venice Marco Polo, 10-min drive; Treviso, 30-min drive

Category: Hotel

NOVECENTO BOUTIQUE HOTEL

SAN MARCO 2684, 30124 VENICE, ITALY
Tel: +39 041 24 13 765 **Fax:** +39 041 52 12 145
Web: www.johansens.com/novecento **E-mail:** info@novecento.biz

Our inspector loved: *The cheerful staff. Everyone smiles at Novecento!*

Price Guide:
room €170-310

Attractions: Accademia Bridge, 5-min walk; St Mark's Square, 10-min walk

Nearby Towns: Mestre, 10-min train/metro; Treviso, 20-min train/metro; Padova, 30-min train/metro
Airports: Marco Polo, 10-min drive; Treviso, 30-min drive

Category: Luxury Guest House

Tucked between St Mark's Square and the Accademia Galleries, this stylish little boutique hotel pays homage to artist and fashion designer Mariano Fortuny who lived in Venice during the 19th century. Local artists are invited to use Novecento as a showcase for their work in rooms filled with furniture and tapestries from the Mediterranean and Far East alongside 21st-century luxuries.

Caché entre la place Saint-Marc et les Galeries de l'Académie, cet élégant petit boutique hôtel rend hommage à l'artiste et dessinateur de mode Mariano Fortuny qui vécut à Venise au XIXe siècle. Les artistes locaux sont invités à utiliser Novecento pour exposer leurs œuvres dans les pièces et chambres remplies de mobilier et de tapisseries venus de Méditerranée et du Moyen-Orient et d'équipements du XXIe siècle.

Escondido entre la Plaza de San Marco y las Galerías Academia, este pequeño y elegante boutique hotel hace homenaje al artista y diseñador de moda Mariano Fortuny que vivió en Venecia en el siglo XIX. Las habitaciones, que combinan mobiliario mediterráneo y tapices del lejano oriente con lujosas comodidades del siglo XXI, son también salas de exposición, pues los artistas locales son invitados a utilizar el Novecento como escaparate para su trabajo.

ALBERGO QUATTRO FONTANE - RESIDENZA D'EPOCA

VIA QUATTRO FONTANE 16, 30126 LIDO DI VENEZIA, VENICE, ITALY
Tel: +39 041 526 0227 **Fax:** +39 041 526 0726
Web: www.johansens.com/quattrofontane **E-mail:** info@quattrofontane.com

Our inspector loved: *The retro atmosphere. This is a true oasis of serenity!*

Price Guide:
single €120-330
double/twin €180-520
apartment €370-630

Attractions: Lido Beach, 100 metres

Nearby Towns: Mainland Venice, 10-min boat ride; St Mark's Square, 15-min boat ride
Airports: Venice Marco Polo, 6km; Treviso, 10km

Category: Charming Hotel
Closed: During November - 20th April

Jump on a water-bus from St Mark's Square and 15 minutes later you can be in the idyllic garden of this distinctive country house. Mr Bevilacqua, whose family has owned the property for over 50 years, has collected unusual artefacts from all over the world. There is even access to a private beach with little beach cabins.

Sautez dans un bateau-bus à Place à Saint-Marc et 15 minutes plus tard vous pouvez être dans le ravissant jardin de cette traditionnelle maison de campagne. Monsieur Bevilacqua, dont la famille est propriétaire de la maison depuis plus de 50 ans, a collectionné des objets originaux du monde entier. Il y a même un accès à une plage privée avec ses petites cabines de plage.

Salte al waterbus en la Plaza de San Marcos y 15 minutos después se encontrará en el idílico jardín de esta peculiar casa de campo. El Siñor Bevilacqua, cuya familia ha sido su propietaria durante más de 50 años, ha hecho colección de inusuales artefactos procedentes de todo el mundo. Hay incluso acceso a una playa privada con pequeños cambiadores.

BELGIUM
GERMANY
FRANCE
Troisvierges
Clervaux
Neuerburg
Bastogne
Wiltz
Bitburg
Vianden
Esch-sur-Sûre
Diekirch
Ettelbruck
Redange-sur-Attert
Mersch
Trier
Arlon
Grevenmacher
Walferdange
Niederanven
Mamer
Luxembourg
Aubange
Hespérange
Pétange
Sanem
Remich
224
Bettembourg
Differdange
Schifflange
Mondorf-les-Bains
Longwy
Esch-sur-Alzette
Dudelange
Kayl
Thionville

LUXEMBOURG (REMICH)

HOTEL SAINT~NICOLAS & SPA

31 ESPLANADE, 5533 REMICH, LUXEMBOURG
Tel: +352 26663 **Fax:** +352 26663 666
Web: www.johansens.com/saintnicolas **E-mail:** hotel@pt.lu

Remich is a picturesque town, and views from this family-run hotel are pretty easy on the eye, as it lies on a prime waterfront location on the banks of the Moselle, looking across the esplanade and lush vineyards. Eclectic in style, the unusual public rooms display interesting paintings, and the fine dining Lohengrin Restaurant serves traditional French cuisine. In the summer, al fresco dining can be enjoyed. Superb spa facilities are now available.

Remich est une ville pittoresque, et les vues depuis cet hôtel familial sont très agréables grâce à sa situation privilégiée sur les berges de la Moselle et à son orientation vers l'esplanade et le luxuriant vignoble. De style éclectique, ses salons inhabituels sont décorés d'intéressantes peintures. Le restaurant Lohengrin sert une cuisine traditionnelle française. L'été, il est possible de dîner à l'extérieur. De superbes équipements de spa sont désormais accessibles.

Remich es una localidad pintoresca, y el panorama que proporciona este hotel de regencia familiar es de lo más agradable, ya que se encuentra ubicado en un lugar privilegiado a orillas del rio Moselle, con vistas a la explanada y exuberantes viñedos. De estilo ecléctico, sus singulares salones se adornan con interesantes lienzos y el restaurante Lohengrin sirve buena cocina tradicional francesa. En verano se puede cenar al aire libre y el hotel también dispone ahora de un fabuloso Spa.

Our inspector loved: *The wonderful location overlooking the Moselle.*

Price Guide: (excluding VAT, car park by reservation available €12 per day)
single €105-140
double/twin/suite €130-165
gastronomic offer (incl 2-night stay) €209-244

Attractions: Moselle Valley and Vineyards, 22km; UNESCO City of Luxembourg, 26km; Mullerthal and Little Switzerland, 40km; The Ardennes and Natural Parks, 85km

Nearby Towns: Luxembourg City, 26km
Airports: Luxembourg Findel, 19km

Category: Hotel

Zebbug
Gharb
San Katald
Gozo
GOZO
Xaghra
Nadur
Qala
Sannat
Xewkija
Comino
MEDITERRANEAN SEA
Marfa
Mellieha
Golden Bay
San Pawl Il-Bahar
Pembroke
226
Gharghur
Mosta
St. Julian's
VALLETTA
227
Mgarr
Rabat
MALTA
Kalkara
Mdina
Dingli
Zeitun
Siggiewi
Luqa
Ghaxaq
Sliema e Marshallok
Qrendi

MALTA (ST JULIANS)

Corinthia Hotel St George's Bay

ST GEORGE'S BAY, ST JULIANS STJ 3301, MALTA

Tel: +356 21374114 **Fax:** +356 21378222

Web: www.johansens.com/corinthia **E-mail:** stgeorges@corinthia.com

Our inspector loved: *The staff, who are always present, friendly and professional.*

Price Guide: (room only, excluding VAT)
de luxe standard room €145-280
ambassador suite €230-365

Attractions: Valletta, 6km; Mdina, 20km; Megalithic Temple Site, 30km; Marsaxlokk Fishermen's Village, 30km

Nearby Towns: St Julians, 0.5km; Sliema, 2.5km; Valletta, 6km
Airports: Malta, 15km

Category: Hotel

This grand, extensive resort is a magnificent feat of modern hospitality. Personal service, stylish contemporary design and an abundance of activities, that include the Apollo Day Spa, a water sports centre, private yacht hire and night clubs, are all under one roof. All this in addition to a superb location directly on St George's Bay. Pure and simple 5-star!

Ce vaste et imposant resort est une magnifique prouesse d'hospitalité moderne. Un service personnalisé, un design chic et moderne et une abondance d'activités, comprenant l'Apollo Day Spa, un centre de sports nautiques, la location d'un yacht privé et des discothèques, sont tous sous le même toit. Tout ceci en plus d'un emplacement magnifique directement sur la baie de St George. Un 5 étoiles purement et simplement.

Este grandioso y extenso centro turístico es un magnífico ejemplo de moderna hospitalidad. Servicio personalizado, diseño moderno y elegante junto a una gran abundancia de actividades, entre las que se incluye el Apollo Day Spa, además de un centro de deportes acuáticos, alquiler de yates privados así como clubes nocturnos, todo esto bajo un mismo techo. Todo ello añadido a su excelente ubicación frente a St George's Bay. Simple y llanamente un 5 estrellas.

Hotel Phoenicia Malta

THE MALL, FRN 1478, FLORIANA, VALLETTA, MALTA
Tel: +356 2122 5241 **Fax:** +356 2123 5254
Web: www.johansens.com/phoeniciamalta **E-mail:** res@phoeniciamalta.com

Our inspector loved: *The "bygone" ambience combined with contemporary touches and the hip clientele.*

Price Guide: (room only, excluding VAT)
classic plus €135-335
executive room €180-395
executive harbour view suite €430-600

Attractions: Valletta Historical City Centre, 2-min walk; St Julians' Night-life, 5km; Dolmen Archaelogical Site, 10km; Marsaxllok Fishermen's Village, 15km

Nearby Towns: Sliema, 3km; St Julians, 5km
Airports: Malta International, 8km

Category: Hotel

Frequented by royalty and socialites since its opening in 1947, much of this 5-star retreat has recently undergone a refurbishment. Enveloped by 7.5 acres of gardens that lead to The Bastion Pool Deck, there is no better place to relax and admire the imposing views. Relax at the Club Bar before dining in one of several available options.

Fréquenté par les royaux et grands de ce monde depuis son ouverture en 1947, la plus grande partie de ce refuge 5 étoiles a été récemment rénovée. Entouré de 3 hectares de jardins menant au Bastion Pool Deck, il n'existe pas de meilleur endroit pour se reposer et admirer les magnifiques vues. Relaxez-vous au Club Bar avant de dîner dans l'un des nombreux restaurants disponibles.

Este lugar de retiro de 5 estrellas, frecuentado por la realeza y famosos desde su inauguración en 1947, ha sido reformado recientemente. Rodeado de 3 hectáreas de jardines que dan al Bastion Pool Deck, no hay mejor lugar para el descanso y el disfrute de las impresionantes vistas. Entre las distintas posibilidades que se le ofrecen está la de relajarse en el Club Bar antes de cenar.

Morocco

SPAIN
Cádiz
Malaga
Gibraltar
Tangier
NORTH
ATLANTIC
OCEAN
Ksar el Kebir
Oujda
Taza
RABAT
Fès
229
Casablanca
El Jadida
Khouribga
Safi
Beni Mellal
Essaouira
Marrakech
230
MOROCCO
Ouarzazate
Tamri
Agadir
ALGERIA
Laayoune
WESTERN
SAHARA
MAURITANIA
MALI
Atar

 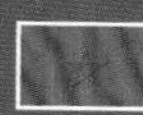

RIAD FÈS

5 DERB BEN SLIMANE, ZERBTANA, FÈS, MOROCCO
Tel: +212 535 94 76 10 **Fax:** +212 535 74 11 43
Web: www.johansens.com/riadfes **E-mail:** contact@riadfes.com

Our inspector loved: *Relaxing in the cool, peaceful riad, then exploring Fès Medina.*

Price Guide: (room only, excluding MAD45.1 tax per person per night)
room MAD1,700-2,000
suite MAD3,000-6,000

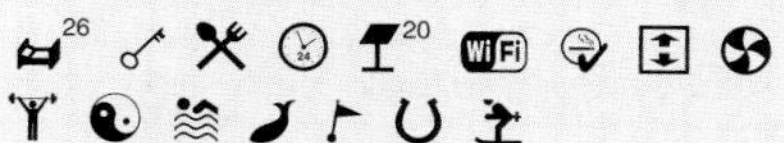

Awards: One of Morocco's Sexiest Hotels, Forbes Traveler 2008

Attractions: Guided Tour of Fès, UNESCO Medina and Souks, close by; 18-hole Golf Club, 10km; The Tanner's Quarter, 15-min walk; Moulay Yacoub Thermal Baths and Hot Springs, 30-min drive

Nearby Towns: Sefrou and the Sebou Gorge, 33km; Volubilis Roman Town, 73km; Horse Riding Excursions in Fès and The Middle Atlas, 25km
Airports: Fès Saïss, 25-min drive

Category: Charming Hotel

You couldn't ask for a more restful hotel in the heart of one of Islam's holiest cities. People live and work here as they have done since medieval times. Riad Fès is renowned for its luxury, service and food. Some of the superb bedrooms have terraces overlooking the sights and sounds of the Medina and chaotic maze of surrounding souks.

Vous ne pourriez souhaiter un hôtel plus paisible au cœur d'une des plus anciennes cités de l'Islam. Les gens vivent et travaillent ici comme ils l'ont toujours fait depuis l'époque médiévale. Le Riad Fès est réputé pour son luxe, son service et sa nourriture. Parmi les superbes chambres, certaines ont des terrasses qui surplombent le quartier ainsi que les bruits et l'agitation des souks alentour.

No se puede pedir un hotel más tranquilo en el corazón de una de las ciudades más sagradas del Islam. Sus habitantes viven y trabajan aquí como lo vienen haciendo desde los tiempos medievales. Riad Fès es célebre por su lujo, servicio y comida. Algunas de sus magníficas habitaciones tienen terraza desde donde podrá contemplar la Medina y su bullicio así como el caótico ajetreo de los zocos circundantes.

Dar Les Cigognes

108 RUE DE BERIMA, MEDINA, MARRAKECH, MOROCCO
Tel: +212 524 38 27 40 **Fax:** +212 524 38 47 67
Web: www.johansens.com/lescigognes **E-mail:** info@lescigognes.com

2 traditional Arabian houses have been transformed into this private, delightful boutique hotel from where views over the medina and snowcapped Atlas peaks are incredible. Behind its inconspicuous door lies a world of Moroccan delights: lavish bedrooms and suites, a restaurant offering national delicacies and daily cookery classes, a rooftop café, spa with hammam, a library and a boutique selling local handicrafts and kaftans!

2 maisons traditionnelles Arabes ont été transformées en charmant boutique hôtel d'où les vues sur la médina et les sommets couverts de neige de l'Atlas sont exceptionnelles. Derrière ses portes discrètes s'ouvre un monde de délices Marocains: chambres et suites somptueuses, un restaurant proposant des mets nationaux et des cours de cuisine quotidiens, un café sur le toit, un spa avec hammam, une bibliothèque et une boutique proposant de l'artisanat local et des caftans!

2 casas Arabes tradicionales se han transformado para crear este encantador boutique hotel privado cuyas vistas a la medina y a las cumbres nevadas del Atlas son increíbles. Tras su discreta puerta encontrará todo un mundo de delicias marroquíes: espléndidas habitaciones y suites, un restaurante que ofrece manjares nacionales y clases de cocina diarias, una cafería-terraza en el último piso, un spa con hammam, una biblioteca y una boutique que vende artesanía local y caftanes.

***Our inspector loved:** Knocking on the door and entering into paradise!*

Price Guide: (including afternoon mint tea with pastries and daily fresh fruit and water)
superior/de luxe room €160-200
suite €240
4-bedroom house €750

Attractions: Medina, The Kasbah, Saadian Tombs and Royal Palaces, on the doorstep; Jemaa el Fna, 5-min walk; The Atlas Mountains, 45-min drive

Airports: Marrakech, 15-min drive

Category: Charming Hotel

NORTH SEA
Den Helder
Leeuwarden
Groningen
Emden
Assen
Emmen
Alkmaar
Purmerend
Lelystad
Zwolle
Nordhorn
Amsterdam
232
Haarlem
Almere
Almelo
Deventer
Hengelo
Enschede
Apeldoorn
Leiden
Amersfoort
The Hague
Zoetermeer
Utrecht
Ede
Gouda
Nieuwegein
Arnhem
Rotterdam
Nijmegen
Dordrecht
Oss
GERMANY
's-Hertogenbosch
Roosendaal
Breda
Tilburg
Helmond
Middelburg
Eindhoven
Duisburg
Essen
Venlo
Antwerp
Wuppertal
Düsseldorf
Mönchengladbach
Ghent
BELGIUM
Cologne
Heerlen
Maastricht
Brussels
Aachen
Bonn
Liège

THE NETHERLANDS (AMSTERDAM)

AMBASSADE HOTEL

HERENGRACHT 341, 1016 AMSTERDAM, THE NETHERLANDS

Tel: +31 20 5550 222 **Fax:** +31 20 5550 277

Web: www.johansens.com/ambassade **E-mail:** info@ambassade-hotel.nl

Our inspector loved: *The float and massage centre, Koan Float, located just a short stroll along the street.*

Price Guide: (breakfast €16, excluding 5% VAT)
single €185
double €185-245
suite €275-375

Attractions: Canal Boat Trips, 300 metres; Anne Frank's House, 500 metres; Rijksmuseum National Gallery, 1km; Van Gogh Museum, 1km

Nearby Towns: Edam, 25km; Marken, 25km; Haarlem, 25km; Volendam, 30km
Airports: Schiphol, 20-min drive

Category: Charming Hotel

11 separate merchant's houses have been combined to make one lovely canal-side hotel, whilst retaining all the erstwhile interior architecture and the external façades. Hunt for famous names in the library, and admire the contemporary paintings on display throughout. Recently refurbished bedrooms combine contemporary design with elegant antique furniture.

11 maisons indépendantes de commerçants ont été rassemblées pour former un séduisant hôtel au bord du canal, tout en conservant l'architecture intérieure d'autrefois et les façades extérieures. Partez à la recherche des noms célèbres dans la bibliothèque et admirez les peintures contemporaines accrochées un peu partout. Les chambres ont été récemment remeublées de façon à combiner le design contemporain et l'élégant mobilier ancien.

11 casas independientes, propiedad de comerciantes, han sido convertido en un hotel con encanto del lado del canal todas en una respetando la arquitectura del antiguo interior así como las fachadas exteriores. Busque en su biblioteca a las grandes personalidades y admire los cuadros contemporáneos que se exhiben por todo el lugar. Las habitaciones han sido recientemente reamuebladas para combinar un diseño moderno con un elegante mobiliario antiguo.

Vigo
Orense
Viana do Castelo
Braga
Chaves
Bragança
Póvoa de Varzim
Guimarães
Oporto & Northern Portugal
Zamora
Porto
Vila Real
Miranda do Douro
ATLANTIC
OCEAN
Vila Nova de Gaia
Espinho
São João da Madeira
Vila Nova de Foz Coa
Aveiro
Viseu
Salamanca
Guarda
Beiras
Figueira da Foz
Coimbra
Covilhã
Marinha Grande
Leiria
Lisbon & Tagus Valley
Tomar
Castelo Branco
Caldas da Rainha
Entroncamento
Santarém
Ponte de Sor
Cáceres
Torres Vedras
251
Portalegre
Vila Franca de Xira
250
CABO DA ROCA
Estoril
242
243
Mora
Cascais
244
245
Lisbon
Elvas
Badajoz
SPAIN
Setúbal
234
235
236
Évora
Alentejo
BAHIA DE SETÚBAL
Grândola
Mourão
Sines
Barrancos
Beja
Aljustrel
ATLANTIC OCEAN
Porto Moniz
Europe
Madeira
Africa
Ourique
Mértola
Madeira
Algarve
252
253
Machico
Lagos
Portimão
240
239
238
241
Huelva
254
Funchal
CABO DE SÃO VICENTE
237
Olhão
Faro
GOLFO DE CÁDIZ

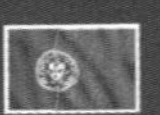

PORTUGAL / ALENTEJO (ÉVORA)

Convento do Espinheiro, A Luxury Collection Hotel & Spa

CANAVIAIS, 7005-839 ÉVORA, PORTUGAL
Tel: +351 266 788 200 **Fax:** +351 266 788 229
Web: www.johansens.com/espinheiro **E-mail:** sales@conventodoespinheiro.com

This former convent is now a luxury hotel with newly decorated bedrooms providing open, stylish spaces. Vestiges from the property's 15th-century past remain such as an olive press and chapel that is perfect for weddings. Set on the doorstep of the Alentejo wine route, sourcing vintages for the daily wine tastings is easy, while the old cellar is home to a gastronomic restaurant. In addition, the new pool-side restaurant is now open to serve snacks.

Cet ancien couvent est dorénavant un hôtel de luxe avec des chambres nouvellement décorées qui offrent des espaces chics. Parmi les vestiges du XVe siècle, l'on trouve une presse à olives et une chapelle, idéale pour les mariages. Situé aux portes de la route des vins de l'Alentejo, la recherche de crus pour les dégustations quotidiennes de vins est facile et l'ancienne cave accueille dorénavant le restaurant gastronomique. Le nouveau restaurant au bord de la piscine sert des snacks.

Este antiguo convento es ahora un hotel de lujo con habitaciones nuevamente decoradas que proporcionan espacios abiertos, con estilo. Entre los vestigios del siglo XV que aún se encuentran en la finca destacan una almazara y una capilla que es ideal para bodas. Situado a las puertas de la ruta vinícola del Alentejo, le resultará fácil proveerse de vinos añejos para su degustación diaria, y en la antigua bodega se encuentra hoy un restaurante gastronómico. Se acaba de abrir otro restaurante al lado de la piscina para comidas ligeras.

***Our inspector loved:** The fabulous, newly designed bedrooms with every comfort.*

Price Guide:
double €240-280
suite €600-850

Attractions: Horse-drawn Carriage Rides, on-site; Évora, 2km; Alentejo Vineyards, 10km; Vila Viçosa, 20-min drive

Nearby Towns: Évora, 10-min drive; Estremoz, 20-min drive; Borba, 30-min drive; Redondo, 30-min drive
Airports: Lisbon, 135km

Category: Hotel

M'AR DE AR AQUEDUTO, HISTORIC DESIGN HOTEL & SPA

RUA CÂNDIDO DOS REIS 72, 7000-582 ÉVORA, PORTUGAL
Tel: +351 266 740 700 **Fax:** +351 266 739 305
Web: www.johansens.com/mardearhotels **E-mail:** geral@mardearhotels.com

Our inspector loved: *The sheer luxury, and attention to detail.*

Price Guide:
single €120-260
double €120-260
suite €231-370

Attractions: Historical Évora, 5-min walk; Estremoz Walled Town, 30-min drive; Redondo Wine Tasting, 30-min drive

Nearby Towns: Évora, 5-min walk; Estremoz, 30-min drive; Redondo, 30-min drive
Airports: Lisbon 1.5-hour drive; Faro 2.5-hour drive

Category: Hotel

Prepare to be surprised by M'AR de Ar Aqueduto. Beyond its 15th-century façade is a modish boutique hotel. Bedrooms contain luxury beds with fluffy, soft duvets and pillows, and extra touches include Nespresso machines in the hallway and free internet access. Relax by the pool, lounge in the bar, visit the wellness area and enjoy the restaurant's cuisine.

Attendez-vous à être surpris par M'AR de Ar Aqueduto. Derrière une façade du XVe siècle se cache un hôtel boutique à la mode. Les chambres offrent des lits luxueux avec des duvets et des oreillers légers et doux. Parmi les touches particulières, des machines Nespresso dans les couloirs et un accès internet gratuit. Détendez-vous au bord de la piscine, flânez dans le bar, visitez le centre de bien-être et dégustez la cuisine du restaurant.

Prepárese para sorprenderse por el M'AR de Ar Aqueduto. Tras su fachada del siglo XV encontrará un moderno y actual hotel boutique. Sus habitaciones disponen de lujosas camas provistas de mullidos y suaves edredones y almohadas. Entre los toques especiales se encuentran las máquinas Nespresso del pasillo y acceso gratuito a internet. Podrá relajarse junto a la piscina o en su bar, visitar la zona wellness y disfrutar de la carta de su restaurante.

PORTUGAL / ALENTEJO (REDONDO)

CONVENTO DE SÃO PAULO

ALDEIA DA SERRA, 7170-120 REDONDO, PORTUGAL
Tel: +351 266 989 160 **Fax:** +351 266 989 167
Web: www.johansens.com/conventodesaopaulo **E-mail:** hotelconvspaulo@mail.telepac.pt

Monks seeking tranquillity built the monastery in 1182, and it's easy to see why the original church and chapel are popular for weddings and special events today. Bedrooms are the old monks' chambers and you can dine beneath 18th-century fresco paintings in the stylish restaurant. The collection of 50,000 original Azulejo tiles is fascinating.

Des moines en quête de tranquillité ont construit ce monastère en 1182 et il est facile de comprendre pourquoi l'église et la chapelle d'origine ont un tel succès aujourd'hui pour les mariages et les occasions spéciales. Les chambres sont situées dans les anciens quartiers des moines et le dîner est servi dans l'élégant restaurant sous des fresques du XVIIIe siècle. La collection de 50. 000 carreaux Azulejo est impressionnante.

Unos monjes en búsqueda de la tranquilidad construyeron el monasterio en 1182 y resulta fácil comprobar por qué su iglesia y su capilla originales son hoy día tan solicitadas para bodas y otros eventos especiales. Las habitaciones son las antiguas celdas de los monjes. Mientras cena podrá admirar las pinturas al fresco del siglo XVIII en el techo de su elegante restaurante. Su colección de 50.000 azulejos procedentes de la zona resulta fascinante.

***Our inspector loved:** The 2 outdoor pools located within absolutely beautiful, natural settings.*

Price Guide:
single/double/twin €90-130
suite €180-200

Attractions: Alentejo Vineyards, 10km; Local Shops of Estremoz, 15-min drive; Historic Vila Viçosa, 20-min drive; Historical Sites of Évora, 20-min drive

Nearby Towns: Redondo, 10-min drive; Évora, 20-min drive; Estremoz, 25km; Borba, 30km
Airports: Lisbon, 150km

Category: Charming Hotel

Quinta Jacintina - My Secret Garden Hotel

GARRÂO DE CIMA, 8135 - 025 ALMANCIL, PORTUGAL
Tel: +351 289 350 090 **Fax:** +351 289 350 099
Web: www.johansens.com/jacintina **E-mail:** info@algarvehotel.co.uk

Our inspector loved: *The tranquillity of this "secret" haven.*

Price Guide:
double €220-500

Attractions: Garão Beach, 3km; Loulé Restaurants and Shops, 15km; Vilamoura Marina, 15km; Historic Silves, 45-min drive

Nearby Towns: Almancil, 5km; Vilamoura, 15km; Loulé, 15km; Faro, 20km
Airports: Faro, 20km

Category: Charming Hotel

A bit of a find, this luxury boutique hotel suits everyone as it's close to Algarve's beaches, superb golf courses, restaurants and shops. Bedrooms are decorated in pretty pastels, and you'll happily spend time in the excellent restaurant and comfortable bar - the perfect meeting place for friends.

Ce tout luxueux boutique hôtel, une véritable trouvaille, convient à tous par sa proximité avec les plages d'Algarve, les superbes parcours de golf, les restaurants et les boutiques. Les chambres sont décorées de charmantes couleurs pastel. Vous passerez d'agréables moments dans l'excellent restaurant et dans le confortable bar, un endroit parfait pour se retrouver entre amis.

Un verdadero hallazgo, este distinguido y lujoso hotel contenta a todo el mundo por su cercanía a las playas del Algarbe, sus magníficos campos de golf, restaurantes y tiendas. Las habitaciones están decoradas en bellos tonos pastel. Le agradará pasar un rato en su excelente restaurante y en su confortable bar, lugar perfecto para reunirse con los amigos.

PORTUGAL / ALGARVE (VILAMOURA)

As Cascatas Golf Resort & Spa

RUA DO BRASIL 4.11.1B, 8125 VILAMOURA, PORTUGAL

Tel: +351 289 304 900 **Fax:** +351 289 304 901

Web: www.johansens.com/ascascatas **E-mail:** reservas.cascatas@imocom-grupo.com

Surrounded by lovely gardens, cascades and rocky grottos, this light and spacious all-suite property is set within an exclusive resort, ideal for both families and couples seeking a peaceful, luxurious holiday. Sample the delights of a variety of restaurants, enjoy a pampering spa treatment, play a round of golf or simply relax by the pool.

Entouré de ravissants jardins, de cascades et de grottes rocheuses, le lumineux et spacieux As Cascatas Hotel Apartamentos est situé au sein d'un complexe luxueux. C'est un endroit parfait aussi bien pour les familles que pour les couples à la recherche de vacances luxueuses et paisibles. Dégustez les mets des nombreux restaurants, appréciez les bienfaits d'un soin au spa, faites une partie de golf ou reposez-vous tout simplement au bord de la piscine.

Rodeado de encantadores jardines, cascadas y grutas rocosas, este complejo formado exclusivamente de suites está situado dentro de un exclusivo resort que resulta ideal tanto para familias como para parejas que buscan unas vacaciones de tranquilidad y de lujo. Saboree las delicias de sus variados restaurantes, déjese mimar con un tratamiento de spa, juegue una partida de golf o descanse simplemente junto a la piscina.

***Our inspector loved:** The stylish décor, and free access to 7Spa.*

Price Guide: (including breakfast and return shuttle to the marina, golf courses and Falésia Beach)
1-4-bedroom suite €225-1,200

Attractions: Golf Course, 50 metres; Beach, 5-min drive; Vilamoura Marina, Casino and Shops, 5-min drive

Nearby Towns: Almancil, 10-min drive; Loule, 15-min drive; Faro, 25-min drive
Airports: Faro Airport, 20-min drive; Lisbon, 2.5-hour drive

Category: Hotel

Hilton Vilamoura As Cascatas Golf Resort & Spa

RUA DA TORRE D'AGUA LOTE 4.11.1B, 8125-615 VILAMOURA, PORTUGAL

Tel: +351 289 304 000 **Fax:** +351 289 304 005

Web: www.johansens.com/hiltonvilamoura **E-mail:** info.vilamoura@hilton.com

Our inspector loved: *The beautifully appointed, comfortable bedrooms.*

Price Guide:
double standard from €179
de luxe/de luxe superior from €214
junior suite from €289

Attractions: Pinhal Oceanico Golf Course, 30 metres; Falesia Beach, 2km; Vilamoura Casino, and Vilamoura Marina, 5-min drive; Loulé Markets, 10-min drive

Nearby Towns: Vilamoura, 3km; Loulé, 15-min drive; Almancil, 15-min drive; Faro, 20-min drive; Albufeira, 20-min drive
Airports: Faro, 20-min drive

Category: Hotel

Suitable for family holidays, romantic getaways, leisure, golf and spa breaks, this fabulous hotel is in a stylish resort near to the buzz of Vilamoura with its marina and shops. Enjoy the magnificent pool area, sample the choice of restaurants and retire to your generous-sized guest room fitted with large bed, marble bathroom and big fluffy towels.

Parfait pour des vacances familiales, une escapade romantique ou des séjours loisirs, golf et spa, ce hôtel est un fabuleux et somptueux resort situé à proximité de à proximité des boutiques animées et de le marina de Vilamoura. Profitez des magnifiques piscines, dégustez grâce au large choix de restaurant et appréciez votre spacieuse chambre équipée d'un grand lit, d'une salle de bain en marbre et de grandes serviettes de toilettes moelleuses.

Ideal para vacaciones familiares, románticas escapadas, ocio, golf y breves estancias en spa, este fabuloso hotel es un elegante resort sito en las cercanías del bullicio del puerto deportivo y tiendas de Vilamoura. Disfrute de su zona de piscina, pruebe su variedad de restaurantes y retírese a descansar en su habitación de generosas proporciones equipada de una amplia cama, cuarto de baño en mármol y grandes y mullidas toallas.

Tivoli Marina Vilamoura

8125-901 VILAMOURA, PORTUGAL
Tel: +351 289 303 303 **Fax:** +351 289 303 345
Web: www.johansens.com/tivolimarina **E-mail:** reservations.htm@tivolihotels.com

Colour and vibrancy describe this hotel perfectly and, with one of the best locations in Vilamoura, there is no better place to admire the view of the ocean or marina than from your terrace. Inside, the wonderfully bright décor creates a uniquely upbeat atmosphere. Outside, there are relaxing pool-side areas, the beach to enjoy and 5 championship golf courses close by that can be reached by the hotel's free shuttle service.

Couleur et résonance décrivent parfaitement cet hôtel et, grâce à son excellente situation dans Vilamoura, il n'y a pas de meilleur endroit pour profiter de la vue sur l'océan et la marina que depuis votre terrasse. A l'intérieur, le décor merveilleusement éclatant crée une ambiance joyeuse unique. A l'extérieur, vous profiterez de la plage, des espaces de repos au bord de la piscine ainsi que des 5 superbes parcours de golf à proximité où vous pourrez vous rendre grâce à la navette gratuite de l'hôtel.

El color y el dinamismo describen este hotel a la perfección. Provisto de uno de los mejores emplazamientos de Vilamoura, no hay lugar mejor para admirar la vista al océano o al paseo marítimo que desde su terraza. En el interior, la vistosa decoración proporciona un singular y vibrante ambiente. En el exterior tendrá a su disposición las relajantes zonas de piscina, la playa y 5 cercanos campos de golf de campeonato accesibles a través del servicio de autobuses del hotel.

Our inspector loved: *The great beach facilities and fantastic spa.*

Price Guide:
single €170-510
double €180-520
suite €350-2,300

Attractions: Marina, 2-min walk; Vilamoura Casino, 5-min walk; Loulé Markets, 10-min drive; Historic Silves, 30-min drive

Nearby Towns: Almancil, 5-min drive; Loulé, 10-min drive; Faro, 15-min drive; Albufeira, 15-min drive
Airports: Faro, 20-min drive

Category: Hotel

TIVOLI VICTORIA

APT. 665, 8125 VILAMOURA, ALGARVE, PORTUGAL
Tel: +351 289 31 7000 **Fax:** +351 289 31 73400
Web: www.johansens.com/tivolivictoria **E-mail:** htvictoria@tivolihotels.com

Our inspector loved: *The super contemporary bedrooms.*

Price Guide:
single from €350
double from €450
suite from €550

Attractions: Victoria Golf Course, 2-min walk; Vilamoura Marina, 5-min drive; Nikki Beach Water Sports and Restaurants, 5-min drive; Loulé Market, 15-min drive

Nearby Towns: Vilmamoura, 5-min drive; Almancil, 15-min drive; Loulé, 15-min drive; Faro, 20-min drive
Airports: Faro, 20-min drive

Category: Hotel

This newly built hotel stands in a quiet area next to Victoria Golf Course, one of the best courses in Europe. However, there is much more to Tivoli Victoria than simply a spectacular golfing experience! Enjoy the Elements Spa by Banyan Tree, the 2 restaurants, 2 pools, pool bar, superbly designed bedrooms and suite butler service.

Cet hôtel, nouvellement construit, se situe dans un quartier calme près du Victoria Golf Course, l'un des meilleurs parcours en Europe. Cependant, il y a plus au Tivoli Victoria qu'une magnifique expérience golfique! Profitez du Elements Spa by Banyan Tree, des 2 restaurants, des 2 piscines, du bar de la piscine, des chambres magnifiquement décorées et du service de majordome dans les suites.

Este hotel de reciente construcción se ubica en una tranquila zona junto al Victoria Golf Course, uno de los campos mejores de Europa. Sin embargo, Tivoli Victoria resulta mucho más que una espectacular experiencia golfista! Disfrute del Elements Spa by Banyan Tree, los 2 restaurantes, las 2 piscinas, el bar de la piscina, las habitaciones de magnífico diseño y el servicio de mayordomo en las suites.

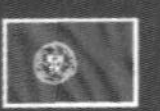

PORTUGAL / LISBON & TAGUS VALLEY (CASCAIS)

Hotel Albatroz

RUA FREDERICO AROUCA 100, 2750-353 CASCAIS, LISBON, PORTUGAL
Tel: +351 21 484 73 80 **Fax:** +351 21 484 48 27
Web: www.johansens.com/albatroz **E-mail:** albatroz@albatrozhotels.com

Our inspector loved: *The hotel's style and class, and home-from-home feeling.*

Price Guide:
single €170-350
double €215-390
suite €300-580

Attractions: Estoril Casino, 5-min drive; Marina Cascais, 5-min drive; Historic Sintra, 20-min drive; Sightseeing in Lisbon and Shopping, 30-min drive

Nearby Towns: Cascais, 5-min walk; Estoril, 5-min drive; Sintra, 20-min drive; Lisbon, 30-min drive
Airports: Lisbon, 30-min drive

Category: Charming Hotel

Perched on the cliffs above Conceição Beach, this former royal summer retreat has cool, characterful rooms and suites, many with panoramic sea views. Dine in the locally renowned restaurant, relax in the bar, meet with colleagues in one of the reception rooms, swim in the salt-water pool, and indulge in one of the hotel's most practised "sports" - sunbathing!

Perché sur la falaise au-dessus de Conceição Beach, cet ancien refuge d'été de la famille royale propose des chambres et suites agréables, pleines de caractère et dont beaucoup offrent des vues panoramiques sur la mer. Dinez au restaurant réputé localement, relaxez-vous au bar, rencontrez vos collègues dans l'une des salles de réception, nagez dans la piscine d'eau salée et adonnez-vous au "sport" le plus pratiqué à l'hôtel - le bain de soleil!

Encaramado en los acantilados que se elevan sobre la playa de Conceição, esta antiguo residencia de descanso veraniego de la realeza dispone de frescas habitaciones y suites rebosantes de personalidad, muchas de las cuales gozan de panorámicas vistas al mar. Podrá cenar en su conocido restaurante de la zona, relajarse en el bar, reunirse con sus colegas en alguna de sus salones de recepción, nadar en su piscina de agua salada o disfrutar de uno de los "deportes" más practicados del hotel: tomar el sol.

Palácio Estoril, Hotel & Golf

RUA PARTICULAR, 2769-504 ESTORIL, PORTUGAL
Tel: +351 21 464 80 00 **Fax:** +351 21 464 81 59
Web: www.johansens.com/estoril **E-mail:** info@hotelestorilpalacio.pt

Our inspector loved: *The fabulous newly decorated terrace.*

Price Guide:
single €190-230
double €230-270
suite €350-450

Attractions: Estoril Casino, 5-min walk; Cascais Restaurants, 10-min drive; Historic Sites of Sintra, 20-min drive; Lisbon Shops and Theatre, 30-min drive

Nearby Towns: Estoril, 5-min walk; Cascais, 10-min drive; Sintra, 20-min drive; Lisbon, 30-min drive
Airports: Lisbon, 30-min drive

Category: Hotel

Exceptionally friendly doormen welcome you to this glamorous 1930s grand old dame. Following a major facelift, the beautiful interior contains huge solid pillars, opulent marble and gorgeous rooms and suites. You may feel something of a starlet yourself in the charming bar, once a favourite haunt of World War II spies!

Des portiers extrêmement chaleureux vous accueillent dans cette élégante et majestueuse adresse des années 30. Depuis une importante rénovation, les superbes intérieures sont composés de piliers massifs, d'une opulence de marbre ainsi que de superbes chambres et suites. Il est facile de se sentir une âme de star dans le charmant bar, autrefois le repère favori des espions de la Seconde Guerre Mondiale!

Unos ujieres de excepcional amabilidad les dan la bienvenida a esta glamorosa anciana y majestuosa dama de la década de los 30. Tras pasar por una considerable operación de cirugía plástica facial, su bello interior acoge ahora sólidas e inmensas columnas, exquisitos mármoles y maravillosas habitaciones y suites. Quizás también Vd. se sentirá especial en el encantador bar, punto de encuentro favorito de muchos espías durante la 2ª guerra mundial!

ALTIS BELÉM HOTEL & SPA

DOCA DO BOM SUCESSO, 1400-038, LISBON, PORTUGAL
Tel: +351 210 400 200 **Fax:** +351 210 400 250
Web: www.johansens.com/altisbelemhotel **E-mail:** reservations@altisbelemhotel.com

Our inspector loved: *The wonderful riverside location and the hotel's imaginative contemporary design.*

Price Guide:
single €296-440
double €336-480
suite €664-1,520

Attractions: Historic Monuments, 5-min walk; Lisbon's Historic Sites, Shops and Restaurants and Centro Cultural de Belém (CCB), 5-min drive; City Centre, 15-min drive; Alfama (Old City), 20-min drive

Nearby Towns: Estoril, 20-min drive; Cascais, 25-min drive

Category: Hotel

An intoxicating mix of cutting-edge design and history, this contemporary hotel is located next to the Tagus River. Rooms themed around discovery have fantastic views with gorgeous linens and the best gowns our Inspector has ever come across! The restaurant comes complete with a Michelin-Starred chef, and spa treatments include sun-deck massages on the terrace overlooking the river.

Situé près du fleuve Tage, cet hôtel contemporain est un grisant mélange d'histoire et de design ultra moderne. Les chambres, sur le thème de la découverte, ont de superbes vues, du linge magnifique et les plus beaux peignoirs de bain jamais rencontrés par notre inspecteur. Le restaurant est géré par un chef étoilé Michelin et les soins du spa proposent notamment des massages sur la véranda surplombant le fleuve.

Una mezcla embriagadora de diseño vanguardista e historia caracteriza a este moderno hotel situado junto al rio Tajo. Las habitaciones, decoradas con temas sobre el descubrimiento, gozan de unas vistas fantásticas y están equipadas con espléndidas ropas de cama y las mejores batas que jamás ha visto nuestro inspector. El restaurante cuenta con un chef galardonado con estrellas de Michelin, y entre los tratamientos que ofrece su spa están los masajes en la terraza con vistas al río.

 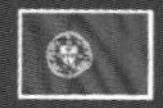

AV. DOS ESTADOS UNIDOS DA AMERICA
AV. DAS FORCAS ARMADAS
AV. DOS COMBATENTES
Jardim Zoologico
Campo Pequeno
AV. DA REPUBLICA
CAMPO PEQUENO
AV. DE BERNA
AV. COLUMBANO BORDALO PINHEIRO
AV. CALOUSTE GULBENKIAN
AV. ANTONIO AUGUSTO DE AGUIAR
AV. ALM. REIS
AV. FONTES PEREIRA DE MELO
Cemetrio do Alto de Sao João
R. MORAIS SOARES
Parque Eduardo VII
Marquês de Pombal
R. JOAQUIM ANTONIO DE AGUIAR
R. ALEXANDRE HERCULANO
249
AV. DA LIBERDADE
248
Jardim Botanico
AV. DE ALVARES CABRAL
247
AV. ALM. REIS
Castelo de S. Jorge
R. DA MADALENA
R. DA PRAIA
R. AUREA
Rossio
Museu Nacional de Arte Contemporânea
AV. INFANTE SANTO
AV. INFANTE DOM HENRIQUE
Praça do Comercio
246
AV. 24 DE JULIO
AV. DA RIBEIRA DAS NAUS
Museu Nacional de Arte Antiga
AV. DE CUEIA
AV. 24 DE JULIO
AV. DE INDIA
RIVER TAGUS

As Janelas Verdes

RUA DAS JANELAS VERDES 47, 1200-690 LISBON, PORTUGAL
Tel: +351 21 39 68 143 **Fax:** +351 21 39 68 144
Web: www.johansens.com/janelasverdes **E-mail:** janelas.verdes@heritage.pt

Tucked away next to the National Art Museum is this small 18th-century palace. A romantic home-from-home, staff are friendly and the style is neoclassical, laced with beautiful paintings. Enjoy a drink on the library's balcony overlooking the River Tagus, and breakfast in the peaceful ivy-covered patio-garden when warm enough!

Caché à côté du Musée National d'Art, se trouve ce petit palace du XVIIIe siècle. C'est une maison romantique décorée dans le style néo-classique, couverte de magnifiques tableaux où l'on se sent comme chez soi et où le personnel est très aimable. Prenez un verre sur le balcon de la bibliothèque qui surplombe la rivière Tage et savourez votre petit-déjeuner dans le patio couvert de lierre, lorsque le temps le permet.

Escondido junto al Museo de Arte Nacional encontramos este pequeño palacio del siglo XVIII, hogareño, de amable personal y de estilo neoclásico, reforzado con preciosas pinturas. Disfrute una copa en la terraza de la biblioteca con vistas al río Tajo y un desayuno en el tranquilo jardín con patio cubierto de hiedra cuando el tiempo es bueno.

Our inspector loved: *The views of the Tagus River from the top-floor terrace.*

Price Guide:
single €147-280
double €161-298

 29     

Attractions: National Ancient Art Museum, next door; Basilica da Estrela, 5-min walk; World Heritage Monuments: Jerónimos Monastery and Tower of Belém, 7-min drive; Old City of Alfama, 10-min drive

Nearby Towns: Lisbon, 2-min drive; Cascais, 30-min drive; Estoril, 30-min drive; Sintra, 30-min drive
Airports: Lisbon, 20-min drive

Category: Luxury Guest House

 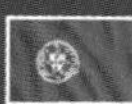

Heritage Av Liberdade

AVENIDA DA LIBERDADE 28, 1250-145 LISBON, PORTUGAL
Tel: +351 213 404 040 **Fax:** +351 213 404 044
Web: www.johansens.com/avliberdade **E-mail:** avliberdade@heritage.pt

Our inspector loved: The style of this chic, extremely well located hotel.

Price Guide:
single €154-295
double €167-325
Heritage €435-560

Awards: Condé Nast Traveler's Hot List 2007

Attractions: Restauradores Square and Tram to Bairro Alto, 2-min walk; Baixa, 5-min walk; World Heritage Monuments: Jerónimos Monastery and Tower of Belém, 15-min drive; Casino, 15-min drive

Nearby Towns: Cascais, 30-min drive; Estoril, 30-min drive; Sintra, 30-min drive
Airports: Lisbon, 20-min drive

Category: Charming Hotel

A great example of Portuguese design, this former palace was renovated by architect Miguel Câncio Martins. The 18th-century façade conceals welcoming town-house interiors, and thankfully the wooden entrance, veranda railings, original ceramics and pieces of furniture remain. Drop your bags and go, you're ideally placed for exploring Lisbon's historic centre.

Superbe exemple de design portugais, cet ancien palais fût rénové par l'architecte Miguel Câncio Martins. La façade du XVIIIe siècle cache des intérieurs accueillants d'hôtel particulier et heureusement l'entrée en bois, la véranda, les céramiques d'origine et des pièces d'ameublement ont été conservées. Vous êtes idéalement situés alors, posez vos sacs et allez explorer le centre historique de Lisbonne.

Excelente ejemplo del arte portugués, este antiguo palacio fue renovado por el arquitecto Miguel Câncio Martins. La fachada del siglo XVIII esconde tras de sí acogedores interiores propios de mansión. Por fortuna perduran su entrada en madera, los pasamanos de la baranda, la cerámica y los muebles originales. Deje su equipaje en este privilegiado enclave y parta desde allí para explorar el centro histórico de Lisboa.

Hotel Britania

RUA RODRIGUES SAMPAIO 17, 1150-278 LISBON, PORTUGAL
Tel: +351 21 31 55 016 **Fax:** +351 21 31 55 021
Web: www.johansens.com/britania **E-mail:** britania.hotel@heritage.pt

Our inspector loved: *The hotel's simple, elegant style. Check out the quirky, old barber's chair!*

Price Guide:
single €133-230
double €147-255

 33     

Attractions: Avenida da Liberdade, nearby; Restauradores Square and Tram to Bairro Alto, 2-min walk; Baixa, 5-min walk; World Heritage Monuments: Jerónimos Monastery and Tower of Belém, 15-min drive

Nearby Towns: Cascais, 30-min drive; Estoril, 30-min drive; Sintra, 30-min drive
Airports: Lisbon, 20-min drive

Category: Charming Hotel

This, the only original art deco hotel left in Lisbon, was designed and opened by famous Portuguese modernist architect Cassiano Branco in 1944. Lovingly restored and family-run with its ambience intact, it's now a classified historic building. You'll find service outstanding, a small library and relaxing, spacious bedrooms that are also delightful.

Cet hôtel, le seul établissement art déco originel à Lisbonne, fût conçu et ouvert par le fameux architecte moderne portugais Cassiano Branco en 1944. Soigneusement restauré et géré en famille avec son ambiance intacte, c'est aujourd'hui un bâtiment classé. Vous apprécierez le service impeccable et la petite bibliothèque, ainsi que les chambres spacieuses et relaxantes.

Este hotel, el único hotel art deco genuino que perdura en Lisboa, fue diseñado e inagurado por el famoso arquitecto modernista portugués Cassiano Branco en 1944. Tras su esmerada restauración, este hotel de gestión familiar, que ha logrado mantener su ambiente intacto, es considerado en la actualidad como edificio de valor histórico. Encontrará su servicio de suma calidad; asimismo su pequeña biblioteca y sus cómodas y amplias habitaciones son una verdadera delicia.

TIVOLI LISBOA

AV. DA LIBERDADE 185, 1269-050 LISBON, PORTUGAL
Tel: + 351 21 319 89 00 **Fax:** + 351 21 319 89 50
Web: www.johansens.com/tivolilisboa **E-mail:** reservas.htl@tivolihotels.com

Our inspector loved: *The newly renovated executive rooms with big beds, fluffy pillows, large plasma TVs, amazing city views and great coffee machines!*

Price Guide:
single €290-480
double €310-580
junior suite €570-660

Attractions: Theatre, 2-min walk; Alfama, 10-min drive; Cascais Marina, 20-min drive; Estoril Casino, 20-min drive

Nearby Towns: Cascais, 20-min drive; Estoril, 20-min drive; Sintra, 25-min drive
Airports: Lisbon, 15-min drive

Category: Hotel

Whilst sitting on the top-floor terrace of this 5-star cosmopolitan hotel and admiring the stunning views over Lisbon, you will feel totally satisfied. Not only are the leisure and business facilities excellent, but staff are exceptionally welcoming and the delicious international cuisine you have just feasted on will certainly contribute to your sense of well-being!

Tandis que vous êtes assis sur le toit terrasse de cet hôtel 5 étoiles cosmopolite, et que vous admirez la vue splendide sur Lisbonne, vous aurez un grand sentiment de satisfaction. Non seulement les loisirs et les équipements pour les hommes d'affaires sont parfaits mais l'équipe est exceptionnellement accueillante. La délicieuse cuisine internationale dont vous ferez un festin, contribuera certainement à votre sensation de bien-être.

Mientras se sienta en la terraza azotea de este cosmopolita hotel de 5 estrellas y admira sus espectaculares vistas de Lisboa, se sentirá plenamente satisfecho. Sus instalaciones de ocio y profesionales son no solo excelentes sino que también su personal es excepcionalmente acogedor. La deliciosa carta internacional que tanto habrá celebrado contribuirá de seguro a su sensación de bienestar.

Tivoli Palácio de Seteais

RUA BARBOSA DU BOCAGE 10, SETEAIS, 2710 SINTRA, PORTUGAL
Tel: +351 219 233 200 **Fax:** +351 219 234 277
Web: www.johansens.com/palaciodeseteais **E-mail:** reservas.hps@tivolihotels.com

Take a trip back in time and experience a bygone era of refined living at this 18th-century palace, a fairy-tale setting surrounded by natural forest and peaceful gardens. The newly refurbished stunning interior reveals frescoed ceilings, restored wall paintings, bedrooms filled with personal touches and the innovative Seteais Restaurant, which overlooks the magnificent grounds and mountains beyond.

Laissez-vous transporter dans le passé et dans le monde du raffinement dans ce palais du XVIIIe siècle. Un cadre digne d'un conte de fées entouré d'une forêt naturelle et de jardins tranquilles. Les somptueux intérieurs, nouvellement restaurés, révèlent de magnifiques fresques et tapisseries, des chambres remplies de touches personnelles et un restaurant innovant, le Seteais, qui surplombe le domaine et les montagnes environnantes.

Realice un viaje en el tiempo y viva la experiencia de una época pasada de refinamiento en este palacio del siglo XVIII, un verdadero emplazamiento de cuento de hadas rodeado de un bosque natural y tranquilos jardines. Su fantástico interior de reciente decoración muestra los frescos de sus techos, pinturas murales restauradas, habitaciones repletas de toques personales y el innovador Seteais Restaurant, con vistas a los magníficos terrenos y montañas en la lejanía.

Our inspector loved: *The magical location!*

Price Guide:
single from €450
double from €480
suite from €550

Attractions: Historical Palaces and Shopping in Sintra, 5-min drive; Shopping in Cascais, 10-min drive; Shopping in Lisbon and Tourist Attractions, 30-min drive

Nearby Towns: Sintra, 5-min drive; Cascais, 10-min drive; Estoril, 15-min drive; Lisbon, 30-min drive
Airports: Lisbon, 30-min drive

Category: Hotel

CampoReal Golf Resort & Spa

RUA DO CAMPO, 2565-779 TURCIFAL, TORRES VEDRAS, PORTUGAL
Tel: +351 261 960 900 **Fax:** +351 261 960 999
Web: www.johansens.com/camporeal

Our inspector loved: *The outstanding service and facilities at this hotel.*

Price Guide: (excluding VAT)
double €140-870

Attractions: Wellington's Citadel (Torres Vedras Defensive Lines), 10-min drive; Wolf Sanctuary, 20-min drive; Buddha Eden Garden, 20-min drive; Silver Coast Beaches, 20-min drive

Nearby Towns: Torres Vedras, 10-min drive; Óbidos, 20-min drive; Cascais, 30-min drive; Lisbon, 30-min drive
Airports: Lisbon, 25-min train/metro; Porto, 250km

Category: Hotel

This sophisticated modern hotel is set amidst quiet countryside and surrounded by its own fantastic golf course. The service is excellent, with the emphasis placed on tranquillity and relaxation. Heavenly beds and subtle décor adorn the large bedrooms, and there is a wonderful spa, several pools and a gym. 3 restaurants serve local and international cuisine.

Cet hôtel moderne et sophistiqué, situé au coeur d'une campagne tranquille, est entouré par son propre parcours de golf fantastique. Le service est parfait, avec une attention particulière portée à la tranquillité et à la relaxation. Les lits sont paradisiaques, le décor des vastes chambres est subtil et l'hôtel possède un magnifique spa, plusieurs piscines et une salle de gym. 3 restaurants servent une cuisine locale et internationale.

Este sofisticado y moderno hotel se encuentra situado en medio de un tranquilo paisaje rural y rodeado de su propio y espléndido campo de golf. Su servicio es excelente, siendo su punto fuerte su tranquilidad y el relax. Sus gloriosas camas y su sutil decorado adornan sus amplias habitaciones. Dispone asimismo de un maravilloso spa, varias piscinas y un gimnasio. Sus 3 restaurantes ofrecen cartas locales e internacionales.

PORTUGAL / MADEIRA (FUNCHAL)

QUINTA DAS VISTAS PALACE GARDENS

CAMINHO DE SANTO ANTONIO 52, 9000-187 FUNCHAL, MADEIRA, PORTUGAL
Tel: +351 291 750 000 **Fax:** +351 291 750 010
Web: www.johansens.com/quintadasvistas **E-mail:** info@charminghotelsmadeira.com

Intimate and stylish, in a striking contemporary building, this welcoming hotel is surrounded by remarkable gardens. Inside, comfortable beds fill elegant, superbly decorated rooms, and a large terrace takes advantage of the gorgeous views. The restaurant serves delicious meals, and the guest relations manager is at hand to make your stay as enjoyable as possible.

Intime et charmant, situé dans un bâtiment moderne étonnant, cet hôtel accueillant est entouré de jardins extraordinaires. A l'intérieur, des lits confortables sont installés dans les chambres élégantes, superbement décorées et une grande terrasse permet de profiter des vues exceptionnelles. Le restaurant sert des plats délicieux et le responsable des relations avec les hôtes est toujours disponible pour faire que votre séjour soit aussi agréable que possible.

Intimista y elegante, sito en un sorprendente edificio contemporáneo, este acogedor hotel se encuentra rodeado de impresionantes jardines. En el interior, sus cómodas camas ocupan sus habitaciones de excelente decoración y su amplia terraza pone a su disposición una vistas inigualables. El restaurante sirve una cocina deliciosa y el gerente encargado de las relaciones con la clientela está a su disposición para hacer su estancia lo más placentera posible.

Our inspector loved: *The lovely, relaxing terraces with breathtaking views.*

Price Guide:
garden view room €163-305
panoramic view room €210-347
de luxe suite €326-483

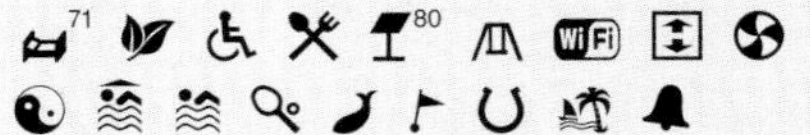

Attractions: Madeira Casino, 5-min drive; Old City of Funchal, 5-min drive; Local Shopping and Restaurants, 5-min drive; Funchal Marina and Boat Trips, 2km

Nearby Towns: Funchal, 5-min drive
Airports: Funchal, 18km

Category: Charming Hotel

Quinta do Monte

CAMINHO DO MONTE 192, 9050-288 FUNCHAL, MADEIRA, PORTUGAL
Tel: +351 291 780 100 **Fax:** +351 291 780 110
Web: www.johansens.com/quintadomonte **E-mail:** info@charminghotelsmadeira.com

Our inspector loved: *The traditional style and good service.*

Price Guide:
double €131-268

Attractions: Monte Palace Gardens, 2-min walk; Levadas, 5-min walk; Funchal Casino, 5-min drive; Funchal Old Town and Marina, 5-min drive

Nearby Towns: Funchal, 5-min drive
Airports: Funchal, 30-min drive

Category: Charming Hotel

This graceful manor house will charm you with its lovely interiors that are reminiscent of Colonial times. Antique furnishings alongside Persian carpets and wooden floors are traditional Madeiran in style, and the sub-tropical gardens are a quiet haven. As a Charming Hotels property, when opting for half board, you can dine at any of the local Charming Hotels restaurants and use their spa facilities for free.

Dès l'instant où vous entrerez dans ce ravissant manoir, vous serez charmés par ses magnifiques intérieurs qui rappellent le temps des colonies. Les meubles anciens sont agrémentés de tapis persans et de parquets traditionnels de madère et les luxuriants jardins subtropicaux sont un havre de paix. Lorsque vous êtes en demi-pension, vous avez la possibilité de dîner dans l'un des restaurants des autres hôtels de la chaîne Charming Hotels à proximité et vous pourrez également utiliser leurs spa gratuitement.

Le encantará esta elegante casa solariega con sus maravillosos interiores de reminiscencias coloniales. Su mobiliario antiguo, alfombras persas y suelos de madera evocan el estilo tradicional de Madeira, y los jardines subtropicales constituyen un tranquilo remanso de paz. Como el hotel forma parte de Charming Hotels, si se aloja con media pensión, puede cenar en cualquiera de los restaurantes de Charming Hotels. Tambien puede utilizar los servicios de spa gratuitamente.

PORTUGAL / MADEIRA (FUNCHAL)

THE VINE

RUA DOS ARANHAS 27-A, MADEIRA, 9000-044 FUNCHAL, PORTUGAL
Tel: +351 291 009 000 **Fax:** +351 291 009 001
Web: www.johansens.com/thevine **E-mail:** info@hotelthevine.com

This sleek, urban retreat is dedicated to the concept of good wine, from the intoxicating art on the walls to the vinotherapy treatments in the spa. Soft lighting and open-plan design set a sophisticated tone throughout the rooms and rooftop restaurant, where the cuisine is prepared under the direction of 3 Star Michelin chef, Antoine Westermann. Here, and from the sundeck and infinity pool, city, sea and mountains views are enjoyed.

Ce refuge urbain aux lignes épurées est dédié au bon vin, de l'art enivrant sur les murs en passant par les soins de vinothérapie au spa. Lumière douce et design paysagé créent un ton sophistiqué dans toutes les chambres et le restaurant sur le toit où office le chef étoiles Michelin, Antoine Westermann. De là, ainsi que du solarium et de la piscine à l'infini, de superbes vues sur la ville, la mer et la montagne peuvent être contemplées.

Este elegante lugar de retiro urbano está plenamente dedicado al concepto del buen vino, desde el embriagador arte expuesto en sus paredes hasta los tratamientos de vinoterapia que se ofrecen en el Spa. La tenue iluminación y el diseño de planta abierta proporcionan un toque de sofisticación a todas las habitaciones y al restaurante situado en la azotea, cuya cocina esta bajo la dirección del chef Antoine Westermann, poseedor de 3 estrellas Michelin. Desde aquí, y desde su solarium con piscina "infinity" podrá disfrutar de vistas al mar, a la ciudad y a las montañas.

Our inspector loved: *The fantastic rooftop terrace with heated outdoor pool.*

Price Guide:
single €191-255
double €221-363
suite €340-662

Attractions: Shopping Centre, 1-min walk; Funchal Marina, 5-min walk; Funchal Casino, 3-min drive

Airports: Funchal, 20-min drive

Category: Hotel

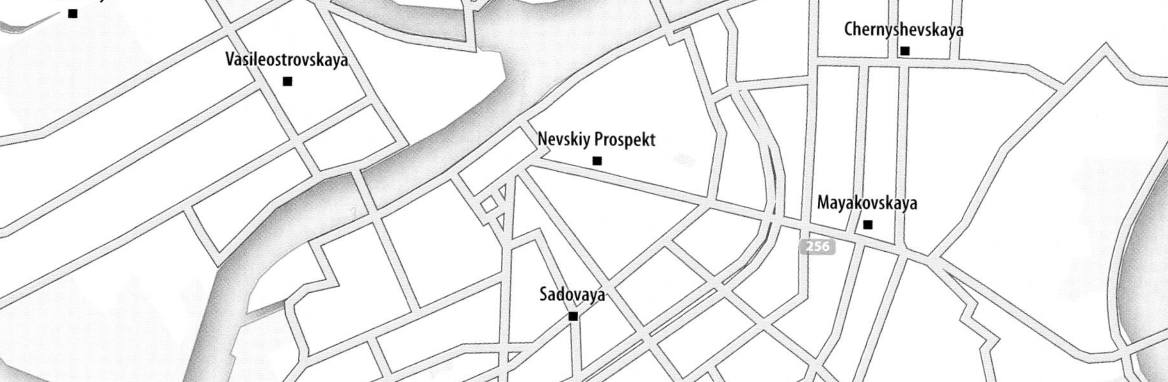
Stantsiya Staraya Derevnya
Stantsiya Novaya Derevnya
Park Tikhiy Otdykh
Vyborgskaya
Chkalovskaya
Petrogradskaya
Ploshchad Lenina
Sportivnaya
Primorskaya
Chernyshevskaya
Vasileostrovskaya
Nevskiy Prospekt
Mayakovskaya
256
Sadovaya

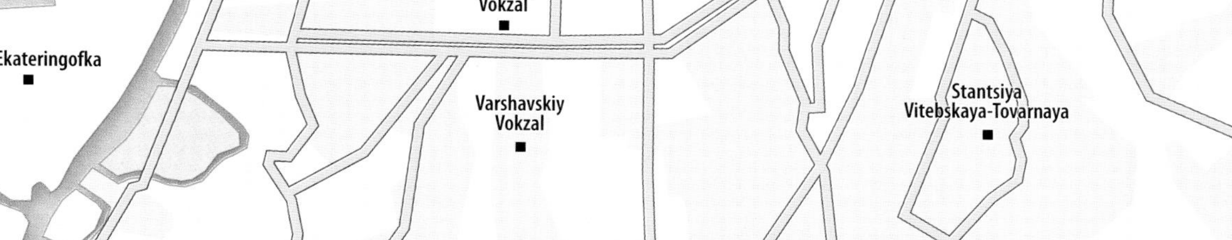
Vitebskiy Vokzal
Baltiyskiy Vokzal
Reka Ekateringofka
Varshavskiy Vokzal
Stantsiya Vitebskaya-Tovarnaya

RUSSIA (ST PETERSBURG)

CORINTHIA HOTEL ST PETERSBURG

NEVSKY PROSPECT 57, ST PETERSBURG, RUSSIA
Tel: +7 812 3802001 **Fax:** +7 812 3801937
Web: www.johansens.com/corinthiastpetersburg **E-mail:** stpetersburg@corinthia.com

With luxury and refined hospitality at its core, this stunning hotel overflows with art, beauty and opulence, invoking images of old fashioned Russian style and modern commodity. You are spoilt for choice when it comes to eating: the restaurants are among the best in the city. The hotel's central location makes access to major sites of interest extremely easy.

Au summum du luxe et de l'accueil raffiné, ce magnifique hôtel débordant d'art, de beauté et d'opulence, évoque le style de l'ancienne Russie avec des équipements modernes. De nombreux choix s'offrent à vous pour la cuisine, les restaurants sont parmi les meilleurs de la ville. L'emplacement central de l'hôtel permet un accès facile aux principaux centres d'intérêts de la ville.

Este impresionante hotel, cuyas características esenciales son el lujo y una refinada hospitalidad, rebosa arte, belleza y opulencia evocando imagines de estilo ruso antiguo así como modernas instalaciones. A la hora de comer tendrá mucho donde elegir: los restaurantes están entre los mejores de la ciudad. La céntrica ubicación del hotel hace enormemente fácil el acceso a los principales lugares de interés.

Our inspector loved: *The excellent service, and surprisingly peaceful ambience in the middle of the busy Nevsky Avenue.*

Price Guide: (room only, excluding VAT. Airport transfers can be organised.)
room €298-345

Awards: 5 Stars Academy Award, The American Academy of Hospitality Science 2009 and 2010; Best Luxury Conference Hotel, World Travel Awards 2009

Attractions: Shopping District, 5-min walk; Boats and Canals, 1km; Theaters, 3km; Palaces and Hermitage Museum, 5km

Airports: St Petersburg, 30-min drive

Category: Hotel

Bad Gastein
Graz
AUSTRIA
HUNGARY
Wolfsberg
Leibnitz
Murska Sobota
Klagenfurt
Dravograd
Maribor
Lendava
Traviso
Ruse
Ptuj
Ormoz
Bled 258
Radoviica
Velenje
Mozirje
Varazdin
Bovec
Kranj
Rogaska Slatina
Tolmin
Zalec
Celje
ITALY
Domzale
Skofija Loka
Idrija
Ljubjana
Udine
Nova Gorica
Sevnica
Vrhnika
Ajdovscina
Brezice
Postojna
Zargreb
Novo Mesto
Sezana
Ribnica
Trieste
Pivka
Kocevje
Ilirska Bistrica
Kope
Crnomelj
Piran
Karlovac
Rijeka
CROATIA
BOSNIA & HERZEGOVINA
Pula
ADRIATIC SEA
Bihac
Jablanac

SLOVENIA (BLED)

HOTEL GOLF BLED

CANKARJEVA 4, 4260 BLED, SLOVENIA
Tel: +386 4579 1700 **Fax:** +386 4579 1701
Web: www.johansens.com/hotelgolfsi **E-mail:** hotelgolf@hotelibled.com

You couldn't ask for more invigorating surroundings: a modern hotel in the heart of Bled, Slovenia's acclaimed alpine and thermal health resort for more than 100 years. In winter this is a wonderland of fresh air, snow and ice, and in summer, a verdant, colourful feast for the senses. Bask in the comfort, enjoy the first-class amenities and take in the bedroom balcony views of the lake, cliff-top castle and mountain peaks.

Vous ne pouviez rêver d'un environnement plus vivifiant: un hôtel moderne situé au coeur de Bled, le complexe thermal alpin le plus réputé de Slovénie depuis plus de 100 ans. En hiver, c'est le pays de l'air pur, de la neige et de la glace. En été, c'est une fête verdoyante et colorée pour les sens. Prélassez-vous dans le confort, appréciez les excellents équipements et profitez des balcons des chambres qui offrent des vues sur le lac, le château perché et les sommets des montagnes.

No podría pedir un entorno más saludable que el de este moderno hotel en pleno corazón de Bled, que ha sido durante mas de 100 años un afamado balneario y destino alpino de Eslovenia. En invierno es un paraíso de aire fresco, nieve y hielo y en verano, una fiesta de colores para todos los sentidos. Disfrute del confort, de las instalaciones de primera clase y del balcón de su habitación, con vistas al lago, al castillo y a las cimas de las montañas.

Our inspector loved: *The live piano music performed in the lobby bar every evening.*

Price Guide:
single €125-165
double €152-190
suite €185-265

Awards: Condé Nast Johansens Most Excellent Resort Hotel Award 2008

Attractions: Island Church, 1km; Bled Castle, 2km; Slovenia's Capital, Ljubljana, 50km; Minimundus, Klagenfurt, Austria, 70km

Nearby Towns: Ljubljana, 50km; Klagenfurt, Austria, 70km; Trieste, Italy, 150km
Airports: Ljubljana, 34km; Klagenfurt, Austria, 61km; Trieste, Italy, 143km

Category: Hotel

Spain

BAY OF BISCAY
FRANCE
Bordeaux
Toulouse
Montpellier
ANDORRA
PORTUGAL
Porto
Bragança
Évora
A Coruña
Lugo
Galicia
Asturias
Gijón
Oviedo
Santander
Cantabria
Bilbao
País Vasco
San Sebastián
Navarra
Pamplona
Vitoria
Pontevedra
Vigo
Orense
Ponferrada
León
Burgos
Castilla y León
Logroño
La Rioja
Huesca
Cataluña
Gerona
Lérida
Manresa
Barcelona
Tarragona
COSTA BRAVA
Zamora
Valladolid
Soria
Zaragoza
Aragón
Salamanca
Segovia
Avila
Madrid
Guadalajara
Plasencia
Teruel
Cuenca
Talavera de la Reina
Toledo
Cáceres
Castellón
Mérida
Badajoz
Extremadura
Castilla~La Mancha
Valencia
Ciudad Real
Albacete
Valdepeñas
Alcoy
Benidorm
Menorca
Mallorca
Palma
Ibiza
Córdoba
Jaén
Murcia
Elche
Alicante
COSTA BLANCA
Sevilla
Huelva
Andalucía
COSTA DE LA LUZ
Jerez
Cádiz
Granada
Málaga
Motril
Almería
Cartagena
Marbella
MEDITERRANEAN SEA
COSTA DEL SOL
Ceuta (Spain)
Tangier
Algiers
ALGERIA
Melilla(Spain)
Oran
MOROCCO
Rabat
Saida
Canary Islands
Lanzarote
Arrecife
ATLANTIC OCEAN
Tenerife
Santa Cruz
Las Palmas
Puerto del Rosario
Gran Canaria
Fuerteventura
288
306
305
316
300
301
299
298
290
302
303
289
307
318
324
322
320
323
319
321
317
272
260
267
268
269
271
261
262
263
264
265
266
270
304

SPAIN / ANDALUCÍA (CÓRDOBA)

Hospes Palacio del Bailío

RAMIREZ DE LAS CASAS DEZA 10-12, 14001 CÓRDOBA, SPAIN
Tel: +34 957 498 993 **Fax:** +34 957 498 994
Web: www.johansens.com/hospesbailio **E-mail:** palaciodelbailio@hospes.es

This magnificent hotel, situated in one of Córdoba's classic Moorish buildings, has carefully preserved its original elements. Admire the Roman ruins beneath the glass floor of one of the patios and the modern design with rich textures and strong colours. The Senzone Restaurant & Tapas Bar serves local-inspired cuisine, and the lovely Bodyna Spa is the perfect place for an indulging experience.

Ce magnifique hôtel situé dans un bâtiment typiquement mauresque de Córdoba a su préservé ses éléments d'origine. Admirez les ruines romaines sous le sol en verre de l'un des patios, ainsi que le design moderne aux textures riches et aux couleurs fortes. Le Senzone Restaurant & Tapas Bar sert une cuisine d'inspiration locale et le splendide Bodyna Spa est l'endroit idéal pour se laisser aller.

Este magnífico hotel es uno de los edificios árabes clásicos de Códoba, que ha conservado con todo cuidado sus elementos originales. Admire las ruinas romanas bajo el suelo de cristal de uno de los patios y el moderno diseño de suntuosas texturas y fuertes colores. El Senzone Restaurant & Tapas Bar sirve una carta inspirada en especialidades locales, y su encantador Bodyna Spa es el lugar perfecto para una experiencia sibarítica.

***Our inspector loved:** The tower suite, and the hotel's Roman hot baths.*

Price Guide: (room only, excluding VAT)
single €145-290
double €145-310
suite €270-655

Awards: Condé Nast Johansens Most Excellent Hotel for Design & Innovation 2009; Best Interior Design in a Hotel in Europe 2008, Prix Villégiature; Best Hotel Design 2007, Sleeper Awards

Attractions: Córdoba Mosque and Jewish Quarter, 10-min walk

Nearby Towns: Sevilla, 138km; Granada, 156km; Málaga, 187km
Airports: Córdoba, 10-min drive; Sevilla, 134km; Málaga, 187km

Category: Hotel

SPAIN / ANDALUCÍA (GRANADA) 

El Ladrón de Agua

CARRERA DEL DARRO 13, 18010 GRANADA, SPAIN
Tel: +34 958 21 50 40 **Fax:** +34 958 22 43 45
Web: www.johansens.com/ladrondeagua **E-mail:** info@ladrondeagua.com

Our inspector loved: *The tower suite and its wonderful views of the Alhambra.*

Price Guide:
single €66-137
double €88-175
suite torreón €174-237

Attractions: Albayzín Monuments and Tapas Bars, 3-min walk; Cathedral, 10-min walk; Alhambra Palace, 15-min walk; Sierra Nevada, 25-min drive

Nearby Towns: Jaen, 95km; Úbeda, 150km; Córdoba, 168km; Sevilla, 253km
Airports: Granada, 15km; Málaga, 145km; Almeria, 190km

Category: Charming Hotel

Lively and exciting, you'll find that this little 16th-century palace on the banks of the River Darro soaks up and reflects life outside its walls. Elegant and simply decorated to enhance the gorgeous architecture, public areas regularly host art exhibitions and recitals. Bedrooms are stylish, and several have exceptional views of the Alhambra.

Gai et vivant, ce petit palais du XVIe siècle situé sur les rives de la rivière Darro s'imprègne et reflète la vie derrière ses murs. Elégantes et décorées avec simplicité afin de mettre en avant la superbe architecture, les pièces communes accueillent régulièrement des expositions d'art et des récitals. Les chambres sont élégantes et plusieurs offrent des vues exceptionnelles sur l'Alhambra.

Vital y sin embargo apacible, así encontrará Vd. este palacio del siglo XVI a orilla del río Darro, que se empapa de animación para a continuación expedirla desde sus muros. Es elegante y está decorado con sencillez para reforzar su impresionante arquitectura. Sus salones comunes acogen regularmente exhibiciones artísticas y recitales. Sus habitaciones tienen estilo y algunas disponen de espectaculares vistas a la Alhambra.

SPAIN / ANDALUCÍA (GRANADA)

Hospes Palacio de los Patos

C/ SOLARILLO DE GRACIA 1, 18002 GRANADA, ANDALUCÍA, SPAIN

Tel: +34 958 535 790 **Fax:** +34 958 536 968

Web: www.johansens.com/hospeslospatos **E-mail:** hospes.palaciopatos@hospes.es

Our inspector loved: *The sumptuous bedrooms in the main palace building.*

Price Guide: (room only, excluding VAT)
single/double €125-340
suite €255-990

Awards: Best Urban Hotel in Spain, Condé Nast Traveller '09; Condé Nast Johansens Most Excellent European Hotel For Design & Innovation Award '08; Best Hotel with Spa, Thermaespa '08

Attractions: Cathedral, 5-min walk; Restaurants and Shopping, 5-min walk; Granada Monuments, 15-min walk; Alhambra Palace, 20-min walk

Nearby Towns: Guadix, 60km; Jaén, 95km; Córdoba, 230km; Sevilla, 255km
Airports: Granada, 15km; Málaga, 145km; Almeria, 190km

Category: Hotel

Effortlessly combining 19th-century grace and character with 21st-century facilities, the Palacio might render you temporarily speechless. The main hotel, a former aristocratic home, features a preponderance of white marble, painted ceilings and a spectacular staircase leading to luxurious bedrooms. The Senzone restaurant, pool, Bodyna Spa and additional guest rooms are located in the new modern building.

Mélangeant naturellement la grâce et le caractère du XIXe siècle avec les équipements du XXIe siècle, le Palacio vous laissera sans voix. Le bâtiment principal, ancienne maison d'aristocrates, est doté d'une prépondérance de marbre blanc, de plafonds peints et d'un spectaculaire escalier menant aux chambres luxueuses. Dans le bâtiment voisin, se trouvent le restaurant Senzone, la piscine, le Bodyna Spa et d'autres chambres.

Mediante la cómoda combinación de la gracia y solera del siglo XIX con instalaciones del siglo XXI, el Palacio podría dejarle temporalmente sin habla. El hotel principal, una antigua mansión aristocrática, presenta un predominio de mármol blanco, techos pintados y una espectacular escalera conducente a sus lujosas habitaciones. El restaurante Senzone, la piscina, el Bodyna Spa y algunas habitaciones se encuentran en el nuevo y moderno edificio.

Barceló La Bobadilla

FINCA LA BOBADILLA, CTRA. SALINAS - VILLANUEVA DE TAPIA, (A-333) KM 65.5, 18300 LOJA, GRANADA, SPAIN
Tel: +34 958 32 18 61 **Fax:** +34 958 32 18 10
Web: www.johansens.com/bobadilla **E-mail:** labobadilla.info@barcelo.com

Our inspector loved: *The attention to detail.*

Price Guide: (excluding VAT)
single €225-389
superior double €382-502
junior/superior/royal suite €432-1,453

Awards: Condé Nast Johansens Most Romantic Hotel 2009

Attractions: Picasso Museum and Coastline, 60km; Alhambra Palace, 70km; Sierra Nevada Ski Resort, 104km; Mezquita de Córdoba, 150km

Nearby Towns: Archidona, 15km; Loja and Iznajar, 20km; Antequera, 35km; Málaga, 60km
Airports: Granada, 35-min drive; Málaga, 40-min drive; AVE Madrid-Antequera Train St, 20-min drive

Category: Hotel

Following a major extension, this beautiful hotel now has 70 bedrooms filled with unique touches and modern facilities such as plasma TVs and playstations by parents' request in the family rooms. All rooms have views to the Granada Hills. El Cortijo restaurant offers a variety of regional dishes, and the spa is an opulent, welcome addition. Jump on a bike, horse, quad-bike or buggie to see the area.

Grâce à une importante extension, cet élégant hôtel se compose dorénavant de 70 chambres toutes avec des touches particulières et avec des équipements modernes tels que des écrans plasma et des playstations, à la demande des parents, dans les chambres familiales. Toutes les chambres offrent de vues sur les collines de Grenade. Le restaurant El Cortijo offre une variété de plats régionaux et amélioré et le spa est une importante addition bienvenue. Sautez sur un vélo, un cheval, un quad ou un buggie pour explorer les environs.

Tras una importante ampliación, este bonito hotel ahora dispone de 70 habitaciones, todas provistas de toques especiales e instalaciones modernas como televisores de plasma y, por la solicitud de muchos padres, playstations en las habitaciones familiares. Todas con perfectas vistas a las montañas de Granada. El restaurante El Cortijo ofrece una variedad de platos regionales y el lujoso Spa es un atractivo adicional que se agradece. Súbase a una bicicleta, un caballo, un quad o un boogie para explorar los alrededores.

Casa Viña de Alcantara

CTRA JEREZ-ARCOS, A382 SALIDA Nº3, A382A KM 8.6, 11400 JEREZ DE LA FRONTERA, CÁDIZ, SPAIN
Tel: +34 956 393 010 **Mobile:** +34 650 907 319
Web: www.johansens.com/vinadealcantara **E-mail:** info@vinadealcantara.com

An ideal stopover on the Jerez to Arcos road if you're touring the "pueblos blancos" or visiting the great sherry bodegas. Family owned and nestling in a grand estate, this country house hotel blends cool interiors with antiques and modern furnishings. Spacious bedrooms are decorated in pale earthy colours. Beautiful and serene.

Une étape idéale sur la route entre Jerez et Arcos si vous visitez les "pueblos blancos" ou les fantastiques distilleries de sherry. Géré en famille et niché dans un grand domaine, cet hôtel de campagne mélange des intérieurs remplis d'antiquités et de meubles modernes. Les chambres spacieuses sont décorées dans des tons pâles et naturels. Magnifique et serein.

Tanto si está viajando por los pueblos blancos como si está visitando las fabulosas bodegas de jerez, este hotel sito en la carretera de Jerez a Arcos resulta una parada ideal. Esta casa-hotel rural de regencia familiar ubicada en una gran finca combina sus refrescantes interiores con las antigüedades y un mobiliario moderno. Las espaciosas habitaciones están decoradas con colores terrosos pálidos. Belleza y serenidad.

***Our inspector loved:** The shady gardens and peaceful atmosphere around the swimming pool.*

Price Guide: (room only, excluding VAT)
double €160-310

Attractions: Bodegas, 5-min drive; Equestrian Shows and Activities, 5-min drive; Beaches, 30-min drive

Nearby Towns: Jerez de la Frontera, 15-min drive; Arcos de la Frontera, 25-min drive; Cádiz, 35-min drive; Sevilla, 1-hour drive
Airports: Jerez de la Frontera, 15-min drive; Gibraltar, 70-min drive

Category: Luxury Guest House

Hotel La Fuente del Sol

PARAJE ROSAS BAJAS, 29260 LA JOYA, ANTEQUERA, SPAIN
Tel: +34 951 70 07 70 **Fax:** +34 951 23 20 90
Web: www.johansens.com/fuentedelsol **E-mail:** info@hotelfuentedelsol.com

Our inspector loved: *The absolute silence.*

Price Guide: (excluding VAT)
single €120
double €150-180
suite €200-250

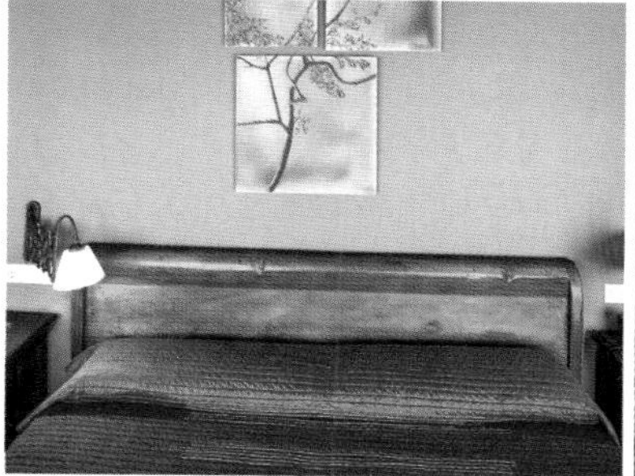

Awards: Best Countryside Hotel in Málaga, Málaga Rural Magazine 2009

Attractions: El Torcal Natural Park, on the doorstep; El Chorro Reservoir, 10-min drive; Antequera, 15-min drive; Beaches, 45-min drive

Nearby Towns: Málaga, 45-min drive; Granada, 1-hour drive; Córdoba, 1-hour drive; Sevilla, 90-min drive
Airports: Málaga, 45-min drive; Granada, 1-hour drive; Sevilla, 1.5-hour drive

Category: Charming Hotel

With uninterrupted views of the mountains, and peace and tranquillity on tap, this is the ideal getaway from the hustle of the city or coast. Décor is comfortable and rustic with modern, high beamed ceilings and a wonderful sense of space. Bedrooms have a cosy, warm atmosphere and some have a Jacuzzi and terrace, while the full-service spa offers massage and treatment rooms, sauna, Turkish bath and a large heated pool.

Avec ses vues ininterrompues sur les montagnes ainsi que sa paix et sa tranquillité à volonté, cet hôtel constitue le repaire idéal pour s'éloigner de l'agitation de la ville ou de la côte. Le décor est rustique et confortable, avec de hauts plafonds modernes aux poutres apparentes et une merveilleuse sensation d'espace. Les chambres ont une atmosphère douillette et chaleureuse; certaines disposent d'un Jacuzzi et d'une terrasse. Le spa offre des massages, plusieurs salles de traitements, sauna, bain turc et une grande piscine chauffée.

Con vistas ininterrumpidas de las montañas donde la paz y la tranquilidad abundan, está el lugar ideal para huir del bullicio de la ciudad o de la costa. Su décor es cómodo y rústico con modernos y altos techos de vigas que dan una sensación maravillosa de espacio. Las habitaciones son acogedoras y de ambiente cálido y algunas disponen de Jacuzzi y terraza. El spa ofrece masajes y tratamientos, sauna, baño turco y una gran piscina climatizada.

SPAIN / ANDALUCÍA (SANLÚCAR DE BARRAMEDA - CÁDIZ)

POSADA DE PALACIO

C/ CABALLEROS, 11, 11540 SANLÚCAR DE BARRAMEDA (CÁDIZ), SPAIN
Tel: +34 956 36 4840 **Fax:** +34 956 36 5060
Web: www.johansens.com/posadadepalacio **E-mail:** reservas@posadadepalacio.com

2 adjacent 18th-century Andalucían-style manor houses, each with a pretty, columned patio, have been transformed into this charming and welcoming guest house situated in an eminent historic and aristocratic town. Large, comfortable and classically furnished rooms open out to flower-filled courtyards and terraces. Everything and everywhere has been stunningly restored to minute detail.

2 manoirs adjacents du XVIIIe siècle au style andalou, ayant chacun un ravissant patio à colonnes, ont été transformés en une charmante et accueillante maison d'hôtes, située dans une ville réputée, historique et aristocratique. Spacieuses, confortables et meublées classiquement, les chambres s'ouvrent sur des cours et des terrasses abondamment fleuries. Tout, partout, a été magnifiquement restauré avec une grande minutie.

2 casas solariegas adyacentes de estilo andaluz del siglo XVIII, cada una de ellas provista de un patio de columnas, han sido transformadas en esta encantadora y acogedora casa de huéspedes situada en una distinguida localidad histórica y aristocrática. Sus amplias, cómodas habitaciones de mobiliario clásico disponen de acceso a patios y terrazas repletas de flores. Todo y en todas partes ha sido exquisitamente restaurado hasta el último detalle.

***Our inspector loved:** The charm and ambience of southern Spain.*

Price Guide:
single €80-107
double €104-136
suite €136-195

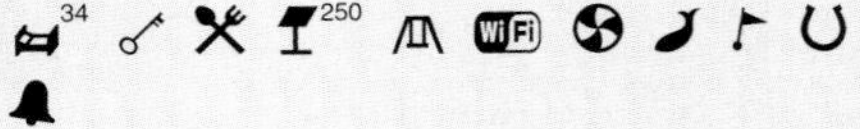

Attractions: Beaches, 5-min drive; Horse Studs and Horse Shows, 20km; Wine and Sherry Bodegas, Jerez, 30km

Nearby Towns: Jerez, 30km; Sevilla, 124km; Cádiz, 30km; Arcos de la Frontera, 1-hour drive
Airports: Jerez de la Frontera, 30km; Sevilla, 135km

Category: Charming Hotel
Closed: 6th January - 6th February

SPAIN / ANDALUCÍA (SANLÚCAR LA MAYOR - SEVILLA) 

Hacienda Benazuza el Bulli Hotel

C/VIRGEN DE LAS NIEVES S/N, 41800 SANLÚCAR LA MAYOR, SEVILLE, SPAIN

Tel: +34 955 70 33 44 **Fax:** +34 955 70 34 10

Web: www.johansens.com/haciendabenazuza **E-mail:** hbenazuza@elbullihotel.com

Our inspector loved: *Walking under the arch into the first patio. It's like stepping into another world.*

Price Guide: (excluding VAT)
double/twin €350-490
suite €455-1,440

Awards: 2 Star Michelin

Attractions: Golf, 10-min drive; Doñana National Park, 40-min drive; Huelva's Beaches, 50-min drive; Sherry Wineries, 1-hour drive

Nearby Towns: Seville, 20km; Cordoba, 165km; Jerez, 100km; Cadiz, 145km
Airports: Seville International, 30km; Jerez, 100km; Faro, Portugal, 180km

Category: Hotel

You may find yourself among high-profile guests here, at one of Spain's most sought after hotels. Let delightful courtyards, gardens and a pool arranged as a series of "water terraces" bring you an instant sense of tranquillity. La Alquería restaurant is world famous and the Sensoria spa area is beautifully decorated and offers exclusive massages and treatments.

Vous serez parmi une clientèle très haut de gamme dans cet hôtel, l'un des plus recherché d'Espagne. Laissez les ravissantes cours intérieurs, les jardins et la piscine arrangée comme une suite de "terrasses d'eau" vous envahir d'un sentiment de tranquillité. Le restaurant La Alquería est mondialement réputé et le spa Sensoria est magnifiquement décoré et propose des massages et des soins exclusifs.

Podrá aquí sentirse parte del grupo de clientes de alto standing en uno de los hoteles más solicitados de España. Déjese llevar por esa instantánea sensación de paz que le proporcionarán sus encantadores patios, jardines y piscina distribuida en forma de "terrazas de agua." El restaurante La Alquería es famoso en el mundo entero y su zona de spa Sensoria goza de una bella decoración y pone a su disposición exclusivos masajes y tratamientos.

SPAIN / ANDALUCÍA (SEVILLA)

CASA NO 7

CALLE VIRGENES NO 7, 41004 SEVILLA, SPAIN
Tel: +34 954 221 581 **Fax:** +34 954 214 527
Web: www.johansens.com/casanumero7 **E-mail:** info@casanumero7.com

You'll find this property simply irresistible. Down a narrow winding street in the middle of Sevilla's buzzing old Jewish Quarter, this protected listed building uncovers a comfortable, private oasis. Each guest room has little extras that make you feel you're staying with friends rather than at a hotel. And the drawing room, with its fireplace, sumptuous sofas and honesty bar, is the perfect spot for unwinding after a day of shopping or sightseeing.

Vous serez merveilleusement séduit par cet établissement. Situé en bas d'une rue étroite et sinueuse au centre du vieux et bouillonnant quartier juif, ce bâtiment classé abrite une confortable oasis privée. Chaque chambre possède de petites particularités qui vous donnent l'impression de séjourner chez des amis plutôt qu'à l'hôtel. Et le salon, avec sa cheminée, ses somptueux canapés et son bar, est l'endroit idéal pour se délasser après une journée de shopping ou de visites.

Encontrará este lugar totalmente irresistible. Dentro de este edificio protegido, situado en una estrecha y sinuosa calle del pintoresco antiguo barrio judío, se descubre un confortable oasis privado. Todas las habitaciones disponen de pequeños detalles que le hará sentirse como si estuviera entre amigos en vez de en un hotel y el salón, con su chimenea, suntuosos sofás y bar abierto, es el lugar ideal para relajarse después de un día de compras o de visitas turísticas.

Our inspector loved: *The warm ambience and the lovely décor; a perfect blend of elegance and comfort.*

Price Guide: (excluding VAT)
double €177

Attractions: Historic Sevilla, 5-min walk; Shopping, 10-min walk; Beaches, 1-hour drive

Nearby Towns: Carmona, Osuna and Ecija, 30-min drive; Jerez, 100km; Córdoba, 150km
Airports: Sevilla, 15-min drive

Category: Luxury Guest House

 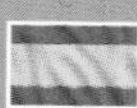

Hospes las Casas del Rey de Baeza

C/SANTIAGO, PLAZA JESÚS DE LA REDENCIÓN 2, 41003 SEVILLA, SPAIN
Tel: +34 954 561 496 **Fax:** +34 954 561 441
Web: www.johansens.com/hospesreydebaeza **E-mail:** hospes.reydebaeza@hospes.es

Our inspector loved: *The rooftop swimming pool and wellness centre.*

Price Guide: (room only, excluding VAT)
single €125-305
double €125-360
suite €300-520

Attractions: Golf, 30-min drive; Donana Nature Reserve, 45-min drive; Beaches of Huelva, 45-min drive

Nearby Towns: Carmona, Ecija, Osuna, 30-min drive; Córdoba, 1-hour drive; Cádiz, 1-hour drive
Airports: Sevilla, 20-min drive

Category: Hotel

Surrounded by churches and palaces in the old quarter of Sevilla, this hotel is filled with light. Walk through a cobbled courtyard, past blue wooden pillars and cascading flowers into relaxing public rooms, and clean, minimalist bedrooms with natural fabrics and dark woods. Views of Sevilla's rooftops from the terrace are enchanting. Don't miss the treatments at Bodyna Spa!

Entouré d'églises et de palais dans le vieux quartier de Séville, cet hôtel est rempli de lumière. Traversez la cour pavée, longez les piliers en bois bleu et les cascades de fleurs pour arriver dans les agréables pièces communes et dans les chambres minimalistes aux tissus naturels et aux bois foncés. Les vues sur les toits de Séville depuis la terrasse sont magiques. Ne manquez pas le Bodyna Spa et ses traitements!

Rodeado de iglesias y palacios en el barrio antiguo de Sevilla, este hotel rebosa luz. Pasee por sus patios adoquinados, pase por azuladas columnas de madera y cascadas de flores antes de llegar a sus relajantes salones comunes y a sus pulcras y minimalistas habitaciones provistas de telas naturales y oscuras maderas. Las vistas de los tejados de Sevilla desde la azotea son verdaderamente encantadoras. ¡No se pierda los tratamientos que ofrece el Bodyna Spa!

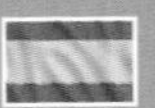

V...

CALLE ROSARIO 11-13, VEJER DE LA FRONTERA, 11150 CÁDIZ, SPAIN
Tel: +34 956 451 757 **Fax:** +34 956 450 088
Web: www.johansens.com/hotelvvejer **E-mail:** info@hotelv-vejer.com

Reached via a narrow street in the middle of town is this exceptional example of clever modern design. From the centuries-old street you enter through a glass door and into a serene world of open space and sleek, inviting interiors. The fantastic rooftop terrace looks out to the Andalucían countryside and ocean, which you can admire from the Jacuzzi.

On rejoint par une petite rue au milieu de la ville cet exemple exceptionnellement délicat de design moderne. Depuis les rues centenaires, on entre par une porte vitrée dans un monde serein fait d'espaces ouverts et d'intérieurs accueillants. La fantastique terrasse sur le toit domine la campagne andalouse et l'océan, que vous pourrez admirer depuis le Jacuzzi.

A través de una estrecha calle en pleno centro de la localidad podrá llegar a esta excepcional muestra de construcción de inteligente y moderno diseño. A través de sus centenarias calles llegará Vd. a una puerta de cristal que le introducirá en todo un sereno mundo de espacios abiertos y de relucientes y acogedores interiores. Su fantástica azotea le proporcionará vistas al campo andaluz y al océano, todo lo cual podrá admirar desde su jacuzzi.

Our inspector loved: *The cooling Jacuzzi on the roof terrace with its 360º views.*

Price Guide:
classic double room from €215
superior double room from €265
2-bedroom suite from €530

Attractions: Golf, 10-min drive; Beach and Water Sports, 10-min drive; Surfing in Tarifa, 30-min drive; Daytrips to Morocco, 30-min drive

Nearby Towns: Cádiz, 30-min drive; Jerez de la Frontera, 45-min drive; Gibraltar, 45-min drive; Sevilla, 90-min drive
Airports: Jerez de la Frontera, 40-min drive; Gibraltar, 45-min drive; Seville, 90-min drive

Category: Luxury Guest House
Closed: During December and January

Hacienda Minerva

CTRA. ZUHEROS-DONA MENCIA KM 9.8 (CO-6203), 14870 ZUHEROS (CÓRDOBA), SPAIN
Tel: +34 957 090 951 **Fax:** +34 957 090 955
Web: www.johansens.com/haciendaminerva **E-mail:** info@haciendaminerva.com

Our inspector loved: *The outdoor passages with hanging flower pots in bloom and names such as "Cat Alley" and "Kiss Alley."*

Price Guide:
single €70-200
double €85-250
suite €190-280

Attractions: Cyclist/Walkers' Track, 50 metres; Sierra Subbeticas Nature Reserve, 100 metres; Cueva Murcielagos Cave, 10-min drive; Golf, 40-min drive

Nearby Towns: Zuheros, 3-min drive; Córdoba, 45-min drive; Ubeda and Baeza, 70-min drive
Airports: Málaga, 1-hour drive; Granada, 70-min drive

Category: Charming Hotel

Like a tiny village with its cobblestone courtyards, arches and flower-filled alleys, this 19th-century hacienda nestles amidst century-old olive groves and a natural park. Spacious rooms are decorated in a traditional Andalucían farmhouse style and retain many original features. The restaurant has an excellent reputation, and various terraces are perfect spots for taking in the countryside views.

Cette hacienda du XIXe siècle, nichée au coeur d'une oliveraie centenaire et un parc naturel, ressemble à un petit village avec ses cours pavées, ses arches et ses allées fleuries. Les chambres spacieuses sont décorées dans un style traditionnel andalou et ont gardé de nombreuses caractéristiques d'origine. Le restaurant a une excellente réputation et les nombreuses terrasses sont autant de lieux d'où admirer les vues sur la campagne.

Al igual que esas pequeñas aldeas de patios adoquinados, arcos y callejones llenos de flores, esta hacienda del siglo XIX está enclavada entre olivos centenarios y un parque natural. Las espaciosas habitaciones están decoradas al estilo tradicional de una alquería andaluza y conserva numerosos elementos originales. El restaurante goza de una excelente reputación, y algunas de las terrazas son lugares perfectos para disfrutar de las vistas que ofrece su paisaje.

Spain (Balearic Islands and Canary Islands)

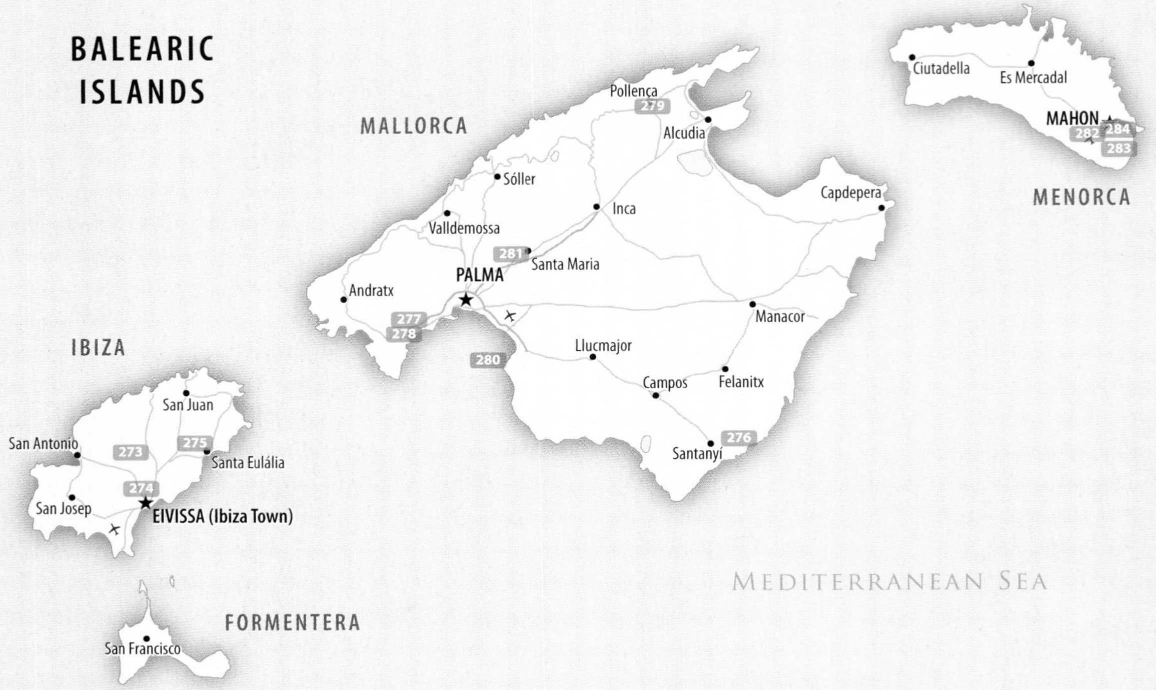

BALEARIC ISLANDS

MALLORCA
Pollença
279
Alcudia
Sóller
Inca
Capdepera
Valldemossa
281
Santa Maria
PALMA
Andratx
277
278
280
Manacor
Llucmajor
Campos
Felanitx
276
Santanyí

MENORCA
Ciutadella
Es Mercadal
MAHON
282
284
283

IBIZA
San Juan
San Antonio
273
275
Santa Eulália
274
San Josep
EIVISSA (Ibiza Town)

FORMENTERA
San Francisco

MEDITERRANEAN SEA

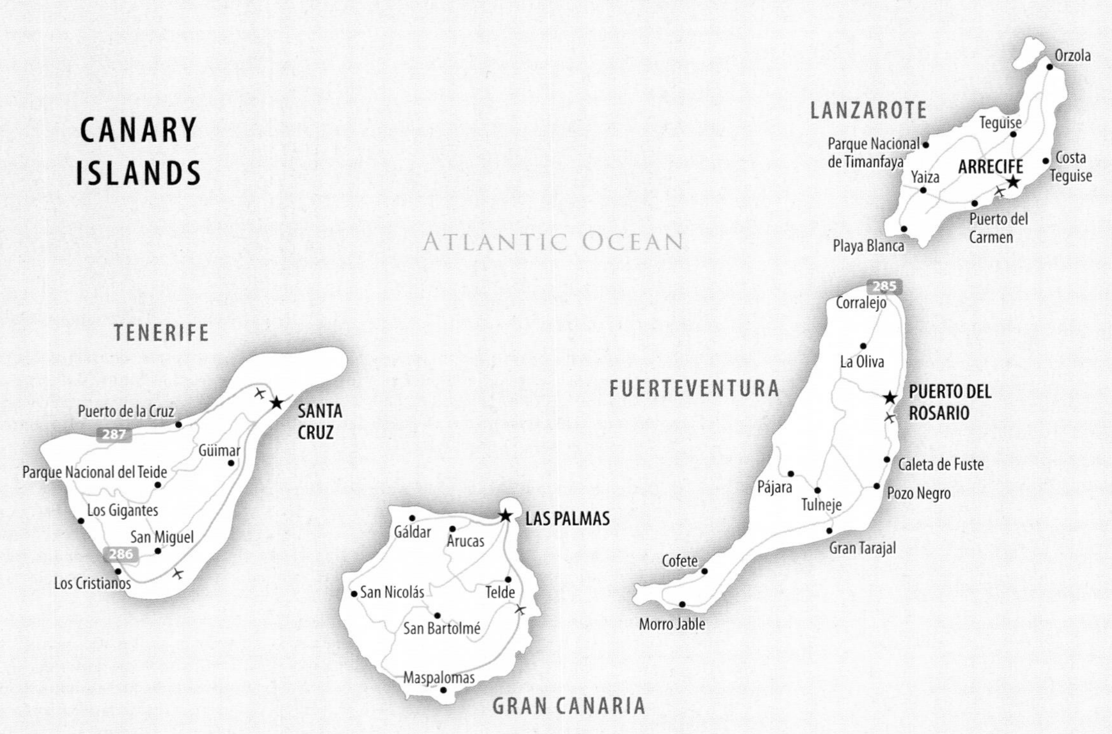

Can Lluc

CRTA. SANTA INÉS, KM 2, 07816 SAN RAFAEL, IBIZA, BALEARIC ISLANDS, SPAIN
Tel: +34 971 198 673 **Fax:** +34 971 198 547
Web: www.johansens.com/canlluc **E-mail:** info@canlluc.com

Our inspector loved: *The quiet nights and peaceful atmosphere.*

Price Guide: (excluding VAT)
double €225-750

Awards: Q - for Quality Spanish Tourist Board Award 2009; ISO 14001 Environmental Management System 2009

Attractions: Sunset Hill Walk, 1km; Beach, 10km; Golf, 16km

Nearby Towns: San Antonio, 11km; Ibiza Town, 10km
Airports: Ibiza, 16km

Category: Charming Hotel

In the heart of the island, Can Lluc captures the tranquillity and magic of rural Ibiza. The main farmhouse has retained its sturdy stone walls and wooden beams and features skylights that let in plenty of natural sunlight. Several bedrooms are located in little houses within the grounds, and the new wellness area is set within the garden. Can Lluc was a Condé Nast Johansens Most Charming Hotel Award finalist, 2009.

Au cœur de l'île, Can Lluc saisit parfaitement la tranquillité et la magie du véritable Ibiza. Le bâtiment principal a conservé ses murs en pierre de taille et ses poutres d'origines tout en béneficiant d'une profusion de lumière naturelle grâce aux fenêtres du plafond. Plusieurs chambres sont situées dans les petites maisons du parc et le nouveau centre de remise en forme se trouve dans le jardin. Can Lluc a été finaliste en 2009 du prix Condé Nast Johansens "Meilleur Hôtel de Charme".

Situado en el corazón de la isla, Can Lluc refleja perfectamente la tranquilidad y la magia de la Ibiza rural. El edificio principal de la hacienda, con gruesas paredes de piedra y vigas de madera, es claro y soleado gracias a las claraboyas del techo. Algunas de las habitaciones se encuentran en pequeñas casas ubicadas en la finca, así como la nueva zona Wellness situada en el jardín. Can Lluc fue finalista en la categoría de Most Charming Hotel de los premios de Condé Nast Johansens 2009.

Cas Gasi

CAMINO VIEJO DE SANT MATEU S/N, PO BOX 117, 07814 SANTA GERTRUDIS, IBIZA, BALEARIC ISLANDS, SPAIN
Tel: +34 971 197 700 **Fax:** +34 971 197 899
Web: www.johansens.com/casgasi **E-mail:** info@casgasi.com

Our inspector loved: *The special atmosphere all year round; outdoors in summer and around the fireplace in winter.*

Price Guide: (excluding VAT)
double €180-399
suite €450-750

Set amidst pretty gardens, almond trees, orchards and olive groves, this former farmhouse has been completely renovated and extended to offer guests an exclusive stay in tranquil surroundings. Feast on the night-life and beaches in summer, or explore the countryside on foot or bicycle during winter. Take a trip on the private yacht and imagine it's yours for a few blissful hours.

Au sein de charmants jardins, d'amandiers, de vergers et d'oliveraies, cet ancien corps de ferme a été complèment rénové et agrandi pour offrir à ses hôtes un sejour exclusif dans un environnement tranquille. Profitez de la vie nocturne et des plages en été ou explorez les environs à pied ou en vélo l'hiver. Naviguez sur le bateau privé de l'hôtel et laissez-vous imaginer qu'il vous appartient pour quelques heures.

Ubicada entre preciosos jardines, almendros, huertas y olivares, esta antigua hacienda ha sido totalmente renovada y ampliada con el propósito de ofrecer a los clientes una estancia exclusiva en un entorno tranquilo. Explore el paisaje a pie o en bicicleta en invierno; en verano vaya a la playa y diviértase por la noche. Navegue en un yate privado e imagínese que es suyo durante unas fantásticas horas.

Attractions: Cycling and Walking Routes; Golf, 10km; Beach, 10km; Hippy Market in San Carlos, 15km

Nearby Towns: Santa Gertrudis, 5km; St Rafael, 5km, Ibiza, Santa Eulàlia and San Antonio 12km
Airports: Ibiza, 18km

Category: Charming Hotel

Quilibra Aguas de Ibiza

C/SALVADOR CAMACHO 9, STA EULALIA DEL RÍO, 07840 IBIZA, BALEARIC ISLANDS, SPAIN
Tel: +34 971 319 991 **Fax:** +34 971 319 869
Web: www.johansens.com/hospesquilibra **E-mail:** quilibra.aguasdeibiza@hospes.es

Our inspector loved: *The attention to detail in the clever interior design.*

Price Guide: (room only, excluding VAT)
junior suite €215-300
suite €310-1,390

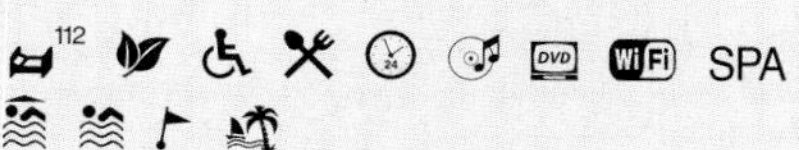

Attractions: Marina, 5-min walk; Golf Club and Beaches, 10-min walk

Nearby Towns: Ibiza, 10-min drive
Airports: Ibiza, 15-min drive

Category: Hotel

Contemporary architecture and cutting-edge interior design distinguish this environmentally conscious resort. The care and attention to style and finish are evident throughout the rooms where views of the sea and the marina can be admired. Highly luxurious rooms, with their own check-in, are situated on the "Cloud Nine" floor. The recently opened Bodyna Spa and Senzone Pool Bar are located on the rooftop.

Une architecture contemporaine et un intérieur à la pointe du design caractérisent ce complexe hôtelier respectueux de l'environnement. L'attention et le soin portés, au style et aux finitions se ressentent dans toutes les chambres d'où l'on peut admirer des vues sur la mer ou la marina. Les chambres extrêmement luxueuses, avec leur propre réception, sont situées au 9e étage, dans les nuages. Le Spa Bodyna récemment ouvert et le Senzone Pool Bar, sont situés sur le toit terrasse.

Una arquitectura contemporánea y un diseño interior vanguardista hacen resaltar a este lugar de vacaciones que es respetuoso con el medio ambiente. El cuidado y la atención puesta respecto al estilo y el acabado, son perceptibles en todas las habitaciones, desde donde podrá admirar vistas al mar y al puerto deportivo. La planta "Cloud Nine" cuenta con unas lujosísimas habitaciones que tienen su propio servicio de recepción. El recientemente inaugurado Bodyna Spa y Senzone Pool Bar se encuentran en el último piso.

SPAIN / BALEARIC ISLANDS (MALLORCA)

Blau Porto Petro Beach Resort & Spa

CARRER DES FAR 16, 07691 PORTO PETRO (SANTANYÍ), MALLORCA, BALEARIC ISLANDS, SPAIN
Tel: +34 971 648 282 **Fax:** +34 971 648 283
Web: www.johansens.com/portopetro **E-mail:** portopetro@blauhotels.com

Next to Porto Petro and the Mondragó Nature Reserve, the resort's rooms, suites and villas have sun terraces and sea views. Gourmet, Japanese, Spanish and buffet dining are available. Children will be kept amused by the 2 beaches, 3 pools and an array of sports, while adults can take advantage of the shuttle service to Vall d'Or golf course and the spa whose menu offers beauty, hydrotherapy, thalasso therapy and personalised treatments.

Situé près de Porto Petro et de la Réserve Naturelle de Mondragó, les chambres, suites et villas de ce resort ont toutes des terrasses solarium et vues sur la mer. Une restauration gastronomique, japonaise, espagnole ou sous forme de buffet est disponible. Les enfants ne s'ennuieront pas avec les 2 plages, les 3 piscines et un large choix de sports pendant que les adultes pourront profiter de la navette vers le parcours de golf du Vall d'Or ou du Spa qui propose hydrothérapie, thalassothérapie, des soins de beauté et des soins personnalisés.

Junto a Porto Petro y a la Reserva Natural Mondragó, las habitaciones, suites y villas de este resort tienen terrazas soleadas y vistas al mar. A su disposición hay cenas: japonesa, española, gourmet o buffet. Los niños son bienvenidos y podrán disfrutar de 2 playas, 3 piscinas y una extensa gama de deportes. Para los adultos hay un servicio de transfer gratuito al campo de golf Vall d'Or y un Spa que ofrece hidroterápia, thalassoterápia así como tratamientos de belleza y personalizados.

Our inspector loved: *The Lomi Lomi massage.*

Price Guide: (per person)
double from €90
suite from €144

319 600 SPA

Awards: EMAS, European Certificate of Compliance with Ecological Regulations 2008

Attractions: Mini Clubs for Children Aged 2-13 years and Teenies Club During High Season for 14-17 year-olds, on-site; Beaches, 2-min walk; Unspoilt Village, 300 metres; Golf, 7km

Nearby Towns: Porto Petro, 5-min walk; Santanyí, 10km; Palma, 60km
Airports: Palma, 50km

Category: Hotel
Closed: During November and December

 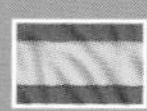

Hospes Maricel

CARRETERA D'ANDRATX 11, 07181 CAS CATALÀ, (CALVIÀ) MALLORCA, BALEARIC ISLANDS, SPAIN
Tel: +34 971 707 744 **Fax:** +34 971 707 745
Web: www.johansens.com/hospesmaricel **E-mail:** hospes.maricel@hospes.es

Our inspector loved: *The fabulous new spa.*

Price Guide: (room only, excluding VAT)
double €189-620
suite €425-1,430

Awards: Best Hotel Suite, Wallpaper Design Awards 2009

Attractions: Beach, 5-min walk; Shopping in Palma, 5km; Golf, 5km

Nearby Towns: Palma, 5km; Port of Andratx, 15km; Sóller, 30km
Airports: Palma, 20km

Category: Hotel
Closed: End of December - February

An exciting fusion of old and new with views of the Mediterranean. The high ceilings and glass windows of the lobby enhance the magnificent scenery. Contemporary bedrooms have bathrooms with traditional tubs, and you can float further from reality on a chartered yacht trip. Enjoy jazz nights at the bar, the menu of Senzone Restaurant, and visit Hearth Spa and Sea Spa, both by Bodyna and each with their own private Zen pool.

Un réjouissant mélange d'ancien et de moderne avec vues sur la Méditerranée. Les hauts plafonds et les baies vitrées du hall mettent en valeur le magnifique paysage. Les chambres contemporaines sont dotées de bains traditionnels. Vous pouvez flotter encore plus loin de la réalité en profitant d'une croisière sur le yacht de l'hôtel. Profitez des soirées jazz au bar, du menu au restaurant Senzone et visitez les Spas Bodyna, Hearth et Sea, ayant chacun de leur propre piscine zen privée.

Una original fusión de antiguo y nuevo con vistas al Mediterráneo. Los altos techos y ventanales del vestíbulo resaltan el magnífico paisaje. Sus modernas y actuales habitaciones disponen de cuartos de baño con bañeras tradicionales y podrá alejarse flotando de la realidad mediante un viaje en yate a su servicio. Disfrute de las noches de jazz en el bar, del menú en el Restaurante Senzone y no se pierda el Hearth Spa y Sea Spa ambos de Bodyna y cada uno con su propia piscina Zen.

SPAIN / BALEARIC ISLANDS (MALLORCA)

HOTEL AIMIA

SANTA MARIA DEL CAMÍ, 1 07108 PORT DE SÓLLER, MALLORCA, BALEARIC ISLANDS, SPAIN
Tel: +34 971 631 200 **Fax:** +34 971 638 040
Web: www.johansens.com/aimia **E-mail:** info@aimiahotel.com

Ultra modern, Hotel Aimia puts its small port and beach resort of northern Mallorca on the map, and if you like a streamlined look you'll be happy, as restful bedrooms and interiors are contemporary with dark wood floors complementing beige, lilac and yellow tones. Make sure you visit the spa with its sauna, cyclonic showers and range of treatments that use natural products only, and enjoy dinner in the elegant restaurant.

L'ultra moderne Hôtel Aimia peut être fier de son petit port et de sa plage au Nord de Majorque. Si vous aimez les lignes pures, vous aimerez les chambres reposantes et les intérieurs contemporains aux parquets sombres qui s'harmonisent avec les tons beiges, lilas et jaunes. N'oubliez pas de visiter le spa avec son sauna, ses douches et ses nombreux soins naturels, ni de dîner dans l'élégant restaurant.

Ultra-moderno, Hotel Aimia logra poner en el mapa su pequeño puerto y complejo playero del norte de Mallorca. Si le gustan las líneas aerodinámicas se alegrará, pues las cómodas habitaciones y el resto del interior son de estilo contemporáneo con suelos de madera oscura combinados con tonos en beis, lila y amarillo. No deje de visitar el Spa con su sauna, duchas ciclónicas y variedad de tratamientos a base de productos naturales, y luego disfrute de una buena cena en el elegante restaurante.

Our inspector loved: *The restaurant staff who are charming and helpful.*

Price Guide:
single €130-160
superior sea-facing room €180-210
junior suite €210-255

Attractions: Beach, on the doorstep; Hiking, on the doorstep; Maritime Museum, 3.5km; Golf, 10km

Nearby Towns: Sóller, 3.5km; Deià, 10km; Valldemossa, 20km; Palma, 38km
Airports: Palma, 45km

Category: Charming Hotel
Closed: During December and January

 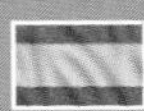

HOTEL CALA SANT VICENÇ

C/MARESSERS 2, CALA SANT VICENÇ, 07469 POLLENÇA, MALLORCA, BALEARIC ISLANDS, SPAIN
Tel: +34 971 53 02 50 **Fax:** +34 971 53 20 84
Web: www.johansens.com/hotelcala **E-mail:** info@hotelcala.com

Our inspector loved: *The quiet location so close to the beach.*

Price Guide:
single €82-175
double/twin €164-299
junior suite €260-351

Attractions: Beaches, 200 metres; Golf, 7km; Inca Market, 25km; Lluc Monastery, 25km

Nearby Towns: Pollença, 5km; Port de Pollença, 9km; Inca, 25km
Airports: Palma, 65km

Category: Charming Hotel
Closed: November - April

A scenic mountain backdrop shields a peaceful village and this pretty terracotta hotel with stone-coloured arches. Just a 200-metre walk means you can feel sand between your toes in a picturesque cove, and bedrooms with balconies provide a restful retreat. Excellent food is offered at the restaurant.

Ce ravissant hôtel en terracotta avec ses arches couleur de pierre est situé dans un village tranquille protégé par les montagnes en toile de fond. Vous pourrez sentir le sable entre vos pieds dans la crique pittoresque située à 200 mètres et les chambres avec balcons vous offrent un refuge reposant. Une délicieuse cuisine est servie au restaurant.

Un espectacular y montañoso telón de fondo mantiene resguardas tanto la tranquila aldea como el pequeño hotel de terracotta de coloridos arcos de piedra. Tras sólo un paseo de 200 metros podrá sentir la arena entre sus pies en la diminuta y pintoresca cala. Las habitaciones provistas de balcones proporcionan el adecuado lugar de retiro para el descanso. Excelente cocina es servida en el selecto restaurante.

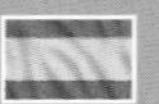

Palacio Ca Sa Galesa

CARRER DE MIRAMAR 8, 07001 PALMA DE MALLORCA, BALEARIC ISLANDS, SPAIN
Tel: +34 971 715 400 **Fax:** +34 971 721 579
Web: www.johansens.com/casagalesa **E-mail:** reservas@palaciocasagalesa.com

Wander into Palma's gothic quarter and stumble across this 16th-century palace with original stained glass, chandeliers and tapestries. Bathrooms offer a "bath menu," featuring a choice of salts, oils, candles and music, or choose from the "massage menu," which includes yoga and t'ai chi classes. Now offering conference facilities, why not hold your board meeting or event here in this elegant setting?

Baladez-vous dans le quartier gothique de Palma et vous tomberez sur ce palais du XVIe siècle avec des vitraux d'origine, des lustres et des tapisseries. Les salles de bains proposent un « menu bain », se composant d'un choix de sels, d'huiles, de bougies et de musiques. Vous pouvez aussi choisir le « menu massage », qui comprend des cours de yoga et de Taï Chi. Comme l'hôtel offre dorénavant des équipements pour les conférences, pourquoi ne pas organiser vos réunions ou vos évènements dans ce décor élégant?

Deambule por el barrio gótico de Palma y se topará con este palacio del siglo XVI de originales vidrios de colores, lámparas araña y tapices. Los cuartos de baño disponen de "carta de baño", que incluye una selección de sales, aceites, velas y música, o alternativamente podrá hacer su elección de la "carta de masajes", que incluye clases de yoga y Tai Chi. Dadas sus estupendas instalaciones, porque no organiza una reunión u otro evento en este elegante entorno?

Our inspector loved: *The personalised service. The staff know what you need before you do!*

Price Guide: (breakfast €24.72)
double €274.13-348.29
suite €415.70-503.33

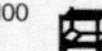

Attractions: Shopping in Palma, 2-min walk; Golf, 5km; Sandy Cove, 25km; Walking in the Mountains, 25-min drive

Nearby Towns: Valldemossa, 20km; Deià, 25km; Sóller, 30km
Airports: Palma, 25-min drive

Category: Luxury Guest House

Read's Hotel & Vespasian Spa

CARRETERA VIEJA DE ALARO S/N, SANTA MARÍA 07320, MALLORCA, BALEARIC ISLANDS, SPAIN
Tel: +34 971 14 02 61 **Fax:** +34 971 14 07 62
Web: www.johansens.com/reads **E-mail:** readshotel@readshotel.com

Our inspector loved: *The beautiful mural on the restaurant walls that continues to evolve.*

Price Guide: (excluding VAT)
double €195-340
suite €245-680

Awards: 1 Star Michelin

Attractions: Wine Bodegas, 2-min drive; Golf Course, 10-min drive; Porta Portals Marina, 25-min drive; Walking in the Mountains, 25km

Nearby Towns: Palma, 20km; Valldemossa, 25km; Sóller, 30km
Airports: Palma, 15km

Category: Hotel

At the foot of the Tramuntana Mountains just 20 minutes from Palma, surrounded by landscaped gardens and vineyard, Read's is a totally unique hotel. Enjoy the $650m^2$ Vespasian Spa with thermal circuit and VIP couple's suite, or an organised day's cycling with mapped route on one of the hotel's GIANT carbon, trekking, road or mountain bikes. Then dine in the Michelin-Starred Bacchus Restaurant or Bistro33 with its summer terraces.

Situé aux pieds des montagnes Tramuntana, à 20 minutes de Palma, entouré par des jardins paysagés et son propre vignoble, Read's est un hôtel absolument unique. Profitez des 650 m^2 du spa Vespasian avec son circuit thermal, la suite VIP pour les couples ou d'une journée cycliste organisée avec des itinéraires tracés sur l'un des incroyables vélos de route ou GIANT en carbone de l'hôtel. Puis dînez au Bacchus, restaurant étoilé Michelin, ou au Bistro33 avec sa terrasse d'été.

A solo 20 minutes de Palma, situado al pie de la sierra de Tramuntana, rodeado por un precioso jardin y con su propio viñedo, el Read's es un hotel verdaderamente único. Disfrute en el Spa "Vespasian" de 650 m^2, con circuito termal y suite VIP para parejas o apuntese a un dia de ciclismo organizado con ruta marcada en una de las bicicletas GIANT para carretera, senderismo o montaña-todo terreno. Despues puede cenar en el restaurante Bacchus, galardonado con una estrella Michelín, o en las terrazas de verano de Bistro33.

SPAIN / BALEARIC ISLANDS (MENORCA)

Biniarroca Country House Hotel

CAMI VELL 57, SANT LUIS, 07710 MENORCA, BALEARIC ISLANDS, SPAIN
Tel: +34 971 150 059 **Fax:** +34 971 151 250
Web: www.johansens.com/biniarroca **E-mail:** hotel@biniarroca.com

It's easy to see where co-owner and impressionist oil painter, Lindsay Mullen, finds her inspiration whose wonderful paintings adorn the stylish interior. Outside, pathways enveloped by lush greenery and exotic plant life lead to romantic corners, pools and the Bar Renoir. French cuisine can be served on the terrace overlooking the rose garden, modelled on Monet's garden.

Cet hôtel est une source d'inspiration pour la co-propriétaire et peintre impressionniste à l'huile, Lindsay Mullen et ses magnifiques tableaux en ornent les intérieurs élégants. A l'extérieur, des sentiers entourés de verdure luxuriante et de plantes exotiques mènent à des recoins romantiques, aux piscines et au Bar Renoir. Une cuisine française peut-être servie sur la terrasse donnant sur la roseraie, inspirée du jardin de Monet.

Es fácil ver dónde encuentra su inspiración Lindsay Mullen, co-proprietaria del inmueble y pintora impresionista cuyos óleos adornan el elegante interior. En el exterior, unos senderos arropados por exuberante vegetación y exóticas plantas le llevarán a románticos rincones, piscinas y al Bar Renoir. Podrá disfrutar de la cocina francesa en la terraza con vistas al jardín de rosales, inspirado en el jardín de Monet.

Our inspector loved: *The peace and tranquillity of this enchanting haven.*

Price Guide:
single €75-160
double €100-215
suite €240-350

18 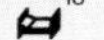    

Attractions: Walking Trails, 5-min drive; Beaches, 10-min drive; Designer Outlet Shopping, 15-min drive; Golf, 20-min drive

Nearby Towns: Mahon, 15-min drive
Airports: Menorca, 20-min drive

Category: Charming Hotel
Closed: November - April

Hotel Sant Joan de Binissaida

CAMI DE BINISSAIDA 108, ES CASTELL, 07720 MENORCA, BALEARIC ISLANDS, SPAIN
Tel: +34 971 35 55 98 **Fax:** +34 971 35 50 01
Web: www.johansens.com/binissaida **E-mail:** santjoan@binissaida.com

Our inspector loved: *The Wagner Suite with its huge terrace and views down to the sea.*

Price Guide: (excluding VAT)
single €70-125
double €130-270
suite €200-350

Attractions: Beach, 10-min drive; Golf, 20-min drive

Nearby Towns: Es Castell, 5-min drive; Sant Lluís, 5-min drive; Mahon, 10-min drive
Airports: Mahon, 20-min drive

Category: Charming Hotel
Closed: January - April and November - December

This old farmhouse has been skilfully converted into an eco-friendly hotel, with hints of its former life merged into graceful modernity. Wooden floors and beamed ceilings complement fresh, white furnishings and traditional furniture. Each bedroom is crisp, cool and comfortable with views over the countryside; some have views to the sea in the distance. The vegetables for the restaurant are all home-grown and taste deliciously fresh.

Cette ancienne ferme a été convertie avec grand soin en hôtel respectueux de l'environnement qui mêle témoignages de sa vie passée et beauté moderne. Les parquets de bois, les poutres des plafonds complètent un mobilier traditionnel et des accessoires blancs. Chaque chambre est claire, calme et confortable avec des vues sur la campagne alentour; certaines ont même des vues sur la mer au loin. Tous les légumes servis dans le restaurant sont produits localement et sont délicieusement frais.

Esta antigua alquería ha sido hábilmente transformada en un hotel ecoamigable combinando algunos de sus antiguos rasgos con una elegante modernidad. Suelos de madera y techos de vigas se complementan con el blanco de sus accesorios y mobiliario tradicional. Las habitaciones son limpias, frescas y confortables, con vistas de la campiña, y desde algunas se vislumbra el mar. Las verduras y hortalizas del restaurante son de la propia huerta y tienen un delicioso y fresco sabor.

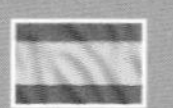

Son Granot

CTRA. DE SANT FELIP S/N, 07720 ES CASTELL, MENORCA, BALEARIC ISLANDS, SPAIN

Tel: +34 971 355 555 **Fax:** +34 971 355 771

Web: www.johansens.com/songranot **E-mail:** hotel@songranot.com

Our inspector loved: *The garden suite with a walled lawn.*

Price Guide: (room only, excluding VAT)
double €105-275
suite €190-310

Attractions: Beach, 5-min drive; Golf, 15-min drive

Nearby Towns: Es Castell, 10-min walk; Mahon, 3km
Airports: Menorca, 5km

Category: Charming Hotel
Closed: 24th -25th December

Uniquely integrated into its rural surroundings, this beautiful Georgian-style hotel, touched with romance, dates back approximately 300 years. The lovely grounds, which incorporate both farmland and gorgeous ecological Mediterranean gardens, provide the restaurant with fresh supplies for their seriously tasty Minorcan dishes. Whilst strolling around the gorgeous grounds, why not take a dip in the pool?

Intégré de manière unique dans son environnement rural, ce magnifique hôtel de style géorgien, touché par la grâce, a environ 300 ans. Le ravissant terrain, qui comprend à la fois des terres cultivées et un somptueux jardin méditerranéen écologique, fournit au restaurant des produits frais pour ses savoureux plats minorquins. Tandis que vous déambulez à travers les jardins, pourquoi ne pas plonger dans la piscine?

Integrado con suma originalidad a su entorno rural, este bello hotel de estilo georgiano de toque romántico se remonta a 300 años atrás. Esta encantadora finca, que incluye tanto terrenos de cultivo como espectaculares jardines mediterráneos ecológicos, les surten al restaurante de verduras y frutas frescas para sus suculentos platos menorquines. Mientras pasea por sus terrenos, ¿por qué no darse un chapuzón en la piscina?

Gran Hotel Atlantis Bahía Real

AVENIDA GRANDES PLAYAS S/N, 35660 CORRALEJO, FUERTEVENTURA, CANARY ISLANDS, SPAIN
Tel: +34 928 53 64 44 **Fax:** +34 928 53 75 75
Web: www.johansens.com/bahiareal **E-mail:** reservations.bahiareal@atlantishotels.com

Our inspector loved: *The funky sushi bar at the Yamatori Japanese restaurant.*

Price Guide:
upon request

Awards: Trivago Site's Best Spa in Spain 2009; Johansens Most Excellent European Hotel Award 2008; Condé Nast Traveler Best Hotel Resort in Spain 2009; IRT Certification Biosphere Hotels 2008

Attractions: Dunas Corralejo Natural Park, 200 metres; Kite Surfing, 5-min walk; Lobos Island, 15-min boat ride; Village of Betancuria, 40km

Nearby Towns: Corralejo, 1.5km; La Oliva, 16km; Puerto del Rosario, 36km
Airports: Fuerteventura, 35km

Category: Hotel

This most luxurious hotel delivers on every level. Enjoy 5-star treatment, spacious accommodation, superb food and endless facilities. Most guest rooms overlook the islands of Lobos and Lanzarote, and your choice of 5 restaurants includes haute cuisine supervised by Michelin-Starred Chef Carles Gaig. The extensive spa is renowned for its lavish treatments, and the pool area is a tropical paradise of lush greenery.

Cet hôtel est extrêmement luxueux à tous les niveaux. Profitez d'un traitement 5 étoiles, d'un hébergement spacieux, d'une délicieuse cuisine et d'équipements infinis. La plupart des chambres offrent des vues sur les îles de Lobos et Lanzarote et votre choix entre 5 restaurants comprend la grande cuisine d'un chef une étoile Michelin, Carles Gaig. L'immense spa est réputé pour ses soins impressionnants et la zone piscine est un paradis tropical de plantes luxuriantes.

Este sumamente lujoso hotel destaca a todos los niveles. Disfrute de un trato de 5 estrellas, salones y habitaciones amplias, una fabulosa carta y multitud de instalaciones. La mayoría de las habitaciones tienen vistas a las islas de Lobos y Lanzarote, y dentro del gran surtido de 5 restaurantes encontrará uno de alta cocina, a cargo del Chef Carles Gaig, poseedor de 1 estrella Michelín. El amplio spa es famoso por sus fastuosos tratamientos, y la zona de la piscina, un paraíso tropical de exuberante verdor.

SPAIN / CANARY ISLANDS (TENERIFE)

Gran Hotel Bahía del Duque Resort

AVDA. DE BRUSELAS S/N, 38660 COSTA ADEJE, TENERIFE, CANARY ISLANDS, SPAIN
Tel: +34 922 746 900 **Fax:** +34 922 746 916
Web: www.johansens.com/bahiaduque **E-mail:** comercial@bahia-duque.com

A colourful private resort situated on a hillside sloping gently down to a beach, this is an oasis of luxury. 19 houses built at the turn of the 20th century form this exclusive complex comprising Corinthian columns, bell towers and vast blue pools. In addition, there are 8 restaurants, 7 bars, 5 nearby golf courses and a stunning new outdoor ESPA managed spa and thalasso as well as 40 villas with butler service and private pools.

Cet ensemble privé, plein de couleurs, situé sur une colline plongeant délicatement sur une plage, est une oasis de luxe. 19 maisons construites au tournant du XXe siècle forment un complexe unique avec ses colonnes corinthiennes, ses clochers et ses vastes piscines bleues. A cela, s'ajoutent également, 8 restaurants, 7 bars, 5 golfs à proximité et un magnifique nouveau spa et un centre de thalasso extérieur gérés par ESPA ainsi que 40 villas avec un majordome et des piscines privées.

Este resort privado, lleno de colorido, situado sobre una colina que se desliza suavemente sobre una playa, es un oasis de lujo. 19 casas construidas a principios del siglo XX conforman este exclusivo complejo que incluye columnas corintias, campanarios y enormes piscinas azules. También cuenta con 8 restaurantes, 7 bares, 5 campos de golf en las cercanías y un impresionante spa y thalasso al aire libre bajo la dirección de ESPA, así como 40 villas con servicio de mayordomo y piscinas privadas.

Our inspector loved: *Getting completely lost in the lush, jungle-like tropical gardens.*

Price Guide:
low season €372
mid season €546
high season €650

Awards: Best Holiday Hotel in Spain, Agenttravel 2008; Tui Holly 2007 Award

Attractions: Puerto Colon Marina, 7-min walk; Siam Park, 6-min drive

Nearby Towns: La Caleta, 15-min walk; Adeje, 10-min drive; Playa de las Americas, 10-min drive
Airports: Tenerife South (Reina Sofia), 20-min drive; Tenerife North (Los Rodeos), 1-hour drive

Category: Hotel

Hotel San Roque

ESTEBAN DE PONTE 32, 38450 GARACHICO, TENERIFE, CANARY ISLANDS, SPAIN
Tel: +34 922 133 435 **Fax:** +34 922 133 406
Web: www.johansens.com/sanroque **E-mail:** info@hotelsanroque.com

Our inspector loved: *The 2-storey stainless steel grasshopper embellishing the interior courtyard.*

Price Guide: (excluding 5% VAT)
double room from €185
duplex room from €205
junior suite from €265

Attractions: Buenavista Golf Course, 10-min drive; Punta de Teno Natural Park, 15-min drive; Loro Park, 20-min drive; Teide National Park, 45-min drive

Nearby Towns: Icod de los Vinos, 5-min drive; Puerto de la Cruz, 20-min drive; La Orotava, 25-min drive; Santa Cruz Capital, 50-min drive
Airports: Tenerife North (Los Rodeos), 45-min drive; Tenerife South (Reina Sofia), 90-min drive

Category: Charming Hotel

The French owners of this luxury boutique hotel have superbly restored this 18th-century mansion, blending traditional Canarian architecture with a twist of Bauhaus-styled furniture. Polished wooden floors, soft lighting and sharp design are the order of the day, and with a staff-to-room ratio of 1:1, it's clear that personal attention is a high priority.

Les propriétaires français de cet boutique hôtel de luxe ont magnifiquement restauré cette maison seigneuriale du XVIIIe siècle en mélangeant une architecture traditionnelle canarienne avec une touche de Bauhaus stylique. Des parquets en bois cirés, une lumière tamisée et un design marqué sont à l'ordre du jour. Avec un ratio de 1/1 entre les chambres et le personnel, il est évident que l'attention personnelle est la principale priorité.

Los propietarios franceses de este hotel de lujo boutique han realizado una excelente restauración de esta mansión del siglo XVIII fusionando la arquitectura tradicional canaria con un toque de diseño en su mobiliario de la época de la Bauhaus. Sus solerías de madera pulida, su suave iluminación y su ingenioso diseño están a la orden del día, y con una proporción de 1 miembro de la plantilla por habitación, está claro que la atención personalizada se convierte en verdadera prioridad.

La Casona de Cosgaya

BARRIO AREÑOS, 39582 COSGAYA, CANTABRIA, SPAIN
Tel: +34 942 733 077 **Fax:** +34 942 733 131
Web: www.johansens.com/casonadecosgaya **E-mail:** recepcion@casonadecosgaya.com

In the heart of a tiny Cantabrian village, this charming 16th-century rural retreat is a comfortable mix of old and new with hunting trophies displayed throughout the bright, refreshing interior. Beamed bedrooms are cosy and decorated in a warm and welcoming rustic style. Game and local dishes are the speciality of the attractive restaurant.

Au cœur d'un minuscule village de Cantabrie, ce charmant refuge rural du XVIe siècle est un mélange confortable d'ancien et de moderne avec notamment des trophées de chasse présentés dans un intérieur clair et agissant comme une bouffée d'air frais. Les chambres avec leurs poutres apparentes sont chaleureuses, accueillantes et décorées dans un style rustique. Gibier et plats locaux sont les spécialités du joli restaurant.

En pleno corazón de una pequeña aldea cántabra, este encantador lugar de retiro rural del siglo XVI es una cómoda combinación de antigüedad y modernidad con trofeos de caza desplegados por todo su radiante y refrescante interior. Las habitaciones provistas de vigas son acogedoras y decoradas con placentero estilo rústico. La caza y los platos locales son la especialidad de su atractivo restaurante.

Our inspector loved: *Relaxing in the spa pool and admiring the magnificent mountains.*

Price Guide:
single €52-70
double €92-140
suite €144-195

Attractions: Salmon and Trout Fishing, 5km; Picos de Europa National Park, 10-min drive; Cross-Country Skiing, 11km

Nearby Towns: Potes, 13km; San Vicente de la Barquera Beaches, 65km; Santillana del Mar, 100km; Santander, 117km
Airports: Santander, 117km; Asturias, 185km; Bilbao, 210km

Category: Charming Hotel

Hotel Rector

C/RECTOR ESPERABÉ 10-APARTADO 399, 37008 SALAMANCA, SPAIN
Tel: +34 923 21 84 82 **Fax:** +34 923 21 40 08
Web: www.johansens.com/rector **E-mail:** info@hotelrector.com

Our inspector loved: *The fine cotton linens and bedroom amenities.*

Price Guide: (breakfast €12, parking €16 per day, excluding VAT)
double/twin €120-145
double/twin de luxe €149-190
junior suite €170-210

 13    

Attractions: Automobile Museum and Roman Bridge, 100 metres; Plaza Mayor, 10-min walk; Art Deco Museum "Casa Lis", 10-min walk; Cathedral, 10-min walk

Nearby Towns: Toledo, 1-hour drive; Valladolid 1.5-hour drive
Airports: Madrid, 2-hour drive

Category: Luxury Guest House

Offering stiff competition to the cathedral it looks up to, a magnificent golden vision when floodlit, this attractive hotel has coolly elegant interiors, with 2 stunning modern stained-glass windows in the main salon. Bedrooms are elegant and comfortable. Enjoy breakfast at the hotel, then explore Salamanca's restaurants for lunch and dinner.

Offrant une concurrence rude à la cathédrale qu'il regarde, une vision magique lorsque illuminée, ce séduisant hôtel offre des intérieurs frais et élégants avec notamment 2 magnifiques vitraux modernes dans le salon principal. Les chambres sont élégantes et confortables et vous pouvez prendre votre petit-déjeuner à l'hôtel puis explorer les restaurants de Salamanca pour le déjeuner et le dîner.

Este atractivo hotel de elegante interior ofrece una dura competencia con la catedral cercana, magnífica panorámica cuando está iluminada, y posee 2 espectaculares vidrieras modernas en el salón principal. Las habitaciones son elegantes y cómodas y puede tomar su desayuno en el hotel después explorar los restaurantes de Salamanca para el almuerzo y la cena.

B30
C16
C58
C33
Sant Cugat del Valles
B20
La Floresta
B10
C31
Parc Güell
AVIG MERIDIANA
CARRER DE PADILLA
GRAN VIA DE LES CORTS CATALANES
AVIG DIAGONAL
292
297
293
VIA AUGUSTA
Parc de Collserola
AVIG DIAGONAL
295
CARRER DE PARIS
CARRER DE BALMES
296
Museo Picasso
Parlament de Catalunya
VIA LAIETANA
Francia
291
CARRER D'ARAGO
Catedral
Estadi Nou Camp
Sants
294
Museo d'Historia
AVIG DEL PARALLEL
Palaou de Congressos
Moll de Barcelona
CARRATERA D'ESPLUGUES
C32
GRAN VIA DE LES CORTS CATALANES
Montjuic
Estadi Olimpic
PASSEIG DE LA ZONA FRANCA
Expo. Feria 2
MEDITERRANEAN SEA
B22
Aeroport de Barcelona

Casanova by Rafael Hotels

GRAN VIA DE LES CORTS CATALANES 559, 08011 BARCELONA, SPAIN
Tel: +34 933 964 800 **Fax:** +34 933 964 810
Web: www.johansens.com/casanova **E-mail:** casanova@rafaelhoteles.com

Our inspector loved: *Having a massage on the spa's relaxing patio surrounded by pretty plants and greenery.*

Price Guide: (buffet breakfast €18.20)
standard €107-379.85
de luxe/superior €133.75-428
junior suite €224.70-497.55

 124     200   

Attractions: Shopping, 5-min walk; Museums, 15-min walk; Beach, 20-min walk

Nearby Towns: Sitges, 40-min drive; Gerona, 90-min drive
Airports: Barcelona, 20-min drive; Gerona, 75-min drive

Category: Hotel

Beyond the original 18th-century limestone façade, a refreshingly modern hotel inspired by Barcelona's arts scene and Gaudí architecture awaits you. Enter through the open-plan lobby where at night guests and locals meet and chat, and at weekends DJs play music. Dine in the exciting Mexiterranée restaurant and visit The Stone Spa to experience aura healing treatments.

Derrière la façade en pierre à chaux du XVIIIe siècle, un hôtel d'une modernité rafraîchissante, inspiré par les scènes artistiques barcelonaises et par l'architecture de Gaudí, vous attend. Entrez dans le lobby paysager où se retrouvent le soir les clients et les habitants locaux et où un DJ officie le week-end. Dînez à l'excitant Mexiterranée et profitez du Stone Spa pour expérimentez les traitements de l'aura.

Más allá de su fachada de caliza del siglo XVIII le espera un hotel refrescante y moderno inspirado en las escenas artísticas de Barcelona y en la arquitectura de Gaudí. Entre en él a través de su sala de recepción de planta abierta donde por la noche se reúnen y charlan los clientes y los barceloneses y donde los fines de semana ponen música los DJs. Cene en su vivaz restaurante Mexiterranée y visite el Spa de Piedra para experimentar sus tratamientos del aura.

HOTEL CASA FUSTER

PASSEIG DE GRÀCIA 132, 08008 BARCELONA, SPAIN
Tel: +34 93 255 30 00 **Fax:** +34 93 255 30 02
Web: www.johansens.com/fuster **E-mail:** hotelcasafuster@hotelescenter.com

Bursting out of its impressive central location, this early 20th-century hotel evokes the 1930s with art deco furniture and rooms and suites in chocolate and blue shades. Dine in the similarly modernist restaurant, Galaxó, and afterwards, sink into huge, red sofas and plush velvet cushions in The Café Vienés with a soothing night cap or head to the roof terrace to admire the impressive views of Paseig de Gràcia and the city.

Bénéficiant d'une situation exceptionnelle en centre ville, cet hôtel du début du XXe siècle rappelle les années 30 avec ses meubles art déco ainsi que ses chambres et suites aux teintes chocolat et bleu. Dînez dans le restaurant, Galaxó, décoré dans un style moderniste semblable et, ensuite, détendez-vous au Café Vienés, dans d'immenses canapés rouges et leurs moelleux coussins de velours, pour un dernier verre, avant d'aller vous coucher où de vous rendre sur le toit terrasse pour admirer les magnifiques vues sur le Passéo de Gràcia et sur la ville.

Pletórico por su impresionante situación céntrica, este hotel de principios del siglo XX evoca la década de los 30 gracias a su mobiliario art déco y a sus habitaciones y suites decoradas en un color chocolate y tonos azulados. Cene el restaurante modernista Galaxó, para después hundirse en los amplios sofás rojos y cojines de terciopelo del Café Vienés con una bebida antes de acostarse, o termine el día admirando las vistas del Paseig de Gràcia y de la ciudad desde la terraza en la azotea.

Our inspector loved: *The live jazz in The Café Vienes.*

Price Guide: (room only, excluding VAT)
single €495
double €495-595
suite €1,700-4,000

 105   200   

Attractions: Shopping, 1-min walk; Bars and Restaurants, 5-min walk; Monuments, 5-min walk; Beaches, 5km

Nearby Towns: Sitges, 40km; Gerona, 90km; Tarragona, 100km
Airports: Barcelona, 15km; Gerona, 80km

Category: Hotel

Hotel Claris

PAU CLARIS 150, 08009 BARCELONA, SPAIN
Tel: +34 93 487 62 62 **Fax:** +34 93 215 79 70
Web: www.johansens.com/claris **E-mail:** claris@derbyhotels.com

Our inspector loved: *The "Kimono" duplex suite with its wonderful antique furniture.*

Price Guide: (breakfast €21, excluding VAT)
single €425
double €475
suite €560-1,210

Awards: Condé Nast Johansens Most Excellent European Marketing Partner 2008

Attractions: Shopping, on the doorstep; Gaudí Route, 5-min walk; Las Ramblas, 15-min walk; Montserrat, 40km

Nearby Towns: Tarragona, 90km; Gerona, 95km; Lleida, 150km; Valencia, 350km
Airports: Barcelona, 20km; Gerona, 90km; Reus, 105km

Category: Hotel

An exciting cocktail of tradition and avant-garde design, this former palace boasts spectacular fully-equipped rooms and suites, adorned with an outstanding collection of millennia-old Egyptian art. The creative feel continues in the Andy Warhol Pop-Art decorated "East 47" serving contemporary Mediterranean cuisine and the poolside rooftop restaurant, "La Terraza del Claris," with its amazing city views.

Extraordinaire cocktail de design traditionnel et avant-gardiste, cet ancien palais peut se vanter de ses spectaculaires chambres entièrement équipées et de ses suites ornées d'une exceptionnelle collection d'art d'egypte ancienne. L'impression de créativité se prolonge au « East 47 » au style Pop Art, décoré par des œuvres d'Andy Warhol, qui sert une cuisine méditerranéenne, ainsi qu'à La Terraza del Claris installé sur le toit au bord de la piscine, avec ses vues magnifiques sur la ville.

Este antiguo palacio, todo un apasionante cóctel de tradición y de diseño vanguardista, dispone de impresionantes habitaciones y suites completamente equipadas y adornadas con una extraordinaria colección de piezas del milenario arte egipcio. El ambiente de creatividad se extiende al "East 47", en el que se exhibe una decoración de arte pop de Andy Warhol a la vez que se sirven platos de la cocina mediterránea contemporánea. El restaurante "La Terraza del Claris", situado en la azotea del hotel junto a la piscina ofrece unas vistas impresionantes de la ciudad.

Hotel Duquesa de Cardona

PASEO COLON 12, 08002 BARCELONA, SPAIN
Tel: +34 93 268 90 90 **Fax:** +34 93 268 29 31
Web: www.johansens.com/duquesadecardona **E-mail:** info@hduquesadecardona.com

Join a noble line of visitors to this restored 19th-century palace, once a refuge to royalty. Stylish and discreetly furnished, there are original and modern features, including an "Ask Me" information desk in the lobby. You're ideally situated here in the cultural Gothic Quarter, and the rooftop pool has spectacular views of Barcelona's harbour.

Rejoignez une lignée de nobles visiteurs dans ce palais restauré du XIXe siècle, autrefois refuge de familles royales. Meublé avec style et discrétion, l'hôtel possède également des équipements modernes dont un bureau de renseignement "Ask Me" dans le hall. Vous êtes idéalement situé dans le Quartier Gothique et pouvez ainsi profiter des vues exceptionnelles qu' offre la piscine du toit sur le port de Barcelone.

Únase a la noble lista de visitantes de este restaurado palacio del siglo XIX, antaño refugio de la realeza. Elegante y de discreta decoración, cuenta con características originales y modernas, que incluyen un mostrador de información "Ask Me" en el vestíbulo. Se encuentra Vd. en el emplazamiento ideal del cultural Barrio Gótico, y la piscina en su azotea dispone de espectaculares vistas al puerto de Barcelona.

Our inspector loved: *The view of the port from the roof terrace.*

Price Guide: (breakfast €15, excluding VAT)
double classic €265
double de luxe €305
junior suite €495

40   32  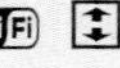 

Attractions: Gothic Quarter, 5-min walk; Museums, 5-min walk; Montserrat Monastery, 40km

Nearby Towns: Vic, 50km; Gerona, 90km; Tarragona, 100km
Airports: Barcelona, 15km; Gerona, 80km

Category: Charming Hotel

SPAIN / CATALUÑA (BARCELONA) 

Hotel Gran Derby

CALLE LORETO 28, 08029 BARCELONA, SPAIN
Tel: +34 93 445 2544 **Fax:** +34 93 419 6820
Web: www.johansens.com/granderby **E-mail:** granderby@derbyhotels.com

Our inspector loved: *Room 541 with its sunny window seat and contemporary furniture.*

Price Guide: (breakfast €16, excluding VAT)
single €250
double €270
suite €305-345

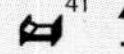     

Awards: Condé Nast Johansens Most Excellent European Marketing Partner 2008

Attractions: Sightseeing Tours, on the doorstep; Shopping, 5-min walk; Barcelona Football Club Stadium (Camp Nou), 5-min drive; Montserrat, 40km

Nearby Towns: Tarragona, 90km; Gerona, 95km; Lleida, 150km; Valencia, 350km
Airports: Barcelona, 20km; Gerona, 90km; Reus, 105km

Category: Hotel

Upon entering the newly designed lobby, filled with funky furniture and sculptures, the scene is set for this highly elegant, tasteful boutique hotel. Located in the city's most exclusive shopping area, all rooms are extremely comfortable, perfect for a relaxing break or hosting small business meetings and social gatherings. Take a dip in the pool on the terrace where a convenient bar service is at your disposal.

En entrant dans le lobby entièrement redécoré, rempli de sculptures et de meubles funky, le ton est donné pour ce boutique hôtel particulièrement élégant. Situé dans l'un des quartiers les plus chics au niveau shopping de Barcelone, toutes les chambres sont extrêmement confortables, parfaites pour un week-end de détente ou pour accueillir de petites réunions professionnelles ou amicales. Plongez dans la piscine située sur la terrasse où un service bar est à votre disposition.

Apenas entrar en el lobby de nuevo diseño, con sus esculturas y muebles "funky", la escena se fija para el resto de este elegantísimo hotel boutique. Situado en la zona comercial más exclusiva de Barcelona, todas sus habitaciones son sumamente confortables e ideales para un fin de semana de descanso o para organizar pequeñas reuniones de negocios y otros eventos sociales. Refrésquese en la piscina de la terraza donde existe un servicio de bar a su disposición.

SPAIN / CATALUÑA (BARCELONA)

Hotel Granados 83

C/ ENRIC GRANADOS 83, 08008 BARCELONA, SPAIN
Tel: +34 93 492 96 70 **Fax:** +34 93 492 96 90
Web: www.johansens.com/granados83 **E-mail:** granados83@derbyhotels.com

Full of surprises, this hotel's classic façade hides contemporary, avant-garde interiors. Go Zen in the central courtyard with spectacular glass roof, and choose between accommodation in a New York style loft, suites, or split-level and 3-level rooms with private pools and terraces. The restaurant, "3", provides creative Mediterranean cuisine whilst rooftop bar "8" and minimalist "GBar" serve exciting cocktails.

Cet hôtel, dont la façade classique cache un intérieur avant-garde, est plein de surprises. Soyez Zen dans la cour centrale à l'impressionnant toit de verre et choisissez entre vous installer dans les suites au style loft new yorkais ou les chambres aménagées sur 2 ou 3 étages avec piscine et terrasse privée. Le restaurant "3" sert une cuisine méditerranéenne créative tandis que le "8" sur le toit ou le minimaliste "GBar" passionnant servent des cocktails.

Hotel lleno de sorpresas donde su clásica fachada esconde interiores contemporáneos y vanguardistas. Descubra su lado Zen en el patio central con su espectacular techo de cristal y elija entre un loft estilo Nueva York, suites o dúplex y habitaciones a 3 niveles con piscinas privadas y terraza. El restaurante "3" sirve cocina creativa mediterránea mientras que el bar de la terraza "8" y el minimalista "GBar" sirven cócteles impresionantes.

Our inspector loved: *The cool duplex rooms with direct access to the pool.*

Price Guide: (breakfast €17, excluding VAT)
single €255-385
double €430
suite €560

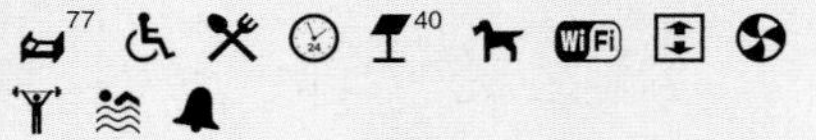

Awards: Condé Nast Johansens Most Excellent European Marketing Partner 2008

Attractions: Shopping, on the doorstep; Gaudí Route, 5-min walk; Las Ramblas, 15-min walk; Montserrat, 40km

Nearby Towns: Tarragona, 90km; Gerona, 95km; Lleida, 150km; Valencia, 350km
Airports: Barcelona, 20km; Gerona, 90km; Reus, 105km

Category: Hotel

Hotel Omm

ROSSELLÓ 265, 08008 BARCELONA, SPAIN
Tel: +34 93 445 40 00 **Fax:** +34 93 445 40 04
Web: www.johansens.com/hotelomm **E-mail:** reservas@hotelomm.es

Our inspector loved: *The lobby bar that is cosy in winter and cool and relaxing in summer.*

Price Guide: (room only, excluding VAT)
double €260-465
superior €360-565
suite €660-865

Awards: Best Foodie Hotel, Tatler Travel Guide 2008; Best European Sommelier of 2008, Roger Viusà of Restaurant Moo; 1 Star Michelin

Attractions: Shopping, on the doorstep; Bars and Restaurants, on the doorstep; Monuments, on the doorstep; Beaches, 3km

Nearby Towns: Sitges, 40km; Gerona, 90km; Tarragona, 100km
Airports: Barcelona, 15km; Gerona, 80km

Category: Hotel

If you like your hotels modern and stylish, Hotel Omm lies discreetly amidst Barcelona's busy streets. The vast bedrooms, minimally and elegantly decorated, place special emphasis on soft mood lighting. Restaurant Moo is run by the well-known Roca brothers and you'll be pleased to find each course comes with a recommended glass of wine.

Si vous aimez les hôtels modernes et avec du style, l'Hôtel Omm se cache au milieu des rues animées de Barcelone. Dans les chambres spacieuses, minimalistes et élégamment décorées l'accent est mis sur un éclairage d'ambiance doux. Le Restaurant Moo est supervisé par les frères Roca et chaque plat est accompagné d'un verre de vin spécifiquement recommandé.

Si le gustan los hoteles modernos y elegantes, el Hotel Omm se sitúa con discreción entre las bulliciosas calles de Barcelona. Sus amplísimas habitaciones, elegantes y sobriamente decoradas, se enorgullecen de su suave iluminación regulable. El Restaurante Moo es gestionado por los conocidos hermanos Roca. Le encantará descubrir que cada plato se sirve con una copa del vino recomendado.

SPAIN / CATALUÑA (COSTA BRAVA)

Hotel Rigat Park & Spa Beach Hotel

AV. AMERICA 1, PLAYA DE FENALS, 17310 LLORET DE MAR, COSTA BRAVA, GERONA, SPAIN
Tel: +34 972 36 52 00 **Fax:** +34 972 37 04 11
Web: www.johansens.com/rigat **E-mail:** info@rigat.com

Pine trees exude their distinctive scent across Rigat Park, the ideal base for exploring Costa Brava's beaches and the nearby Catalan towns. Once you've tired of sightseeing, relax on the beach, swim in the pool, or take time out in the spa. 21 Mediterranean-style suites have tiled floors and marble bathrooms.

Les pins dégagent leur senteur particulière à Rigat Park, base idéale pour explorer les plages de la Costa Brava ainsi que les villes catalanes voisines. Après vos visites, vous pourrez vous relaxer sur la plage, nager dans la piscine ou profiter du spa. Les 21 suites de style Méditerranéen ont un sol carrelé et des salles de bain en marbre.

Los pinares exhalan su distintivo aroma por todo el Rigat Park, enclave ideal para explorar las playas de la Costa Brava y las cercanas localidades catalanas. Cuando se canse de hacer turismo, podrá relajarse en la playa, darse un baño en la piscina o hacer uso de su spa. Sus 21 suites de estilo mediterráneo disponen de suelos de baldosas y cuartos de baño de mármol.

Our inspector loved: *The subtle colours of the newly decorated bedrooms.*

Price Guide: (room only, excluding VAT)
double €192-340
suite €320-1,950

SPA

Attractions: Santa Clotilde Gardens, 2km; Catamaran Trips, 3km; Golf PGA, 20km

Nearby Towns: Gerona, 20km; Barcelona, 60km
Airports: Gerona, 29km; Barcelona, 75km

Category: Hotel
Closed: 26th October - March

SPAIN / CATALUÑA (COSTA BRAVA) 

Hotel Santa Marta

PLAYA DE SANTA CRISTINA, 17310 LLORET DE MAR, SPAIN
Tel: +34 972 364 904 **Fax:** +34 972 369 280
Web: www.johansens.com/santamarta **E-mail:** info@hotelsantamarta.net

Our inspector loved: *The pathways from the hotel to the beach, and surrounding peaceful pine woods.*

Price Guide: (room only)
single €125-205
double €179-294
family room €283-470

Attractions: Water Sports, 5-min walk; Golf, 3km; Santa Clotilde Gardens, 3km

Nearby Towns: Tossa del Mar, 7km; Gerona, 30km; Barcelona, 80km; Cadaques, 100km
Airports: Gerona, 25km; Barcelona, 90km

Category: Hotel
Closed: 20th December - 7th February

Bathe in the Mediterranean's warm, translucent waters from the spectacular sandy beach, or if you're feeling energetic, seek out the hotel's extensive sport and leisure facilities. Alternatively, visit the new spa comprising 8 massage cabins, a pool and hairdressers. Furnishings and décor are classic, and guest rooms have shady balconies to show off the views. First-class cuisine is served in a traditional-style restaurant.

Baignez-vous dans les eaux tièdes et transparentes de la Méditerranée depuis la superbe plage de sable ou si vous avez de l'énergie, profitez des nombreux équipements de sports et de loisirs de l'hôtel. Sinon, visitez le nouveau spa avec ses 8 cabines de soins, une piscine et un salon de coiffure. Ameublements et décoration sont classiques et les chambres ont des balcons ombragés pour admirer les vues. Une cuisine de premier ordre est servie dans le restaurant de style traditionnel.

Suméjase en las templadas y transparentes aguas del Mediterráneo desde la espectacular playa arenosa o, en cambio, si se siente lleno de energía, haga uso de las amplias instalaciones deportivas y de ocio que ofrece el hotel. También puede visitar el nuevo Spa, con sus 8 cabinas para masajes, piscina y peluquería. El mobiliario y la decoración son clásicas y las habitaciones disponen de balcones sombreados para disfrutar de las vistas. En el restaurante de estilo tradicional se sirve cocina de primera.

Hospes Villa Paulita

AV. PONS I GASH, 15, 17520 PUIGCERDÀ (GERONA), SPAIN
Tel: +34 972 884 662 **Fax:** +34 972 884 632
Web: www.johansens.com/hospesvillapaulita **E-mail:** hospes.villapaulita@hospes.es

Our inspector loved: *The tranquil, lakeside views.*

Price Guide: (room only, excluding VAT)
double €105-225
junior suite €280-520
suite €479-885

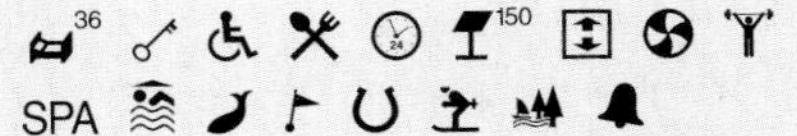

Attractions: Walking/Hiking, 2km; Skiing, 10km

Nearby Towns: Andorra la Vella, Andorra, 40km; Gerona, 90km; Barcelona, 120km
Airports: Gerona, 90km; Barcelona, 120km; Toulouse, France, 120km

Category: Hotel

Built on the shore of a lake and surrounded by forested land, this private villa, with its vivid red façade and elegantly decorated rooms, is a tranquil hideaway. Stroll through the charming gardens before treating yourself to a meal in L'Estany gourmet restaurant, that will reveal the delectable flavours of the Cerdanya region. The Bodyna Spa is an exclusive retreat and a personal trainer is available at the gym.

Construite sur les rives d'un lac et entourée de forêts, cette villa privée, avec sa façade rouge vive et ses chambres élégamment décorées, est une retraite tranquille. Promenez-vous dans les ravissants jardins avant de vous régaler d'un repas au restaurant gastronomique L'Estany qui vous fera découvrir les délicieux arômes de la région de Cerdanya. Le spa Bodyna est un refuge exclusif et un coach particulier est à votre disposition dans la salle de gym.

Construido a la orilla de un lago y rodeado de bosques, esta villa privada con su fachada en rojo vivo y habitaciones elegantemente decoradas es un rincón tranquilo. Pasee por los encantadores jardines antes de disfrutar de una comida en el restaurante gourmet L'Estany, donde descubrirá los deliciosos sabores de la Cerdanya. Se recomienda el spa Bodyna, un refugio exclusivo, y si desea un entrenador personal lo encontrara en el gimnasio.

SPAIN / CATALUÑA (ROSES) 

Romantic Villa - Hotel Vistabella

CALA CANYELLES PETITES, PO BOX 3, 17480 ROSES (GERONA), SPAIN
Tel: +34 972 25 62 00 **Fax:** +34 972 25 32 13
Web: www.johansens.com/vistabella **E-mail:** info@vistabellahotel.com

Our inspector loved: *The cliff-top location.*

Price Guide: (excluding VAT)
double €130-310
suite €295-990

Attractions: Walking Paths and Water Sports, on the doorstep; Golf, 20km; Dalí Museum, Figueres, 20km; Roman Ruins, Empuries, 20km

Nearby Towns: Cadaqués, 5km; Figueres, 20km; Gerona, 70km; Barcelona, 160km
Airports: Gerona, 75km; Perpignan, France, 75km; Barcelona, 170km

Category: Hotel
Closed: October - April

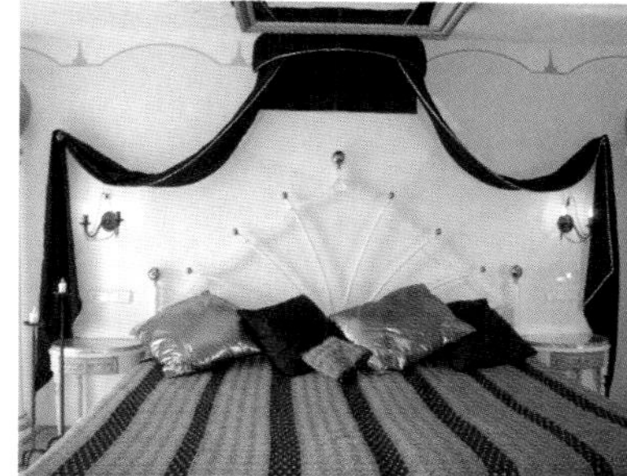

Vistabella enjoys culturally rich surroundings, between the natural parks of Aiguamolls of l'Empordà and the Cap of Creus. Bedrooms and suites are individually decorated and most have sea views. The wellness centre is ideal for relaxing treatments. Exercise your tastebuds in no less than 4 restaurants, including the acclaimed Els Brancs.

Le Vistabella est situé entre les parcs naturels du Cap de Creus et des Aiguamolls de l'Empordà, dans un environnement culturellement riche. Les chambres et suites ont, pour la plupart, une vue sur la mer et sont décorées individuellement. Le centre wellness est l'endroit idéal pour des soins relaxants. Exercez votre palais dans les 4 différents restaurants, dont le renommé Els Brancs.

El Vistabella está situado en una rica zona cultural entre los parques naturales de Cap de Creus y Els Aiguamolls de l'Empordà. Cada habitacion y suite está decorada de estilo individual y la mayoria tiene vistas al mar. El centro wellness resulta un lugar ideal para sus tratamientos relajantes. Puede ejercitar sus papilas gustativas en cualquiera de sus 4 restaurantes, entre los que se encuentra el reputado Els Brancs.

Dolce Sitges Hotel

AV. CAMI DE MIRALPEIX 12, SITGES 08870, SPAIN
Tel: +34 938 109 000 **Fax:** +34 938 109 001
Web: www.johansens.com/dolcesitges **E-mail:** info_sitges@dolce.com

Our inspector loved: *The spacious rooms, and the views over Sitges and the sea.*

Price Guide: (excluding VAT)
room €175-500
presidential suite €1,100

Attractions: Beach, 2km; Garraf Natural Park, 5km; Wine Routes, 20km

Nearby Towns: Barcelona, 25km; Tarragona, 50km
Airports: Barcelona, 25km

Category: Hotel

An injection of colour has been introduced to this modern hotel with fine dining, extensive spa facilities and a relaxing, revamped pool area. On a hilltop overlooking the Mediterranean and city of Sitges, its elegant bedrooms have terraces with sea, garden or pool views. Choose to have dinner in the intimate Restaurant Esmarris or go exclusive with private dining in Racó de la Calma. The hotel is also ideal for meetings and special events.

Un flot de couleurs a été injecté dans cet hôtel moderne, avec une excellente restauration, un vaste spa et une piscine totalement repensée et idéale pour la relaxation. Sur une colline surplombant la Méditerranée et la ville de Sitges, les chambres élégantes disposent de terrasses donnant sur la mer, le jardin ou sur la piscine. Vous pouvez dîner dans l'intime Restaurant Esmarris ou en privé à l'exclusif Racó de la Calma. L'hôtel est également idéal pour des réunions et événements.

Un nuevo toque de color ha sido introducido a la decoración de este moderno hotel con excelente cocina, amplias instalaciones de spa y relajante zona de piscina recientemente renovada. Situado sobre una colina que mira al Mediterráneo y a la ciudad de Sitges, sus elegantes habitaciones tienen terrazas con vistas al mar, al jardín o a la piscina. Podrá cenar en el íntimo Restaurant Esmarris o en privado en el exclusivo Racó de la Calma. El hotel también es ideal para celebrar reuniones y otros eventos.

San Sebastian Playa Hotel

CALLE PORT ALEGRE 53, 08870 SITGES (BARCELONA), SPAIN
Tel: +34 93 894 86 76 **Fax:** +34 93 894 04 30
Web: www.johansens.com/sebastian **E-mail:** hotelsansebastian@hotelsansebastian.com

Our inspector loved: *The view over Sitges beach.*

Price Guide:
single €118-214
double €129-305
suite €205-350

Attractions: Beaches, 1-min walk; Shopping, 2-min walk; Bars and Night-life, 5-min walk; Wine Routes, 15km

Nearby Towns: Barcelona, 30km; Tarragona, 45km
Airports: Barcelona, 15km

Category: Hotel

With glistening white balconies overlooking the bay of cosmopolitan Sitges, the hotel offers friendly Spanish hospitality. You must try El Posit, set directly on the sea front, which specialises in fresh local seafood. And with no less than 17 beaches and abundant restaurants and museums nearby, you'll find something to please everyone.

Avec ses balcons d'un blanc resplendissant surplombants la baie de la ville cosmopolite de Sitges, cet hôtel offre une accueillante hospitalité espagnole. Vous devez essayer El Posit, situé directement sur la mer, et spécialisé en produits locaux et frais de la mer. Avec pas moins de 17 plages, de nombreux restaurants et musées à proximité, il y en a pour tous les goûts.

Con sus balcones de blanco resplandeciente con vistas a la bahía de la cosmopolita Sitges, este hotel le ofrece la afabilidad de la hospitalidad española. No deje de probar El Posit, en plena línea de mar, especializado en marisco fresco del lugar. Con no menos de 17 playas y numerosos restaurantes y museos en los alrededores, hay siempre algo de interés para todos.

CASA PALACIO CONDE DE LA CORTE

PLAZA PILAR REDONDO 2, 06300 ZAFRA (BADAJOZ), SPAIN
Tel: +34 924 563 311 **Fax:** +34 924 563 072
Web: www.johansens.com/condedelacorte **E-mail:** reservas@condedelacorte.com

Our inspector loved: *The classic elegance of the house and gardens.*

Price Guide:
single €85
double €105-130
suite €160

Step inside this small palace from one of Zafra's picturesque town squares and be swept up by its inviting private mansion atmosphere. Think opulence and comfort, as the hotel is awash with paintings, period furnishings, wall friezes and hand-painted trinkets. The cosy living room and terraced garden with pool are perfect places to relax.

Pénétrez dans ce petit palais de una pintoresca plaza de Zafra et laissez-vous envahir par l'atmosphère d'une demeure privée. Pensez opulence et confort en admirant les nombreux tableaux, meubles d'époque, frises murales et babioles artisanales. Le salon confortable et la terrasse avec piscine sont parfaits pour se relaxer.

Entre en este palacete de la pintoresca plaza de la ciudad de Zafra y quedará impresionado por el acogedor ambiente propio de mansión privada. Opulencia y confort sirven para definirlo, dado que el hotel está rebosante de lienzos, muebles de época, frisos y objetos decorativos pintados a mano. La placentera sala de estar y su jardín en terraza con piscina son lugares perfectos para el descanso.

Awards: Condé Nast Johansens Most Excellent European Value for Money Hotel 2008

Attractions: Conde Corte Bull Breeding Hacienda, 20km; Jamon Iberico Tasting, 60km; Shopping, 60km; Monfrague Nature Reserve, 130km

Nearby Towns: Merida, 100km; Caceres, 100km; Sevilla, 130km; Córdoba, 150km
Airports: Sevilla, 130km; Lisbon, 250km

Category: Charming Hotel

NOVAVILA

SANTO TOMÉ DE NOGUEIRA, 36637 MEIS, PONTEVEDRA, SPAIN
Tel: +34 986 716954 **Fax:** +34 986 712499
Web: www.johansens.com/novavilariasbaixas **E-mail:** info@novavilariasbaixas.com

Our inspector loved: *The dovecote's contemporary bedroom and the home-produced Albariño wine!*

Price Guide:
double €150-200

Attractions: Wine Tasting, on-site; Golf, 10km; Beaches, 20km; Santiago Cathedral, 50km

Nearby Towns: Pontevedra, 10-min drive; Sanxenxo, 15-min drive; Vigo, 35-min drive; Santiago, 45-min drive
Airports: Vigo, 35-min drive; Santiago, 45-min drive; Oporto, 90-min drive

Category: Luxury Guest House

Seek solace at the peaceful and private Novavila, a rural, small country house surrounded by pretty gardens. The owner's passion for his authentic yet modernly furnished Spanish home and Galician and Spanish wine, is positively contagious! Rooms come in all shapes and sizes filled with designer furniture and objets d'art that are all for sale!

Trouvez refuge dans cette petite maison de campagne, calme et intime, entourée de ravissants jardins. La passion du propriétaire pour cette authentique maison espagnol, meublée de manière moderne, et pour les vins espagnols et galiciens, est tout simplement contagieuse! Les chambres sont toutes de formes et de tailles différentes avec des meubles design et des objets d'arts qui sont disponibles à la vente!

Encontrará el sosiego en la tranquila y recogida Novavila, una pequeña casa solariega rural rodeada de bellos jardines. La pasión de su propietario por su casa española, de genuino mas moderno mobiliario, así como por los vinos españoles y gallegos, resulta verdaderamente contagiosa. Las habitaciones se presentan en todo tipo de tamaños y formas, provistas de muebles de diseño y objetos de arte, todos a la venta.

SPAIN / GALICIA (SANXENXO - PONTEVEDRA)

AUGUSTA SPA RESORT

LUGAR DE PADRIÑÁN NO. 25, 36960 SANXENXO, GALICIA, SPAIN
Tel: +34 986 72 78 78 **Fax:** +34 986 72 70 60
Web: www.johansens.com/augustasparesort **E-mail:** reservas@augustasparesort.com

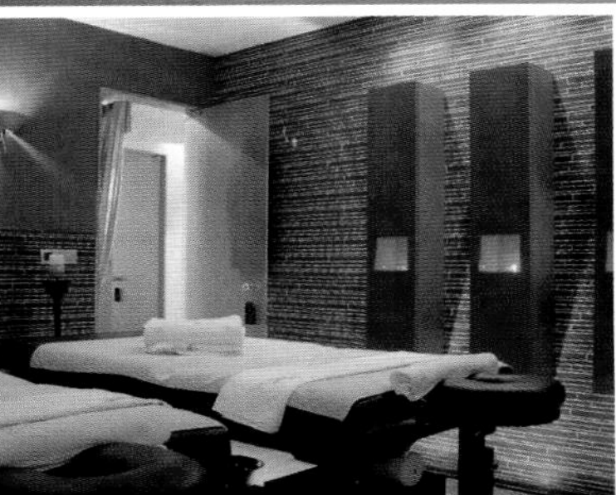

If you're seeking extensive spa treatments, tranquil gardens, a chill-out bar, relaxation area, eco-friendly kitchen garden, 3 restaurants and numerous activities, then this resort is for you! Close to the town centre and Silgar beach, each hotel, one classic, the other modern, has every comfort and convenience for its particular clientele. A complimentary Smart car is at guests' disposal to use between the hotels.

Si vous êtes à la recherche d'un séjour proposant de nombreux soins au spa, des jardins tranquilles, un bar accueillant, un coin détente, un potager respectueux de l'environnement, 3 restaurants et de nombreuses activités, alors ce complexe hôtelier est pour vous! Proche du centre de ville et de la plage de Silgar, chacun des hôtels, l'un classique et l'autre moderne, offre tout le confort à sa clientèle. Une voiture Smart est à la disposition gratuite des clients pour circuler entre les hôtels.

Si busca un lugar con una extensa carta de tratamientos spa, pacíficos jardines, zona relax-chillout, un huerto ecológico, 3 restaurantes, y numerosas actividades, entonces este resort es para usted. Cerca del centro de la ciudad y de la playa de Silgar, cada uno de sus hoteles, uno clásico y el otro moderno, proporciona todo confort para su particular clientela. Un coche Smart esta a disposición gratuita de los clientes para que puedan trasladarse de un hotel al otro.

Our inspector loved: *The attention to detail.*

Price Guide: (room only, excluding 7% VAT)
single/double €78.50-175
family suite for 6 people €120-298

Awards: Q - for Quality Spanish Tourist Board Award 2003-2009

Attractions: Traditional Galician Gastronomy, 5-min walk; Hotel's Boat for Excursions, 5-min drive; Golf, 10-min drive; Wine Cellars, 10-min drive

Nearby Towns: La Toja, 10-min drive; Pontevedra, 20-min drive; Vigo, 30-min drive; Santiago de Compostela, 50-min drive
Airports: Vigo, 40km; Santiago de Compostela, 60km

Category: Hotel

El Cervellón
Aeropuerto de Madrid - Barajas
Coslada
La Partija Santa Mónica
La Moraleja
El Encinar de los Reyes
Parque Juan Carlos I
Museo de la Ciudad
Estadio Santiago Bernabeu
Charmartín
Parque del Retiro
Museo del Prado
Atocha
Palacio de Justicia
Plaza Mayor
Ciudad Universitaria
Norte
Imperial
Parque de Entrevías
Perales del Rio
Palacio de Cristal
Casa de Campo
Parque de la Cuña Verde
Leganés
Arroyo de Meaques
Fortuna
Monte del Pardo
Pozuelo de Alarcón
Monte del Pilar
Monteclaro
Monte Alina
Prado Largo
Ventorro del Caño
Venta la Rubia
Alcorcón
Móstoles
Majadahonda
Bonanza
Las Lomas
Boadilla del Monte
Las Rozas de Madrid
M12
M14
M21
M40
M11
M30
N-11
E-90
A-3
A6
A-5
E-5
Paseo de la Castellana
308
309
310
311
312
313
314
315

SPAIN / MADRID (MADRID)

AC Hotel Santo Mauro

C/ZURBANO 36, 28010 MADRID, SPAIN
Tel: +34 91 319 69 00 **Fax:** +34 91 308 54 77
Web: www.johansens.com/santomauro **E-mail:** santo-mauro@ac-hotels.com

The Duke of Santo Mauro's former residence, this centrally located palace will surpass your grandest expectations. Comprising 3 areas: the Duke's palace, his daughter's palace and the converted stables, you will want for nothing. The superb 21st-century design respects the past while embracing modern style and the needs of the discerning traveller.

Ancienne résidence du Duc de Santo Mauro, ce palais du centre ville surpassera vos plus grandes attentes. Il est composé de 3 parties: le palais du Duc, le palais de sa fille et les écuries aménagées, où rien va vous manquer. Le superbe design du XXIe siècle respecte le passé tout en intégrant un style moderne et les besoins des voyageurs exigeants.

Antigua residencia del Duque de Santo Mauro, este palacio de céntrica ubicación superará sus mayores expectativas. Comprende 3 zonas: el palacio del Duque, el palacio de su hija y los establos reconvertidos y no le faltará nada más. Su extraordinario diseño propio del siglo XXI respeta su pasado a la vez que se abraza al estilo moderno y a las necesidades del viajero exigente.

Our inspector loved: *The quiet, city centre location with peaceful gardens offering a haven of tranquillity and privacy.*

Price Guide: (room only)
single €280
double €338-365
suite €464-985

Attractions: Chic Shopping in Calle Serrano, 10-min walk; Archaelogical Museum, 10-min walk; El Prado Museum, 20-min walk; Plaza Mayor, 10-min drive

Nearby Towns: El Escorial, 45-min drive; Segovia, 1-hour drive; Toledo, 1-hour drive; Avila, 75-min drive
Airports: Madrid, 20-min drive

Category: Hotel

Gran Meliá Fénix

HERMOSILLA 2, 28001 MADRID, SPAIN
Tel: +34 91 431 67 00 **Fax:** +34 91 576 06 61
Web: www.johansens.com/granmeliafenix **E-mail:** gran.melia.fenix@solmelia.com

Our inspector loved: *The "royal service" offered to guests in the suites and VIP top-floor rooms.*

Price Guide: (breakfast €29, per person)
deluxe €195-395
premium €230-430
executive suite €560-3,000

Attractions: National Archaeological Museum, 1-min walk; National Museum Library, 1-min walk; Chic Shopping in the Calle Serrano, 3-min walk; Prado and Thyssen Galleries, 15-min walk

Nearby Towns: El Escorial, 45km; Segovia, 85km; Toledo, 85km; Avila, 95km
Airports: Madrid - Barajas, 20-min drive

Category: Hotel

With one of the best locations in the city, everything about this hotel cries luxury, and the grand exterior reveals opulent public and guest rooms with every modern facility. The service is exceptional and The Presidential Suite is eye-wateringly impressive, boasting some of the best views in Madrid. A visit to Epoque by Gran Meliá restaurant, serving delicious Mediterranean gastronomic cuisine, is not to be missed!

Avec l'un des meilleurs emplacement de la ville, tout dans cet hôtel respire le luxe et derrière la magnifique façade se cachent des salons et des chambres opulentes, avec tout le confort moderne. Le service est exceptionnel et la suite Présidentielle est réellement impressionnante, offrant les plus belles vues sur Madrid. Une visite au restaurant Epoque by Gran Meliá qui sert une délicieuse cuisine gastronomique Méditerranéenne est à ne pas manquer!

Ubicado en uno de los mejores sitios de la ciudad, este hotel rezuma lujo por todas partes y su gran fachada exterior refleja la opulencia de los salones y las habitaciones equipadas con las más modernas instalaciones. El servicio es excepcional y la Suite Presidencial le dejará boquiabierto con sus impresionantes vistas de Madrid. No deje de visitar el restaurante Epoque by Gran Meliá, donde se sirve una deliciosa cocina gourmet mediterránea.

SPAIN / MADRID (MADRID)

Hospes Madrid

PLAZA DE LA INDEPENDENCIA, 3, 28001 MADRID, SPAIN
Tel: +34 914 322 911 **Fax:** +34 914 322 912
Web: www.johansens.com/hospesmadrid **E-mail:** hospes.madrid@hospes.es

This city hotel, with views of the Puerta de Alcalá and Retiro Park, is a serene haven. Featuring beautifully restored architecture and contemporary interiors, accommodations include duplex and grand suites. Dining options are plentiful with the gourmet Senzone Restaurant, Senzone Chill-Out Terrace and Senzone Lounge Bar. The Bodyna Spa offers a wide range of treatments and includes a hairdressers and fitness room.

Ce hôtel de ville, avec ses vues sur la Puerta de Alcalá et le Parc du Retiro, est un havre de paix. Avec leur architecture magnifiquement restaurée et leurs intérieurs contemporains, les hébergements incluent des duplex et des grandes suites. Avec le restaurant gastronomique Senzone, la zone Senzone Chill-Out sur la terrasse et le Senzone Lounge Bar, vous aurez de nombreuses options pour dîner. Le Spa Bodyna propose une gamme complète de soins, un salon de coiffure et une salle de gym.

Este nuevo urbano, con vistas a la Puerta de Alcalá y al Parque del Retiro, es un verdadero paraíso de paz y tranquilidad. Además de la bella restauración de su arquitectura y sus modernos interiores, sus habitaciones incluyen duplex y grand suites. Las opciones para cenar son abundantes gracias al restaurante gourmet Senzone, la terraza Senzone Chill-Out y el Senzone Lounge Bar. El Bodyna Spa ofrece una gran variedad de tratamientos asi como peluquería y sala de fitness.

***Our inspector loved:** The modern décor.*

Price Guide: (breakfast €28, excluding 7% VAT)
double €240-510
suite €395-1,600

41 40 SPA

Awards: Best Sommelier of the Year 2008, Madrid Fusión Gastronomic Summit; Best Chef of the 21st Century 2008, Cocinero Gastronómico; Restaurant Revelation of the Year 2007 and Best Sommelier 2007, El Mundo Spanish Metrópoli Awards

Attractions: Chic Shopping in Calle Serano, 5-min walk; Prado and Thyssen Art Museums, 5-min walk; National Library/Archaeological Museum, 10-min walk; Plaza Mayor, 20-min walk

Nearby Towns: El Escorial, 45-min drive; Aranjuez, 80km; Toledo, 110km; Segovia, 120km
Airports: Madrid - Barajas, 15km

Category: Hotel

HOTEL ORFILA

C/ORFILA, NO 6, 28010 MADRID, SPAIN
Tel: +34 91 702 77 70 **Fax:** +34 91 702 77 72
Web: www.johansens.com/orfila **E-mail:** inforeservas@hotelorfila.com

Our inspector loved: *The elegant period décor and furnishings.*

Price Guide: (breakfast €30, excluding VAT)
double €233-405
suite €335-1,320

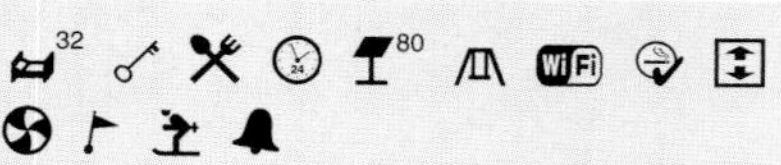

Awards: Condé Nast Johansens Most Excellent European Charming Hotel 2008

Attractions: Restaurants and Bars, 2-min walk; Prado and Thyssen Museums, 1km; Plaza Mayor, 2km; Chic Shopping in the Calle Serrano, 5-min walk

Nearby Towns: El Escorial, 45-min drive; Segovia, 1-hour drive; Toledo, 1-hour drive; Avila, 75-min drive
Airports: Madrid, 25-min drive

Category: Charming Hotel

The hotel retains its stately 19th-century air and stands among friends in a quiet residential area. Bedrooms have hydro-massage baths to rejuvenate you in time for dinner at the small restaurant opening onto a terrace and pretty garden. It would be impolite not to try a cocktail, reputedly among the best in Madrid.

L'hôtel a su garder sa stature du XIXe siècle et se dresse parmi d'autres bâtiments similaires dans un quartier résidentiel tranquille. Les chambres ont des baignoires à hydromassage, idéales pour vous revigorer avant de dîner dans le petit restaurant qui s'ouvre sur la terrasse et le ravissant jardin. Les cocktails servis au bar sont réputés pour être parmi les meilleurs de Madrid.

Este hotel conserva su señorial aspecto decimonónico y se erige con familiaridad en una tranquila zona residencial. Las habitaciones disponen de cuartos de baño con hidromasaje para que pueda rejuvenecerse justo antes de cenar en el pequeño restaurante con entrada a una terraza y a su lindo jardín. Sería impropio que no se dignase probar un cóctel, con fama de ser de los mejores de Madrid.

Hotel Selenza Madrid

C / CLAUDIO COELLO 67, 28001 MADRID, SPAIN

Tel: +34 917 810173 **Fax:** +34 915 767741

Web: www.johansens.com/selenza **E-mail:** madrid@selenza.com

Our inspector loved: *The spectacular black and white marble and mosaic floor.*

Price Guide:
superior €200-330
junior suite €240-900

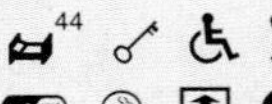

Attractions: Designer Shopping, 1-min walk; El Retiro Park, 10-min walk; Prado and Thyssen Art Galleries, 15-min walk; Plaza Mayor, 15-min drive

Nearby Towns: El Escorial, 35-min drive; Aranjuez, 40-min train/metro; Toledo, 40-min train/metro; Segovia, 1-hour drive
Airports: Madrid, 18km

Category: Charming Hotel

Join Madrid's smart set in the chic shopping neighbourhood of Salamanca. Refurbished with respect for its 19th-century history, the hotel displays flashes of colour and stunning features: a floor-to-ceiling ribbon sculpture adorns the original staircase. Ramón Freixa Madrid is the new exciting gastronomic offer, and bedrooms strike the perfect balance between design and comfort.

Mêlez-vous à la haute société madrilène dans le quartier chic du shopping de Salamanca. Rénové en respectant son histoire du XIXe siècle, l'hôtel affiche des touches de couleur et des particularités uniques: un ruban en sculpture habille l'escalier d'origine du sol au plafond. Ramón Freixa Madrid est la nouvelle adresse gastronomique à la mode et les chambres sont à la fois design et confortables.

Forme parte de la élite de la elegancia de Madrid en este hotel situado en el distinguido barrio comercial de Salamanca. El hotel, que ha sido restaurado respetando todo su valor histórico del siglo XIX, hace gala de vivos colores y otras impresionantes características: una escultura que llega hasta el techo realizada con cintas que adorna su original escalera. Su nueva apasionante oferta gastronómica viene del restaurante Ramón Freixa Madrid. Destaca la perfecta armonía entre el diseño y el confort que ofrecen sus habitaciones.

SPAIN / MADRID (MADRID) 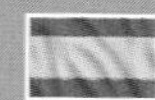

Hotel Urban

CARRERA DE SAN JERÓNIMO 34, 28014 MADRID, SPAIN
Tel: +34 91 787 77 70 **Fax:** +34 91 787 77 99
Web: www.johansens.com/urban **E-mail:** urban@derbyhotels.com

Our inspector loved: *The exhibits, in particular, the spectacular Egyptian pieces.*

Price Guide: (breakfast €21, excluding VAT)
single €425
double €475
suite €645-1,210

Awards: Condé Nast Johansens Most Excellent European Marketing Partner 2008; Condé Nast Johansens Most Excellent European Hotel 2007

Attractions: Prado and Thyssen Art Museums, 5-min walk; Plaza Mayor, 10-min walk; Chic Shopping at Calle Serrano, 10-min walk; Opera and Theatre, 15-min walk

Nearby Towns: El Escorial, 45km; Segovia, 85km; Toledo, 85km; Avila, 90km
Airports: Madrid, 15km

Category: Hotel

Located in the city's most cultural and artistic area, the fashionable Hotel Urban has become the reference point for quality and style, thanks to its clever, contemporary design that mixes chrome, iron, glass, light and wood. Try the Glass Bar, Madrid's "coolest" hot spot, the gourmet "Europa Decó" restaurant and the pool-side rooftop La Terraza del Urban and El Cielo del Urban with their fabulous views.

Situé dans l'un des quartiers les plus artistique et culturel de la ville, le très à la mode Hotel Urban, est devenu une référence pour sa qualité et son style, grâce à son utilisation fine du design contemporain, mélangeant chrome, fer, verre, lumière et bois. Testez le Glass Bar, la boite la plus branchée de Madrid, le restaurant gastronomique "Europa Decó" ainsi que La Terrazza et El Cielo del Urban, sur le toit, au bord de la piscine, avec ses vues fabuleuses sur la ville.

Situado en la zona más artística y cultural de la ciudad, el moderno Hotel Urban se ha convertido en referente de calidad y estilo gracias a su ingenioso diseño contemporáneo en el que combinan el cromo, el hierro, el vidrio, la luz y la madera. Visite el Glass Bar, el lugar más "de moda" y popular de Madrid, el restaurante gourmet "Europa Decó" además de La Terraza y El Cielo del Urban, la piscina en la azotea que ofrece unas fabulosas vistas.

SPAIN / MADRID (MADRID)

Hotel Villa Real

PLAZA DE LAS CORTES 10, 28014 MADRID, SPAIN
Tel: +34 914 20 37 67 **Fax:** +34 914 20 25 47
Web: www.johansens.com/villareal **E-mail:** villareal@derbyhotels.com

Our inspector loved: *The Andy Warhol Marilyn prints in the East 47 hotel bar-restaurant.*

Price Guide: (breakfast €21, excluding VAT)
single €385
double €430
suite €645-1,210

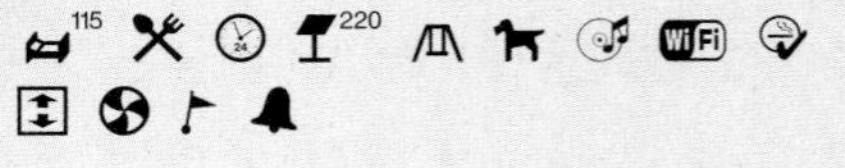

Awards: Condé Nast Johansens Most Excellent European Marketing Partner 2008

Attractions: Opera and Theatre, 1km; Chic Shopping in Calle Serrano, 1km; Thyssen, Prado and Reina Sofía Museums, 5-min walk; Plaza Mayor, 10-min walk

Nearby Towns: El Escorial, 45km; Segovia, 85km; Toledo, 85km; Avila, 95km
Airports: Madrid, 15km

Category: Hotel

In the heart of Madrid's cultural hub, this prestigious hotel provides exceptional service and cleverly designed rooms. Many of the suites boast hydro-massage baths and saunas, as well as terraces with unbeatable views over the city. Be inspired by the magnificent collection of Roman mosaics and Greek ceramics displayed throughout the hotel; truly amazing!

Au cœur du centre culturel de Madrid, cet hôtel prestigieux fournit un service exceptionnel et des chambres savamment conçues. La plupart des suites possèdent baignoires à hydro massages et saunas, ainsi que des terrasses ayant une vue imprenable sur la ville. Soyez attentifs à la formidable collection de mosaïques romaines et de céramiques grecques répartie dans l'hôtel; c'est vraiment magnifique!

Ubicado en pleno meollo del Madrid cultural, este prestigioso hotel ofrece un servicio excepcional y habitaciones de ingenioso diseño. Muchas de las suites disponen de baños de hidromasaje y saunas además de terrazas y de unas inmejorables vistas a la ciudad. Sienta la inspiración de la magnífica colección de mosaicos romanos y de piezas de cerámica griega expuesta por todo el hotel; es realmente increíble.

SPAIN / MADRID (MADRID - BOADILLA DEL MONTE) 

ANTIGUO CONVENTO

C/ DE LAS MONJAS, S/N BOADILLA DEL MONTE, 28660 MADRID, SPAIN

Tel: +34 91 632 22 20 **Fax:** +34 91 633 15 12

Web: www.johansens.com/elconvento **E-mail:** informacion@elconvento.net

Our inspector loved: *The selection of guest rooms with magnificent four-poster beds.*

Price Guide: (excluding VAT)
single €142-180
double €161-200
suite €248-500

Attractions: Museums, 17km; Opera, 17km; Shopping, 17km; Theatre, 17km

Nearby Towns: Madrid, 17km; El Escorial, 30km; Toledo, 83km
Airports: Madrid, 30km

Category: Charming Hotel

Dating from the 17th century, this former convent has been beautifully refurbished with modern fittings, antiques and harmonious period details. The former nuns' rooms have been imaginatively decorated; skylights and a large covered patio create light and space. Stroll through the ornamental gardens and visit the restaurant offering superb cuisine. Extensive business facilities are also provided.

Ce couvent du XVIIe siècle a été admirablement rénové avec des installations modernes, des antiquités et d'harmonieux détails d'époque. Les anciennes chambres de nonnes sont décorées de manière originale, les lucarnes et le grand patio créent lumière et espace. Promenez-vous les jardins ornementaux ou déguster l'excellente cuisine du restaurant. D'importants équipements d'affaires sont également disponibles.

Este convento del siglo XVII ha sido elegantemente renovado con accesorios modernos, antigüedades y armoniosos detalles del periodo. Las antiguas celdas de las monjas han sido decoradas con imaginación y tanto los tragaluces como su amplio patio cubierto proporcionan luz y espacio. Dese un paseo por sus decorativos jardines y visite el restaurante, que sirve una excelente cocina. Hay también disponibles generosas instalaciones para los negocios.

HOTEL ETXEGANA

IPIÑABURU 38, ZEANURI, 48144 BIZKAIA, SPAIN
Tel: +34 946 338 448 **Fax:** +34 946 338 449
Web: www.johansens.com/etxegana **E-mail:** info@etxegana.com

Our inspector loved: *The unique rural location, which is at the epicentre of so many interesting excursions.*

Price Guide:
classic €125-140
de luxe €135-175
suite €175-325

This traditional Basque-style hotel is located in unspoilt countryside, with views of the mountains and century-old woods. The bedrooms, with hydromassage baths and lounges, have been lovingly decorated with antique English and French furniture, as well as exotic pieces collected by the owners from far-flung places. The excellent home-cooked meals, the good wine selection and wellness centre make for a truly enjoyable stay.

Cet hôtel de style traditionnel basque est situé dans une campagne intacte, entourée de montagnes et d'anciennes forêts. Les chambres, avec des baignoires à hydromassage, et les salons sont décorées avec des meubles anciens anglais et français et objets exotiques ramenés des pays lointains par les propriétaires. La délicieuse cuisine faite maison, la bonne sélection de vins et le centre de bien-être rendront votre séjour très agréable.

Este hotel de estilo vasco tradicional se encuentra en pleno campo, con vistas a los montes y bosques centenarios. Sus amplias habitaciones, todas con hidromasaje, y salones han sido decoradas exquisitamente con mobiliario antiguo de origen inglés, frances y exoticas piezas traidas de lejanos paises por sus propietarios. El spa, la excelente comida casera y su completa selección de vinos, le permitiran disfrutar de una estancia inolvidable.

Attractions: Natural de Gorbea Park, on-site; Guggenheim Bilbao Museum, 30km; Reserva de la Biosfera (Urdaibai), 30km; Bodegas de la Rioja and Ruta del Vino Rioja Alaves, 70km

Nearby Towns: Bilbao, 30km; Vitoria, 30km; San Sebastián, 100km
Airports: Bilbao (Loiu), 25km; Vitoria (Foronda), 25km; Hondarribia, 100km

Category: Charming Hotel

SPAIN / VALENCIA (ALICANTE) 

Hospes Amérigo

C/ RAFAEL ALTAMIRA 7, 03002 ALICANTE, SPAIN
Tel: +34 965 14 65 70 **Fax:** +34 965 14 65 71
Web: www.johansens.com/hospesamerigo **E-mail:** amerigo@hospes.es

Our inspector loved: *The Bodyna Spa and the view from the rooftop pool.*

Price Guide: (room only, excluding VAT, parking is available at the hotel)
single €115-280
double €115-280
suite €300-795

Awards: Condé Nast Johansens Most Excellent European Hotel for Design & Innovation 2007

Attractions: Alicante Marina, 5-min walk; Chic Shopping, 5-min walk; Alicante Castle, 1km; Terra Mitica Theme Park, 40km

Nearby Towns: Murcia, 70km; Albacete, 170km; Valencia, 200km
Airports: Alicante, 10km; Murcia, 90km

Category: Hotel

Almost unrecognisable as its former guise, this 16th-century convent today wears marble, stone, leather and chrome creating a luxurious yet functional 21st-century space. Well-groomed bedrooms and bathrooms possess all mod-cons, and you can appreciate 2 restaurants: Senzone Restaurant and Senzone Tapas Bar. There is also a roof terrace, an indoor pool with retractable roof and Bodyna Spa.

Pratiquement méconnaissable par rapport à son apparence d'origine, ce couvent du XVIe siècle s'habille aujourd'hui de marbre, de pierre, de cuir et de chrome créant ainsi une espace luxueux mais fonctionnel du XXIe siècle. Les chambres et salles de bain bien pensées offrent tout le confort moderne et vous pourrez profiter des 2 restaurants, le restaurant Senzone et le Bar à tapas Senzone, de la terrasse sur le toit, de la piscine intérieure avec un toit rétractable et Bodyna Spa.

Casi irreconocible en su aspecto anterior, este convento del siglo XVI se reviste hoy en día de mármol, piedra, cuero y cromo para crear un lujoso y no menos funcional espacio propio del siglo XXI. Sus habitaciones y cuartos de baño perfectamente acondicionados disponen de todos los servicios. Podrá también apreciar sus 2 restaurantes, Senzone Restaurant y Senzone Tapas Bar, una terraza en lo alto, una piscina cubierta con techo móvil y Bodyna Spa.

Hotel Termas Marinas el Palasiet

PARTIDA CANTALLOPS S/N, 12560 BENICÀSSIM, CASTELLÓN, COSTA DEL AZAHAR, SPAIN
Tel: +34 964 300 250 **Fax:** +34 964 302 236
Web: www.johansens.com/termasmarinas **E-mail:** reservas@termasmarinas.com

Experience a wide range of new, medically controlled health and beauty treatments at this thalassotherapy spa, the first of its kind to open in Spain. Enjoy Mediterranean cuisine focused on healthy eating, and explore your surroundings on a hotel bicycle. Alternatively, soak up the Old World charm at this wonderful hotel furnished with Spanish tiles, wooden floors and wall frescoes, and relax on your bedroom balcony overlooking the bay.

Découvrez un large choix de nouveaux soins de santé et de beauté, contrôlés médicalement, dans ce spa thalasso, le premier de ce genre à ouvrir en Espagne. Dégustez une cuisine méditerranéenne centrée sur la diététique et explorez les alentours sur les vélos de l'hôtel. Sinon imprégnez-vous du charme de l'ancien monde dans ce magnifique hôtel composé de carrelages espagnols, de parquets en bois et de fresques murales et relaxez-vous sur le balcon de votre chambre surplombant la baie.

Disfrute de una amplia gama de nuevos tratamientos de salud y belleza controlados por médicos en este Spa de Thalasssoterapia, el primero en España. Deléitese de la cocina mediterránea con especialidad en platos saludables y descubra los bellos alrededores en una bicicleta del hotel. Si prefiere, puede descansar en el balcón de su habitación con vistas a la bahía y empaparse del encanto de otros tiempos que emana el hotel con sus azulejos españoles, solerías de madera y frescos murales.

Our inspector loved: *The wonderfully professional therapists in the luxurious spa.*

Price Guide:
standard double €169-196
superior double €195-228
superior double with sitting room €218-246

Attractions: El Desierto de las Palmas Park and 17th-Century Monastery, 7km; Castellón Cathedral, 12km; Villafames Castle, 20-min drive; Vall Torta Museum, 40km

Nearby Towns: Oropesa, 6km; Castellón, 12km; Peñiscola, 57km; Valencia, 75km
Airports: Valencia, 50-min drive; Tarragona, 80-min drive

Category: Hotel
Closed: January - February

La Madrugada

PARTIDA BENIMARRAIG, 61 B, 03720 BENISSA, SPAIN
Tel: +34 965 733 156 **Fax:** +34 966 489 649
Web: www.johansens.com/lamadrugada **E-mail:** info@lamadrugada.es

Our inspector loved: *The stylish and successful transformation from Mediterranean villa into charming hotel.*

Price Guide: (breakfast €12, excluding VAT)
double €95-135
suite €240-270

Attractions: Casa del Maco Restaurant, 1km; Calpe Marina and Beaches, 5km; Benissa Historic Town Centre, 10-min drive; Guadelest Historic Centre and Moraira Marina, 13-15-min drive

Nearby Towns: Benissa, 2km; Calpe, 5km; Moraira, 15-min drive; Altea, 30-min drive
Airports: Alicante, 80km; Valencia, 120km

Category: Charming Hotel
Closed: During February

Leave your worries behind and lose yourself in the serenity of this picturesque sanctuary surrounded by exotic plants and palm trees. This stylish and comfortable villa not only offers wonderfully classically-styled bedrooms and a luxury suite with mini kitchen but has a relaxing lounge with games area, bar and breakfast salon with terrace.

Laissez vos soucis derrière vous et plongez-vous dans la sérénité de ce sanctuaire pittoresque entouré de plantes exotiques et de palmiers. Cette villa élégante et confortable offre non seulement de magnifiques chambres de style classique et une suite luxueuse équipée d'une mini-cuisine mais possède également un salon relaxant avec coin jeu, un bar et une salle de petit-déjeuner avec terrasse.

Deje sus preocupaciones a un lado y déjese llevar por la serenidad de este pintoresco santuario rodeado de exóticas plantas y palmeras. Esta elegante y cómoda villa no sólo pone a su disposición encantadoras habitaciones de estilo clásico y una suite de lujo con mini-cocina sino que también dispone de un relajante salón con zona de juegos, bar y salón para desayunos con terraza.

SPAIN / VALENCIA (BOCAIRENT)

HOTEL FERRERO

CTRA. ONTINYENT-VILLENA, KM 16 46880, BOCAIRENT, VALENCIA, SPAIN
Tel: +34 962 35 51 75 **Fax:** +34 962 35 06 41
Web: www.johansens.com/hotelferrero **E-mail:** info@hotelferrero.com

This superb example of 21st-century design is a stunning getaway for leisure, fitness and relaxation. Amidst 30 acres of land, each contemporary suite is a tranquil sanctuary fitted with the newest technology, and the small spa and gym are superbly equipped. Restaurant Ferrero by Francisco Morales and Rut Cotroneo presents a seasonal, creative menu with modern and traditional options.

Ce magnifique exemple de design du XXIe siècle est un superbe refuge pour les loisirs, le fitness et la relaxation. Au cœur de 12 hectares de terres, chacune des suites contemporaines est un véritable sanctuaire tranquille équipé du meilleur de la technologie moderne. Le petit spa et la salle de gym sont magnifiquement équipés. Le Restaurant Ferrero, par Francisco Morales et Rut Cotroneo, propose un menu créatif, adapté aux saisons et qui offre des options aussi bien modernes que traditionnelles.

Este magnifico ejemplo de diseño del siglo XXI es un cobijo ideal para disfrutar del ocio, del deporte y el relax. Ubicado en una finca de 12 hectáreas, cada una de sus suites contemporáneas son remansos de paz dotados de la más moderna tecnología, y su pequeño Spa y gimnasio están equipados a la perfección. El Restaurante Ferrero, gestionado por Francisco Morales y Rut Cotroneo ofrece un menú creativo que varía según la estación, combinando platos modernos con los tradicionales.

Our inspector loved: *The Ferrero restaurant, where the freshest of ingredients are used to create contemporary and traditional dishes.*

Price Guide: (excluding 7% VAT)
standard double €195-230
junior suite €290-340
suite €340-390

Attractions: Natural Park Sierra Mariola, 1km; Historic Bocairent, 1km; Historic Villena, 25km; Gandia Coastal Town, 40-min drive

Nearby Towns: Bocairent, 1km; Ontinyent, 12km; Villena, 25km; Xativa, 30km
Airports: Alicante, 50-min drive; Valencia, 1-hour drive; Murcia, 75-min drive

Category: Hotel
Closed: 7th January - 1st February

VILLA MARISOL

URB. MARISOL PARK 1-A, 03710 CALPE, ALICANTE, SPAIN
Tel: +34 96 587 57 00 **Fax:** +34 96 583 85 44
Web: www.johansens.com/marisol **E-mail:** info@marisolpark.com

Our inspector loved: *The Mediterranean cuisine served al fresco on the terrace.*

Price Guide:
double €110-140
junior suite €140-180
suite €320

Attractions: Calpe Marina, 1km; Desafio Medieval Castillo Conde Alfaz de Pí, 25km; Terra Mitica, 30km; Aqualandia and Mundomar, 30km

Nearby Towns: Moraira, 12km; Altea, 15km; Javea, 15km; Benidorm, 30km
Airports: Alicante, 70km; Valencia, 80km; Murcia, 150km

Category: Charming Hotel

Embracing modern style, this large Mediterranean villa awaits discovery in the quiet beach-side town of Calpe. Treat yourself and visit the hotel's mini-spa before retiring to your comfortable guest room where carefully selected and tasteful splashes of colour have been chosen to complement the neutral, clean lines. For a light snack or special gourmet dining experience head to Villa Marisol Restaurant and Terrace.

De style moderne, cette grande villa méditerranéenne attend qu'on la découvre dans la tranquille station balnéaire de Calpe. Faites vous plaisir en visitant le mini spa de l'hôtel avant de vous rendre dans votre confortable chambre où les touches de couleurs élégantes ont été choisies avec soin afin de compléter les lignes pures. Pour un déjeuner léger ou pour un dîner gastronomique rendez-vous au Villa Marisol Restaurant et Terrasse.

De estilo moderno, esta gran villa mediterránea en el tranquilo pueblo playero de Calpe espera aun ser descubierta. Porqué no se regala una visita al mini-spa del hotel, para luego descansar en su confortable habitación de lineas limpias y neutrales con acentos de color cuidadosamente escogidos. Para comidas ligeras o experiencias culinarias especiales a la hora de la cena, diríjase a Villa Mairsol Restaurante y Terrazas.

Hotel Mont Sant

SUBIDA AL CASTILLO, S/N JÁTIVA - XÀTIVA, 46800 VALENCIA, SPAIN
Tel: +34 962 27 50 81 **Fax:** +34 962 28 19 05
Web: www.johansens.com/montsant **E-mail:** mont-sant@mont-sant.com

Once a Moorish palace and then a monastery, the hotel has stunning views of the "mini Alhambra" hilltop fortification, which was the birthplace to 2 Spanish popes. Rustic décor has made it cosy, and food served in the restaurant is superb. Unsurprisingly, you can enjoy an abundance of walking and sightseeing in the area.

Cet hôtel, qui fût autrefois un palais mauresque puis un monastère, possède des vues exceptionnelles sur la colline et les fortifications du « mini Alhambra », qui a vu naître 2 Papes espagnols. Un décor rustique lui confère une atmosphère charmante et la cuisine servie dans le restaurant est délicieuse. Vous ne serez pas surpris d'avoir une abondance de randonnées et de lieux à visiter dans la région.

Antaño palacio árabe y con posterioridad monasterio, este hotel dispone de maravillosas vistas a la fortificación sobre la colina conocida como "mini Alhambra", lugar de nacimiento de 2 Papas españoles. Su decoración de estilo rústico le ha proporcionado su acogedor aspecto y la carta de su restaurante es extraordinaria. No resulta nada sorprendente que pueda Vd. disfrutar de generosas oportunidades de pasear y de hacer turismo por la zona.

Our inspector loved: *The hillside location with wonderful 360º views of Játiva town below and the impressive Játiva Castle above.*

Price Guide: (room only, excluding VAT)
single €70-90
double €110-180
junior suite €180-350

Attractions: Játiva Castle and Fortification, 0.5km; Játiva Basilica, 1km; Valencia Port and City Centre, 65km; Almansa Castle, 65km

Nearby Towns: Valencia, 65km; Alicante, 85km
Airports: Valencia, 60km; Alicante, 80km

Category: Charming Hotel

Hotel Swiss Moraira

C / HAYA 175, TEULADA, MORAIRA, 03724 ALICANTE, SPAIN
Tel: +34 965 747 104 **Fax:** +34 965 747 074
Web: www.johansens.com/swisshotelmoraira **E-mail:** info@swisshotelmoraira.com

Our inspector loved: *The idyllic Mediterranean location surrounded by semi-tropical vegetation.*

Price Guide: (room only)
double €140-210
suite €350-380

Attractions: Moraira Marina and Shopping, 2km; Sandy Beaches, 2km; Javea, 10km; Terra Mitica and Aqualandia, Benidorm, 50km

Nearby Towns: Javea, 10km; Denía, 25km; Benidorm, 50km
Airports: Alicante, 80km; Valencia, 110km

Category: Hotel

Enveloped by vegetation and lush gardens is the delightful Hotel Swiss Moraira. Beyond the entrance hall is a relaxing lounge, small wellness centre, café/bar and Al Punt restaurant where modern and traditional Mediterranean cuisine is served. Guest rooms feature a décor that is sophisticated, cool Mediterranean and have terraces overlooking the courtyard with pool.

Le ravissant Hôtel Swiss Moraira est entouré de végétation et de jardins luxuriants. Derrière le hall d'entrée se cache un salon agréable, un petit centre de bien-être, un café/bar et le restaurant Al Punt où est servie une cuisine méditerranéenne à la fois moderne et traditionnelle. Les chambres offrent un décor à la fois sophistiqué et méditerranéen et ont des terrasses donnant sur la cour et sa piscine.

Arropado por vegetación y suntuosos jardínes se encuentra el encantador Hotel Swiss Moraira. Traspasado el vestíbulo de la entrada se encontrará con un relajante salón, un pequeño centro wellness, un café/bar y el restaurante Al Punt donde se sirve cocina moderna y tradicional mediterránea. Las habitaciones disponen de una decoración sofisticada y refrescantemente mediterránea así como de terrazas con vistas al patio y la piscina.

SPAIN / VALENCIA (VALENCIA)

Hospes Palau de la Mar

NAVARRO REVERTER 14, 46004 VALENCIA, SPAIN
Tel: +34 96 316 2884 **Fax:** +34 96 316 2885
Web: www.johansens.com/hospespalaudelamar **E-mail:** palaudelamar@hospes.es

Our inspector loved: *Without doubt, the stimulation of the senses!*

Price Guide: (room only, excluding VAT, private hotel parking available)
single €125-500
double €125-500
suite €505-700

Attractions: Valencia Port and Marina, 1km; Valencia Science/Museum Park, 1km; Valencia Historic Centre, 5-min walk; Shopping, 10-min walk

Nearby Towns: Sagunto, 30km; Játiva, 50km; Castellon, 75km
Airports: Valencia, 10km

Category: Hotel

Aristocratic and beautiful, style floods from every corner of this hotel, even before you walk up the exceptional staircase with its magnificent stained-glass skylight depicting ocean waves. Floors are individually designed, with some rooms placed around an open landscaped patio. Massages and therapies are offered in the specially created cabins of the Bodyna Spa.

Un style noble et magnifique déborde de tous les coins de cet hôtel, même avant que vous soyez monté par l'exceptionnel escalier avec son magnifique vitrail au plafond représentant les vagues de l'océan. Chaque étage à son propre design et certaines chambres se trouvent autour d'une cour intérieure paysagée. Des soins et massages sont proposés dans les cabines spécialement conçues du Bodyna Spa.

Bella y aristocrática, su estilo fluye por todos los rincones de este hotel, incluso antes de subir por su excepcional escalera con su magnífico tragaluz de vidrio de colores con motivos de olas del océano. Sus solerías muestran diseños individuales y algunas de sus habitaciones se sitúan alrededor de una patio abierto al paisaje. A su disposición tendrá masajes y terapias en las cabinas del Bodyna Spa.

NORWEGIAN SEA
NORTH SEA
SWEDEN
NORWAY
FINLAND
DENMARK
ESTONIA
LATVIA
LITHUANIA
BELARUS
GERMANY
POLAND
Luleå
Skellefteå
Umeå
Omskoldsvik
Gåvle
Karlstad
STOCKHOLM
326
Våstervik
Goteborg
Jonkoping
Kariskrona
Malmo
COPENHAGEN
OSLO
HELSINKI
TALLINN
RIGA
VILINIUS
MINSK

SWEDEN (STOCKHOLM)

Lydmar Hotel

SÖDRA BLASIEHOLMSHAMNEN 2, BOX 161 96, 10324 STOCKHOLM, SWEDEN
Tel: +46 8 22 31 60 **Fax:** +46 8 22 31 70
Web: www.johansens.com/lydmar **E-mail:** info@lydmar.com

Our inspector loved: *The impressive views over Stockholm's waterfront.*

Price Guide:
room SEK2,800-12,500

Attractions: National Museum of Art, next door; Cafés, Bars, Restaurants and Designer Shopping, on the doorstep; Museum of Modern Art and Galleries, close by; Stockholm Annual Jazz Festival 15-19th July, 10-min walk

Airports: Stockholm, 30-min drive; Arlanda Express Train, 20-min train/metro

Category: Hotel

Impressive, elegant, spacious and stylish with panoramic views of Stockholm's waterfront, this is one of the city's newest places to visit and be seen in, where the relaxed atmosphere is enhanced by professional and friendly staff. You will love the location, the décor, the antiques and the chic, unpretentious bar-restaurant, which attracts the beautiful people!

Impressionnant, élégant, spacieux et stylé, avec ses vues sur le front de mer de Stockholm, c'est l'un des nouveaux endroits à fréquenter absolument, avec son ambiance détendue et son équipe professionnelle et conviviale. Vous adorerez l'emplacement, le décor, les meubles anciens et le chic sans prétention du bar-restaurant qui attire la haute société!

Este impresionante, elegante, amplio y refinado hotel con vistas panorámicas al paseo marítimo de Estocolmo es uno de los lugares más modernos de la ciudad para visitar y para dejarse ver, y donde un personal profesional y eficiente contribuye a realzar su ambiente relajado. Le encantará su ubicación, la decoración, sus antigüedades así como el elegante y modesto bar-restaurante que atrae a la jet set.

Stuttgart
Strasbourg
Augsburg
GERMANY
FRANCE
Freiburg
Belfort
Schaffhausen
Frauenfeld
Basel
Liestal
Winterthur
Sankt Gallen
Bregenz
Aarau
Herisau
Delémont
Zürich
Appenzell
Solothurn
AUSTRIA
Zug
LIECHTENSTEIN
Biel
Lucerne
Glarus
329
Schwyz
Neuchâtel
Bern
Stans
Sarnen
Altdorf
Chur
Freiburg
Thun
Yverdon-les-Bains
Zernez
330
St. Moritz
Lausanne
Lauterbrunnen
Münster
Sils
Brig
328
Geneva
St-Maurice
Sion
Bellinzona
Martigny
Lugano
Trento
Como
Aosta
Chambéry
Milan
FRANCE
Turin
ITALY
Parma
Gap

SWITZERLAND (CRANS~MONTANA)

LeCrans Hotel & Spa

3963 CRANS~MONTANA, SWITZERLAND
Tel: +41 27 486 60 60 **Fax:** +41 27 486 60 61
Web: www.johansens.com/lecrans **E-mail:** info@lecrans.com

At the summit of Crans-Montana ski resort, this exclusive and peaceful hotel and spa affords breathtaking views of the snowcapped Swiss Alps. While the warm, private home ambience of the interior beckons you in, the spa will tempt you to experience its extensive Cinque Mondes treatments, the variety of cuisine will fulfil your appetite and the impressive Vinothèque will excite the taste buds!

Situé au sommet du complexe de ski de Crans-Montana, ce luxueux hôtel et spa offre des vues à couper le souffle sur les sommets enneigés des Alpes suisses. Tandis que l'intérieur vous invitera par son ambiance chaleureuse et authentique, le spa vous proposera d'essayer toute la variété de ses soins Cinque Mondes, la diversité offerte en cuisine comblera votre appétit et l'impressionnante Vinothèque éveillera vos papilles!

En la cima de la estación de eskí de Crans-Montana se encuentra este tranquilo y selecto hotel-spa con impresionantes vistas a las cumbres nevadas de los Alpes suizos. El acogedor y privado ambiente hogareño del interior le invita a entrar al tiempo que el spa le incita a probar sus numerosos tratamientos de Cinque Mondes. La variedad de su cocina saciará su apetito y la impresionante Vinothèque conseguirá despertar sus papilas gustativas.

***Our inspector loved:** The peace and quiet, and magical view over the snowcapped Alps.*

Price Guide: (airport transfers can be arranged)
double CHF550-1,280
suite CHF1,250-5,000

Awards: 15/20 Gault Millau

Attractions: Crans-Montana Cafés, Restaurants, Boutique Shopping, Casinos and Nightclubs, nearby; Crans-Montana Ski Resort, 100 metres; Severiano Ballesteros-Designed Golf Course (during summer), 10-min drive;

Nearby Towns: Lausanne, 90-min drive; Geneva, 2-hour drive
Airports: Geneva, 2-hour drive

Category: Hotel

Park Hotel Weggis

HERTENSTEINSTRASSE 34, 6353 WEGGIS, SWITZERLAND
Tel: +41 41 392 05 05 **Fax:** +41 41 392 05 28
Web: www.johansens.com/weggis **E-mail:** info@phw.ch

Our inspector loved: *The newly extended spa.*

Price Guide: (room only, excluding tourist tax)
single/double CHF265-610
suite CHF710-3,200

Awards: Wine Spectator Best of Award of Excellence 2009; 14/20 Gault Millau; 15/20 Gault Millau; 1 Star Michelin

Attractions: Lake Lucerne; Rigi Mountain, 2km; Lake Zug, 16km; Pilatus Mountain, 30km

Nearby Towns: Lucerne, 21km; Zürich, 55km; Basel, 115km
Airports: Zürich, 65km; Mulhouse-Basel, 131km; Bern, 151km

Category: Hotel

Relaxation is the emphasis at this luxury hotel with gorgeous views over Lake Lucerne and the Alps. Enjoy the spa's beauty and massage treatments, and dine in style at the gourmet, 15/20 Gault Millau awarded and Michelin-starred Annex restaurant or 14/20 Gault Millau awarded Sparks restaurant. Bedrooms and suites are awash with Designers' Guild fabrics, Philippe Starck lighting and Molteni furniture.

La relaxation est le maître mot dans cet hôtel de luxe aux vues magnifiques sur le lac de Lucerne et les Alpes. Laissez-vous aller dans l'extraordinaire spa qui offre des soins de beauté et des massages. Dînez avec style dans le restaurant gastronomique l'Annex, étoilé au Michelin et noté 15/20 au Gault et Millau ou au restaurant Sparks, noté 14/20 Gault et Millau. Les chambres et suites sont remplies de tissus Designers' Guild, de luminaires Philippe Starck et de mobilier Molteni.

El énfasis de este lujoso hotel con vistas espectaculares al lago de Lucerna y a los Alpes es la relajación. Descanse con los inspiradores masajes y tratamientos de belleza que se ofrecen en el Spa, y cene de lujo en el restaurante gourmet Annex, galardonado con estrella Michelin y adjudicado 15/20 en la guía gastronomica Gault Millau, o en el restaurante Sparks, 14/20 en la guía Gault Millau tambien. Las habitaciones y suites están decoradas con telas del Designers' Guild, alumbrado de Philippe Starck y mobiliario de Molteni.

HOTEL CAPRICE

3823 WENGEN, SWITZERLAND
Tel: +41 33 856 06 06 **Fax:** +41 33 856 06 07
Web: www.johansens.com/caprice **E-mail:** hotel@caprice-wengen.ch

Our inspector loved: *The ski slopes right on the doorstep.*

Price Guide:
standard CHF300-580
de luxe CHF350-680
suite CHF450-920

20     

Awards: 14/20 Gault Millau

Attractions: Hiking, on the doorstep; Skiing, 3-min walk; Golf at Interlaken and Thun, 30-min train/metro

Nearby Towns: Interlaken, 20km; Lauterbrunnen, 20-min train ride
Airports: Bern, 60km; Zurich, 120km; Geneva, 200km

Category: Charming Hotel

If skiing or hiking are your passions, then head to Hotel Caprice in the buzzing, car-free village of Wengen. Families are more than welcome and rest comfortably in the 2-bedroomed suites and rooms with picture-perfect views from windows and balconies. Creative French fare is available in the restaurant and cocktails in the lounge bar.

Si vous êtes passionnés de ski ou d'escalade, alors venez à l'Hôtel Caprice, dans le très actif village de Wengen où les voitures sont interdites. Les familles sont particulièrement bienvenues et séjournent confortablement dans les 2 suites et les chambres, dont les vues depuis les fenêtres et les balcons ont la perfection de cartes postales. Une cuisine française créative est servie dans le restaurant ainsi que des cocktails dans le bar.

Si le apasiona el ski o el excursionismo, venga al Hotel Caprice en Wengen, bulliciosa aldea libre de coches. Las familias son más que bienvenidas. Podrán descansar cómodamente en sus suites y habitaciones de 2 dormitorios con vistas de película desde sus ventanas y balcones. En el restaurante encontrará una creativa carta francesa así como cócteles en el bar.

UKRAINE
Kichinev
ROMANIA
Odesa
Braila
Sevastopol
Constanja
BULGARIA
Varna
Burgas
BLACK SEA
Istanbul
Sisli
Kagithane
Besiktas
Beyoglu
Faith
Eminonu
Uskudar
Zeytinburnu
335
338
336
337
Sukhum
Mahackala
Vladikavkaz
Telav
GEORGIA
T'bilisi
Kirklareli
Edirne
Komotini
Tekirdag
Istanbul
Zonguldak
Sinop
Samsun
Artvin
Gyumri
Ganca
Izmil
Bolu
Trabzon
Ordu
Kars
ARMENIA
Yerevan
Canakkale
Bursa
Cankiri
Amasya
Bayburt
Ankara
Eskisehir
Kirikkale
Sivas
Erzincan
Erzurum
Agri
Balikesir
Kutahya
Afyon
Manisa
Izmir
Kayseri
341
342
343
Malatya
Elazig
Bitlis
Van
IRAN
Tabriz
Denizli
Isparta
Konya
Nigde
Diyarbakir
Batman
333
Kahramanmaras
Sirnak
Bodrum
Mugla
Sanliurfa
334
340
Antalya
332
Mersin
Adana
Osmaniye
Gaziantep
Al-Hasaka
Rodos
339
Hatay
Aleppo
Kirkuk
Hamah
SYRIA
Nicosia
Larnaca
CYPRUS
Beirut
LEBANON
MEDITERRANEAN SEA
Damascus
IRAQ
Baghdad
Jerusalem
Amman
ISRAEL
JORDAN
Cairo
SAUDI ARABIA
EGYPT

TURKEY (ANTALYA)

Cornelia Diamond Golf Resort and Spa

ISKELE MEVKII, BELEK, ANTALYA, TURKEY

Tel: +90 242 710 1600 **Fax:** +90 242 715 3353

Web: www.johansens.com/corneliadiamond **E-mail:** sales@corneliadiamond.com

Luxury, comfort, service and relaxation are emphasised at this crescent-shaped, 5-star hotel with its own sandy beach, tournament golf course and plethora of waterside activities. Bedrooms are crisp, modern, equipped with every amenity and have far-reaching views across the gardens and Mediterranean. Enjoy relaxing around the huge swimming pool or destressing in the spa.

Luxe, confort, service et relaxation sont les mots clés de cet hôtel 5 étoiles en forme de croissant qui possède sa propre plage de sable privée, son tournoi de golf et d'innombrables activités nautiques. Les chambres sont impeccables, modernes, équipées de tout le confort et offrent des vues infinies sur les jardins et la Méditerranée. Relaxez-vous au bord de l'immense piscine ou destressez-vous au spa.

El lujo, el confort, el servicio y el relax constituyen los puntos fuertes de este hotel de 5 estrellas de forma de luna creciente provisto de su propia playa arenosa, campo de golf de campeonato y todo un despliegue de actividades acuáticas. Las habitaciones son impecables, modernas, equipadas de todas las posibles instalaciones y de vistas a la lejanía a través de sus jardines y al Mediterráneo. Disfrute relajándose junto a su inmensa piscina o dejando el estrés a un lado en el spa.

Our inspector loved: *The attention to detail, and luxury facilities.*

Price Guide: (all inclusive)
single €210-315
double €280-370
suites and lake houses upon request

Attractions: "Blue" Flag Beach, on-site; ESPA Certified Crassula Spa Centre, on-site; Nick Faldo Championship Golf Course, 2-min buggy ride; Aspendos Theatre, 20-min drive

Nearby Towns: Belek, 5km; Side, 25km; Antalya, 50km; Alanya, 80km
Airports: Antalya, 40km

Category: Hotel

Ada Hotel

BAGARASI MAHALLESI, PK 350, GÖL - TÜRKBÜKÜ, BODRUM, TURKEY
Tel: +90 252 377 59 15 **Fax:** +90 252 377 53 79
Web: www.johansens.com/adahotel **E-mail:** info@adahotel.com

Our inspector loved: *Enjoying Bodrum from this elegant, stylish hotel.*

Price Guide: (breakfast US$20)
luxury US$445-520
de luxe US$495-570
suite US$750-1,035

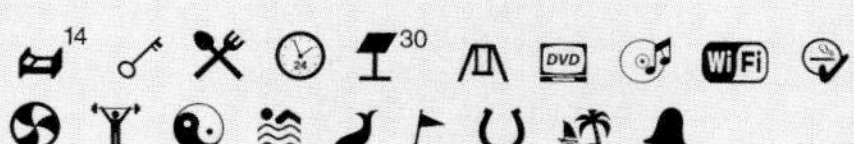

Attractions: Bodrum Museum of Underwater Archaeology, 20-min drive; Castle of the Knights and St John, 20-min drive; Mausoleum, One of the Seven Wonders of the World, 20-min drive; Bodrum Night-life and Blue Cruise, 20-min drive

Nearby Towns: Göl - Türkbükü Beach, 5-min walk; Bodrum, 20-min drive
Airports: Milas - Bodrum, 45-min drive

Category: Hotel
Closed: 10th October - 1st May

Join Istanbul's glitterati and stay at this luxury boutique hotel in the beach resort area of Bodrum. A stone's throw from the sea and exclusive beach club, this is a private and tranquil sanctuary offering spacious rooms and suites, and exceptional personal service. The 2-storey wellness centre houses a Turkish bath, medieval-styled restaurant, meeting area and cinema room.

Rejoignez les paillettes d'Istanbul et séjournez dans ce boutique hôtel de luxe situé dans la partie balnéaire de Bodrum. A quelques mètres de la mer et d'un beach club exclusif, c'est un sanctuaire privé et tranquille qui offre des chambres et suite spacieuses et un service exceptionnel et attentif. Le centre de bien-être sur 2 étages offre des bains turques, un restaurant de style médiéval, un lieu de réunion et une salle de cinéma.

Únase a las celebridades de Estambul hospedándose en este lujoso boutique hotel del complejo-playa de Bodrum. A un paso del mar y de un selecto club de playa, este santuario privado y tranquilidad ofrece espaciosas habitaciones y suites así como un excepcional servicio personal. El centro wellness, de 2 plantas, contiene un baño turco, un restaurante de estilo medieval, un área de reuniones y un sala de cine.

KEMPINSKI HOTEL BARBAROS BAY

KIZILAGAC KOYU, GERENKUYU MEVKII, YALICIFTLIK, 48400 BODRUM, TURKEY
Tel: +90 252 311 0303/11 **Fax:** +90 252 311 0300
Web: www.johansens.com/barbaros **E-mail:** reservations.barbaros@kempinski.com

The setting is spectacular, facilities and service superb. This secluded cliff-top hotel has everything for guests seeking tranquillity, excellent cuisine and pampering Six Senses spa treatments. With a fabulous serenity pool, stunning views of the Aegean over and beyond a private bay, this is an unrivalled choice for visitors favouring luxurious elegance and style with famous Turkish hospitality.

L'emplacement est spectaculaire, les équipements et le service excellents. Cet hôtel isolé en haut d'une falaise possède tout ce que recherchent des hôtes en quête de tranquillité, d'une cuisine délicieuse et d'agréables soins au spa Six Senses. Avec une fabuleuse piscine à débordements, des vues exceptionnelles sur la mer Egée, sur une baie privée et bien au-delà, cet endroit est un choix incontournable pour les visiteurs qui privilégient luxe, élégance et style avec la non moins fameuse hospitalité turque.

El emplazamiento es espectacular, y las instalaciones y servicios excepcionales. Este apartado hotel situado sobre un acantilado dispone de todo lo necesario para los clientes que buscan tranquilidad, una excelente cocina y mimosos tratamientos en Six Senses Spa. Gracias a su fabulosa piscina, espectaculares vistas del mar Egeo mas allá de la bahía privada, este es un lugar inigualable para aquellos que valoran el lujo, la elegancia y el estilo combinados con la famosa hospitalidad turca.

Our inspector loved: *The serenity pool.*

Price Guide:
single €120-470
double €160-510
suite €263-7,000

Awards: Condé Nast Traveller Readers' Best Hotel Spa Award 2008

Attractions: Gulet Cruise, on the doorstep; "Blue" Flag Beach, on-site; Bodrum Castle, 14km; Golf in Bodrum, 30-min drive

Nearby Towns: Bodrum, 14km; Turkbuku, 15km; Kos, 40-minute boat ride from Bodrum; Ephesus, 2.5-hour drive from Bodrum
Airports: Milas-Bodrum, 38km

Category: Hotel

TURKEY (ISTANBUL) 

A'JIA HOTEL

AHMET RASIM PASA YALISI, ÇUBUKLU CADDESI, NO 27, KANLICA, ISTANBUL, TURKEY
Tel: +90 216 413 9300 **Fax:** +90 216 413 9355
Web: www.johansens.com/ajiahotel **E-mail:** info@ajiahotel.com

Our inspector loved: *The uniqueness of this Ottoman mansion in the city of 2 continents.*

Price Guide:
single/double €255-355
suite €455-855

Awards: Condé Nast Johansens Most Excellent Charming Hotel 2009

Attractions: Bosphorus, 5 metres; Museums, 10-min drive; European Side of Istanbul, 10-min boat ride; Old City, 30-min drive

Nearby Towns: Istanbul Old City, 30-min drive
Airports: Sabiha Gokcen, 35-min drive; Ataturk, 50-min drive

Category: Charming Hotel

This superbly restored Ottoman mansion sparkles white, contrasting beautifully with deep blues of the Bosphorus Sea, over which it regally rises. Comfortably blending old and new, the exterior and surrounds are traditional while inside you'll find a tasteful modern, almost minimalist style. Indoor and outdoor dining is quite an experience, complemented by the views.

Cette demeure ottomane superbement restaurée, d'un blanc chatoyant, contraste magnifiquement avec les eaux bleues profondes du Bosphore au-dessus duquel elle s'élève majestueusement. Mariant confortablement l'ancien et le moderne, les extérieurs et ses environs sont traditionnels alors que l'intérieur est décoré avec goût dans un style moderne presque minimaliste. Le dîner servit dedans ou dehors est une expérience, agrémentée de superbes vues.

Esta mansión otomana de excelente restauración brilla en su blancura, lo cual resalta en bello contraste con los profundos azules del mar del Bósforo, sobre la cual majestuosa se erige. Tras combinar con toda comodidad lo antiguo con lo nuevo, su exterior y sus alrededores constituyen su lado tradicional mientras en su interior podrá comprobar que su estilo es elegante y moderno, casi minimalista. Las cenas, tanto bajo techo como al aire libre, son todo una experiencia realzada por las vistas.

TURKEY (ISTANBUL)

Bosphorus Palace Hotel

YALIBOYU CADDESI NO 64, BEYLERBEYI, 34676 ISTANBUL, TURKEY
Tel: +90 216 422 00 03 **Fax:** +90 216 422 00 12
Web: www.johansens.com/bosphoruspalace **E-mail:** reservation@bosphoruspalace.com

Superbly restored to its original neo-Ottoman grandeur, this hotel is ideally situated for exploring the historic city centre and the Beylerbeyi Straits. Luxurious with classical style, guest rooms are particularly palatial and opulent. You will enjoy the stunning views over the waters of the Bosphorus and excellent international cuisine in the plush restaurant.

Superbement restauré afin lui redonner sa grandeur néo-ottomane d'origine, cet hôtel est idéalement placé pour explorer le centre historique de la ville et le détroit de Beylerbeyi. Les chambres, de style classique, sont particulièrement somptueuses et opulentes. Vous apprécierez les vues exceptionnelles sur le Bosphore et l'excellente cuisine dans le restaurant cossu.

Espectacularmente restaurado a su grandeza original neo-otomana, este hotel se encuentra en una situación ideal para explorar el histórico centro de la ciudad y los estrechos de Beylerbeyi. Fastuoso y pródigo de estilo clásico, sus habitaciones son especialmente señoriales y suntuosas. Disfrutará de las espléndidas vistas a las aguas del Bósforo y su excelente carta internacional en el lujoso restaurante.

Our inspector loved: *The unique restaurant located on the ground floor where "kayik" boats used to moor.*

Price Guide:
single/double €250-550
Bosphorus palace room €850

Attractions: Beylerbeyi Palace, 1km; City Centre, 1km; Fethi Pasha Forest, 2km; Anadolu Kavagi Seaside Village, 15km

Nearby Towns: Uskudar (Asia Side), 10-min boat ride; Kadiköy Centre (Asia Side), 20-min drive
Airports: Sabiha Gokcen, 25-min drive; Ataturk International, 30-min drive

Category: Hotel

SIRKECI KONAK

TAYA HATUN SOKAK, NO 5, 34120 SIRKECI - ISTANBUL, TURKEY
Tel: +90 212 528 4344 **Fax:** +90 212 528 4455
Web: www.johansens.com/sirkecikonak **E-mail:** info@sirkecikonak.com

Our inspector loved: *The historical atmosphere of old Istanbul.*

Price Guide:
single/double €136-200
superior €238-255
de luxe €290-325

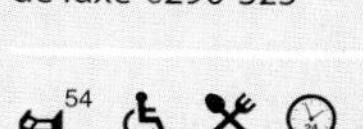

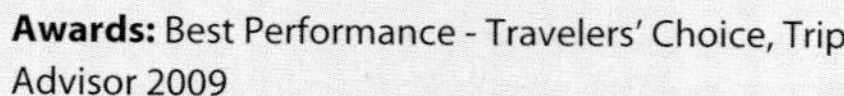

Awards: Best Performance - Travelers' Choice, Trip Advisor 2009

Attractions: Basilica Cistern, 3-min walk; Hagia Sophia, 3-min walk; Blue Mosque, 5-min walk; Topkapi Palace, 5-min walk

Nearby Towns: Asian Side of Istanbul, 20-min boat ride; Princess Islands, 90-min boat ride; Bursa, 2-hour boat ride; Edirne, 2-hour drive
Airports: Istanbul Ataturk, 20km

Category: Charming Hotel

This former Ottoman residence in the centre of Istanbul's old town combines modern amenities with local handicrafts. The atmosphere is relaxed and friendly, and the bedrooms are comfortable with pretty textiles and elegant wooden floors. For leisure, take a dip in the pool, enjoy the sauna and Jacuzzi or head to the hotel's traditional Turkish bath.

Cette ancienne résidence ottomane au coeur de la vieille ville d'Istanbul mélange les équipements modernes et l'artisanat local. L'atmosphère y est relaxante et accueillante et les chambres sont confortables avec de ravissants tissus et d'élégants parquets en bois. Pour les loisirs, plongez dans la piscine, profitez du sauna et du jacuzzi ou rendez-vous au bain turque traditionnel de l'hôtel.

Esta antigua residencía otomana del centro del casco antiguo de Estambul combina las instalaciones modernas con las artesanías locales. El ambiente es relajado y cordial y las habitaciones son cómodas, provistas de lindas telas y elegantes suelos de madera. Para el ocio, se podrá dar un chapuzón en la piscina, disfrutar de la sauna y jacuzzi o dirigirse al tradicional baño turco del hotel.

TURKEY (ISTANBUL)

SUMAHAN ON THE WATER

KULELÍ CADDESI NO 51, ÇENGELKÖY, 34684 ISTANBUL, TURKEY
Tel: +90 216 422 8000 **Fax:** +90 216 422 8008
Web: www.johansens.com/sumahan **E-mail:** info@sumahan.com

A hotel on the water, the charming Sumahan offers a personalised service. Set beside the Bosphorus Straits, which separate Europe from Asia, sit back and watch the boats and ships sailing by from your bedroom. And dine in the award-winning seafood restaurant, Kordon, or at the Waterfront Terrace restaurant for Turkish and international cuisine. The atmosphere is calm and the hamman and wellness centre is an ideal place to relax.

Un hôtel sur l'eau, Sumahan est une charmante propriété qui offre un service personnalisé. Installée à côté du détroit du Bosphore qui sépare l'Europe de l'Asie, détendez-vous et regardez les bateaux et les voiliers depuis votre chambre. Dinez au restaurant primé de poisson et fruits de mer Kordon ou au restaurant Waterfront Terrace pour une cuisine turque et internationale. L'atmosphère est calme; le hammam et le centre de remise en forme sont des endroits parfaits pour se détendre.

Un hotel sobre el agua, el encantador Sumahan ofrece un servicio personalizado. Está ubicado en el estrecho del Bósforo que separa Europa de Asia, y desde la ventana de su habitación podra contemplar los barcos y los veleros que navegan por esas aguas. Puede cenar en el galardonado restaurante de marisco "Kordon" o en el restaurante Waterfront Terrace donde se sirve cocina turca e internacional. El ambiente es tranquilo y el centro wellness con hamman es el lugar ideal para el relax.

Our inspector loved: *The history of this stylish hotel, and the wonderful Bosphorus views from every room.*

Price Guide: (complimentary scheduled boat shuttle service available)
double €240-295
suite €280-550

Attractions: Bosphorus, 5 metres; Shopping and Museums, 10-min drive; Beylerbeyi Palace, 10-min drive; Nightclubs, 15-min drive

Nearby Towns: Old City, 30-min drive
Airports: Istanbul Ataturk, 35km; Istanbul Sabiha Gökçen, 35km

Category: Charming Hotel

Villa Mahal

PO BOX 4 KALKAN, 07960 ANTALYA, TURKEY
Tel: +90 242 844 32 68 **Fax:** +90 242 844 21 22
Web: www.johansens.com/villamahal **E-mail:** info@villamahal.com

Our inspector loved: *The romantic ambience, and updates made to the villa each year!*

Price Guide:
moonlight standard/de luxe €160-230
sunset de luxe €260-290
sunset suite €310-340

Awards: Condé Nast Johansens Most Excellent Romantic Hotel 2007

Attractions: Daily Gulet Cruise, 5-min walk; Yacht Harbour, 20-min walk; Patara Beach, 15-min drive; Xanthos Ancient Site, 30-min drive

Nearby Towns: Kas, 27km; Fethiye, 75km
Airports: Dalaman, 125km

Category: Charming Hotel
Closed: November - April

An ocean lover's paradise, stone steps plunge to the villa's beach platforms and an infinity pool with integrated Jacuzzi. Hypnotise yourself with views from bright, airy and stylish bedrooms or the sound of waves lapping as you relax with a massage. Turkish specialities are on offer for breakfast, lunch and dinner. One of few hotels in Kalkan with a private beach club.

Un paradis pour amoureux de l'océan : un escalier en pierres plonge vers les pontons privés de la villa et une piscine à débordements avec un jacuzzi intégré. Vous serez hypnotisés par les vues depuis les chambres lumineuses, spacieuses et élégants ou par le clapotis des vagues pendant que vous vous détendez grâce à un massage. Des spécialités turques sont proposées au petit-déjeuner, au déjeuner et au dîner. C'est l'un des rares hôtels à Kalkan a posséder une plage privée.

Un verdadero edén para el amante de los océanos. Unos escalones de piedra bajan hasta sumergirse en el apeadero de la playa de la villa y en una gigantesca piscina provista de jacuzzi integrado. Hipnotícese con las vistas que se contemplan desde las luminosas, espaciosas y con estilos habitaciones o con el cantar de las olas mientras se relaja con un masaje. Las especialidades turcas están a su disposición para el desayuno, almuerzo y cena. Es uno de los escasos hoteles de Kalkan que disponen de club de playa privado.

TURKEY (MARMARIS)

Golden Key Bördübet

BÖRDÜBET MEVKII, MARMARIS, MUGLA, TURKEY

Tel: +90 252 436 92 30 **Fax:** +90 252 436 90 89

Web: www.johansens.com/goldenkey **E-mail:** bordubet@goldenkeyhotels.com

Our inspector loved: *The quasi-tropical, lush landscape and the private beach.*

Price Guide: (including dinner)
de luxe €180-260
African suite €230-290
forest house €450-550

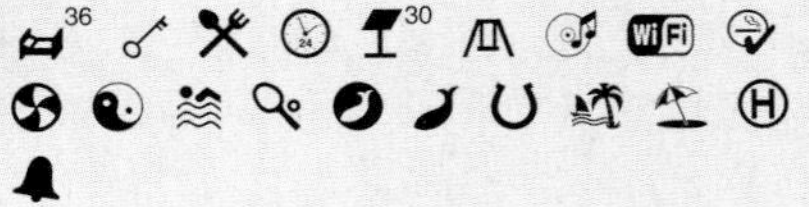

Attractions: Daily Gulet Cruise, 35km; Knidos, 60km; Kaunos/Dalyan, 90km; Ephesus, 280km

Nearby Towns: Marmaris, 25km; Datca, 45km; Bodrum, 190km

Airports: Dalaman, 125km; Bodrum, 175km; Izmir, 350km

Category: Hotel

Closed: November - April

Escape from the world and head to this secluded forest hideaway, enveloped by pine trees and lush gardens. Relax and fall asleep listening to the gentle flow of the stream running through the grounds. Comfortable bedrooms are fitted with bespoke country-style furnishings. You'll enjoy the short boat ride to the hotel's fully-equipped private beach club.

Fuyez le monde et soyez le premier dans ce refuge forestier, enveloppé par des pins et des jardins luxuriants. Détendez-vous et endormez vous au son du léger courant qui coule à travers le parc. Des meubles de style campagnard, faits sur mesure, ornent les chambres confortables. Vous apprécierez la courte promenade en bateau pour rejoindre la plage privée et son club tout équipé.

Aléjese del mundanal ruido en este apartado rincón de bosque arropado de pinos y exuberantes jardines. Relájese y duérmase mientras escucha el suave fluir del riachuelo que recorre el lugar. Sus cómodas habitaciones están provistas de un mobiliario de estilo rural diseñado en exclusividad. Disfrutará del breve paseo en bote hasta el club de playa privado del hotel, plenamente equipado para su confort.

Argos in Cappadocia

UÇHISAR, 50240 NEVSEHIR (CAPPADOCIA), TURKEY
Tel: +90 384 2193130 **Fax:** +90 384 219 2055
Web: www.johansens.com/argos **E-mail:** aic@argos.com.tr

Our inspector loved: *The simple elegance and modern design that respects the building's history.*

Price Guide:
room €110-1,200

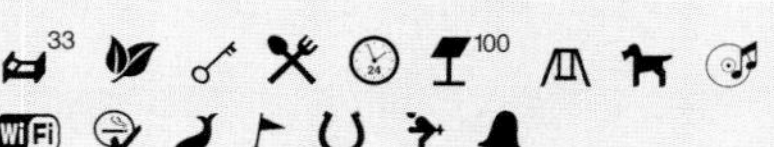

Attractions: Hiking in Valleys, 2-min walk; Göreme Open-Air Museum, 5-min drive; Uçhisar Castle, 10-min walk; Underground City, 20-min drive

Nearby Towns: Uçhisar, 5-min walk; Göreme, 5-min drive; Nevsehir, 10-min drive; Urgup, 15-min drive
Airports: Nevsehir, 35-min drive; Kayseri, 60-min drive

Category: Charming Hotel

Ancient houses, caves and tunnels have been uniquely transformed into an amazing holiday location of modern luxury and spaciousness in the old town of Uchisar. Bedrooms and public rooms are enchanting and interconnected with lush gardens and sun-soaked terraces. There are inviting nooks and crannies, views towards majestic Mount Erciyes and a fairy-tale ambience to enchant every visitor.

D'anciennes maisons, des caves et des tunnels ont été transformés de manières exceptionnelles en un lieu de vacances moderne, luxueux et spacieux dans la vieille ville de Uchisar. Les chambres et espaces communs sont un enchantement et fusionnent avec des jardins luxuriants et des terrasses ensoleillées. Il y a d'invitants coins et recoins, des superbes vues sur le majestueux Mont Erciyes et une ambiance de conte de fées qui ravira tous les visiteurs.

Varias casas ancestrales, cuevas y túneles se han transformado de manera inigualable para crear un asombroso destino de vacaciones, amplio y de moderno lujo, en la antigua ciudad de Uchisar. Sus habitaciones y dependencias comunes son encantadoras y están conectadas entre sí con frondosos jardines y soleadas terrazas. El lugar cuenta con numerosos y atractivos rincones y escondrijos, vistas al majestuoso Monte Erciyes y un ambiente propio de cuento de hadas que cautiva a todo visitante.

Cappadocia Cave Resorts & Spa

TEKELLI MAHALLESI, GÖREME CADDESI 83, 50240 UÇHISAR-CAPPADOCIA, NEVSEHIR, TURKEY
Tel: +90 384 219 3194 **Fax:** +90 384 219 3197
Web: www.johansens.com/ccrhotels **E-mail:** info@ccr-hotels.com

Our inspector loved: *The excellent amenities, and great views.*

Price Guide:
double €302
de luxe €399
suite €499-1,187

Attractions: Göreme Open-Air Museum, a UNESCO World Heritage Site, 3km; Pigeon Valley, 10-min walk; Underground Cities, 30km; Ihlara Gorge, 60km

Nearby Towns: Göreme, 3km; Nevsehir, 5km; Avanos, 12km; Kayseri, 70km
Airports: Nevsehir, 40km; Kayseri, 75km

Category: Hotel

Comprising old houses and cave homes on a sloping hill below the magnificent Uchisar Castle, rooms enjoy magical views over to the Red Valley, Mount Erciyes and Göreme. Traditional Turkish style meets modern luxury, and first-class resort facilities match the exceptional personal service. With the only spa in Cappadocia, it is a must to experience!

Composé de vieilles maisons et de caves situées sur la pente d'une colline sous le majestueux château Uchisar, les chambres profitent de magnifiques vues sur la Vallée Rouge, le Mont Erciyes et Göreme. Le style traditionnel turque se mélange au luxe moderne et les équipements de premier ordre rivalisent avec un service personnalisé exceptionnel. Faites l'expérience du seul spa de Cappadocia!

Este complejo vacacional lo componen casas antiguas y casas-cueva situadas en la ladera de una colina bajo el magnífico Castillo de Uchisar. Las habitaciones gozan de mágicas vistas al Valle Rojo, Monte Erciyes y Göreme. El estilo tradicional turco se combina con el lujo moderno, y las instalaciones de primera clase en todo el complejo están a la altura de su excepcional servicio personalizado. ¡Con su spa, el único de Cappadocia, resulta una experiencia que no puede perderse!

SACRED HOUSE

DUTLU CAMI MAHALLESI, BARBAROS HAYRETTIN SOKAK, NO 25, 50400 ÜRGÜP - CAPPADOCIA, TURKEY
Tel: +90 384 341 7102 **Fax:** +90 384 341 6986
Web: www.johansens.com/sacredhouse **E-mail:** info@sacred-house.com

Our inspector loved: *The excellent blend of history, charm and elegance.*

Price Guide: (10% discount applicable for cash payments)
standard US$210
de luxe US$300
superior de luxe US$500

Attractions: Turkish Bath, 2-min walk; Wineries, 4km; Göreme Open-Air Museum, a UNESCO World Heritage Site, 8km; Underground Cities, 35km

Nearby Towns: Göreme, 8km; Avanos, 9km; Nevsehir, 17km; Kayseri, 65km
Airports: Nevsehir, 45km; Kayseri, 70km

Category: Charming Hotel

Welcome to the mystical world of Sacred House. A former mansion, now a stylish boutique hotel, prepare to be "wowed" by the unique design that oozes medieval majesty. Emotive lighting, custom-ordered fabrics, wooden carvings, antiques and exposed stone walls are found throughout. You'll love the little restaurant with its ancient Anatolian-inspired menu.

Bienvenue dans le monde mystique de Sacred House. Dans cet ancien manoir, devenu un élégant boutique hôtel, préparez-vous à être séduit par sa conception unique qui respire l'atmosphère médiévale. Lumière douce, tissus fabriqués sur-mesure, sculptures sur bois, antiquités et sols en pierres apparentes sont présents dans tout l'hôtel. Vous adorerez le petit restaurant avec son menu inspiré par l'Anatolie ancienne.

Bienvenido al místico mundo de Sacred House, antigua mansión convertida en la actualidad en un boutique hotel. Déjese cautivar por su singular diseño que rezuma una majestuosidad propia del Medievo. Encontrará una iluminación emotiva, telas de encargo, grabados en madera, antigüedades y paredes de piedra al descubierto por todas partes. Le encantará el pequeño restaurante con su carta inspirada en platos de la antigua Anatolia.

Hotels, Great Britain & Ireland

Properties listed below can be found in our Recommended Hotels & Spas, Great Britain & Ireland 2010 Guide.

Properties from our Recommended Hotels & Spas, Great Britain & Ireland 2010 Guide

Channel Islands

Braye Beach Hotel	Alderney	+44 (0)1481 824300
Fermain Valley Hotel	Guernsey	+44 (0)1481 235 666
The Atlantic Hotel and Ocean Restaurant	Jersey	+44 (0)1534 744101
The Club Hotel & Spa, Bohemia Restaurant	Jersey	+44 (0)1534 876500
Longueville Manor	Jersey	+44 (0)1534 725501

England

The Bath Priory Hotel, Restaurant & Spa	B & NE Somerset	+44 (0)1225 331922
Dukes Hotel	B & NE Somerset	+44 (0)1225 787960
Homewood Park	B & NE Somerset	+44 (0)1225 723731
Hunstrete House	B & NE Somerset	+44 (0)1761 490490
The Royal Crescent & The Bath House	B & NE Somerset	+44 (0)1225 823333
Luton Hoo Hotel, Golf & Spa	Bedfordshire	+44 (0)1582 734437
Moore Place Hotel	Bedfordshire	+44 (0)1908 282000
Cantley House Hotel	Berkshire	+44 (0)118 978 9912
Cliveden & The Pavilion Spa	Berkshire	+44 (0)1628 668561
Fredrick's – Hotel Restaurant Spa	Berkshire	+44 (0)1628 581000
The French Horn	Berkshire	+44 (0)1189 692204
Stirrups Country House Hotel	Berkshire	+44 (0)1344 882284
Danesfield House Hotel and Spa	Buckinghamshire	+44 (0)1628 891010
Hartwell House Hotel, Restaurant & Spa	Buckinghamshire	+44 (0)1296 747444
Stoke Park	Buckinghamshire	+44 (0)1753 717171
Rowton Hall Hotel, Health Club & Spa	Cheshire	+44 (0)1244 335262
Budock Vean - The Hotel on the River	Cornwall	+44 (0)1326 252100
The Cornwall Hotel, Spa & Estate	Cornwall	+44 (0)1726 874545
Hell Bay	Cornwall	+44 (0)1720 422947
The Lugger Hotel	Cornwall	+44 (0)1872 501322
Meudon Hotel	Cornwall	+44 (0)1326 250541
The Nare Hotel	Cornwall	+44 (0)1872 501111
The Polurrian Hotel	Cornwall	+44 (0)1326 240421
Rose-In-Vale Country House Hotel	Cornwall	+44 (0)1872 552202
St Michael's Hotel & Spa	Cornwall	+44 (0)1326 312707
Armathwaite Hall Country House Hotel and Spa	Cumbria	+44 (0)17687 76551
Dale Head Hall Lakeside Hotel	Cumbria	+44 (0)17687 72478
Farlam Hall Hotel	Cumbria	+44 (0)16977 46234
Holbeck Ghyll Country House Hotel	Cumbria	+44 (0)15394 32375
The Inn on the Lake	Cumbria	+44 (0)17684 82444
Lakeside Hotel on Lake Windermere	Cumbria	+44 (0)15395 30001
Linthwaite House Hotel	Cumbria	+44 (0)15394 88600
The Lodore Falls Hotel	Cumbria	+44 (0)17687 77285
Lovelady Shield Country House Hotel	Cumbria	+44 (0)1434 381203
Netherwood Hotel	Cumbria	+44 (0)15395 32552
Rothay Manor	Cumbria	+44 (0)15394 33605
The Samling	Cumbria	+44 (0)1539 431 922
Sharrow Bay	Cumbria	+44 (0)1768 486 301
Tufton Arms Hotel	Cumbria	+44 (0)17683 51593
Callow Hall	Derbyshire	+44 (0)1335 300900
Cathedral Quarter Hotel	Derbyshire	+44 (0)1332 546080
The Izaak Walton Hotel	Derbyshire	+44 (0)1335 350555
Losehill House Hotel & Spa	Derbyshire	+44 (0)1433 621219
Risley Hall Hotel and Spa	Derbyshire	+44 (0)115 939 9000
Riverside House	Derbyshire	+44 (0)1629 814275
Buckland-Tout-Saints	Devon	+44 (0)1548 853055
Combe House	Devon	+44 (0)1404 540400
Gidleigh Park	Devon	+44 (0)1647 432367
Hotel Riviera	Devon	+44 (0)1395 515201
Lewtrenchard Manor	Devon	+44 (0)1566 783222
Mill End	Devon	+44 (0)1647 432282
Northcote Manor Country House Hotel	Devon	+44 (0)1769 560501
Orestone Manor & The Restaurant at Orestone Manor	Devon	+44 (0)1803 328098
Soar Mill Cove Hotel	Devon	+44 (0)1548 561566
The Tides Reach Hotel	Devon	+44 (0)1548 843466
Watersmeet Hotel	Devon	+44 (0)1271 870333
Alexandra Hotel and Restaurant	Dorset	+44 (0)1297 442010
Captain's Club Hotel	Dorset	+44 (0)1202 475111
The Priory Hotel	Dorset	+44 (0)1929 551666
Stock Hill Country House Hotel & Restaurant	Dorset	+44 (0)1747 823626
Summer Lodge Country House Hotel, Restaurant and Spa	Dorset	+44 (0)1935 482000
Rockliffe Hall	Durham	+44 (0)1325 729999

Seaham Hall & The Serenity Spa	**Durham**	**+44 (0)1915 161 400**
Maison Talbooth	Essex	+44 (0)1206 322367
Bibury Court	Gloucestershire	+44 (0)1285 740337
Burleigh Court	Gloucestershire	+44 (0)1453 883804
Calcot Manor Hotel & Spa	Gloucestershire	+44 (0)1666 890391
Charingworth Manor	Gloucestershire	+44 (0)1386 593555
The Greenway	Gloucestershire	+44 (0)1242 862352
Lower Slaughter Manor	Gloucestershire	+44 (0)1451 820456
The Manor House Hotel	Gloucestershire	+44 (0)1608 650501
Washbourne Court	Gloucestershire	+44 (0)1451 822143
Thornbury Castle	S Gloucestershire	+44 (0)1454 281182
Chewton Glen	Hampshire	+44 (0)1425 275341
New Park Manor and Bath House Spa	Hampshire	+44 (0)1590 623467
Tylney Hall	Hampshire	+44 (0)1256 764881
Castle House	Herefordshire	+44 (0)1432 356321
Down Hall Country House Hotel	Hertfordshire	+44 (0)1279 731441
Great Hallingbury Manor Hotel	Hertfordshire	+44 (0)1279 506475
Eastwell Manor	Kent	+44 (0)1233 213000
The George Of Stamford	Lincolnshire	+44 (0)1780 750750
41	London	+44 (0)20 7300 0041
51 Buckingham Gate, Taj Suites and Residences	London	+44 (0)20 7769 7766
Beaufort House	London	+44 (0)20 7584 2600
The Egerton House Hotel	London	+44 (0)20 7589 2412
Hotel Verta	London	+44 (0)20 7978 0875
Jumeirah Carlton Tower	London	+44 (0)20 7235 1234
Jumeirah Lowndes Hotel	London	+44 (0)20 7823 1234
Kensington House Hotel	London	+44 (0)20 7937 2345
The Mandeville Hotel	London	+44 (0)20 7935 5599
The Mayflower Hotel	London	+44 (0)20 7370 0991
Milestone Hotel	London	+44 (0)20 7917 1000
The New Linden Hotel	London	+44 (0)20 7221 4321

Hotels & Small Hotels, Great Britain & Ireland

Properties listed below can be found in our Recommended Hotels & Spas, Great Britain & Ireland 2010 Guide and our Recommended Small Hotels, Inns & Restaurants, Great Britain 2010 Guide.

Sofitel London St James	London	+44 (0)20 7747 2200
St James's Hotel and Club	London	+44 (0)20 7316 1600
Twenty Nevern Square	London	+44 (0)20 7565 9555
Westbury Hotel	London	+44 (0)20 7629 7755
The Wyndham Grand London Chelsea Harbour	London	+44 (0)20 7823 3000
Congham Hall	Norfolk	+44 (0)1485 600250
Rushton Hall Hotel & Spa	Northamptonshire	+44 (0)1536 713001
Doxford Hall Hotel and Spa	Northumberland	+44 (0)1665 589700
Lace Market Hotel	Nottinghamshire	+44 (0)115 852 3232
Ye Olde Bell Hotel & Restaurant	Nottinghamshire	+44 (0)1777 705121
Bicester Country Club	Oxfordshire	+44 (0)1869 241204
Le Manoir aux Quat' Saisons	Oxfordshire	+44 (0)1844 278881
Old Bank Hotel	Oxfordshire	+44 (0)1865 799599
The Old Parsonage Hotel	Oxfordshire	+44 (0)1865 310210
Weston Manor	Oxfordshire	+44 (0)1869 350621
Hambleton Hall	Rutland	+44 (0)1572 756991
The Castle at Taunton	Somerset	+44 (0)1823 272671
The Mount Somerset	Somerset	+44 (0)1823 442500
Ston Easton Park	Somerset	+44 (0)1761 241631
Hoar Cross Hall Spa Resort	Staffordshire	+44 (0)1283 575671
Hintlesham Hall	Suffolk	+44 (0)1473 652334
Kesgrave Hall	Suffolk	+44 (0)1473 333741
Ashdown Park Hotel and Country Club	East Sussex	+44 (0)1342 824988
Dale Hill	East Sussex	+44 (0)1580 200112
The Grand Hotel	East Sussex	+44 (0)1323 412345
Horsted Place Country House Hotel	East Sussex	+44 (0)1825 750581
Newick Park	East Sussex	+44 (0)1825 723633
Amberley Castle	West Sussex	+44 (0)1798 831992
Bailiffscourt Hotel & Spa	West Sussex	+44 (0)1903 723511
Felbridge Hotel & Spa	West Sussex	+44 (0)1342 337700
Ockenden Manor	West Sussex	+44 (0)1444 416111
The Spread Eagle Hotel & Spa	West Sussex	+44 (0)1730 816911
The Vermont Hotel	Tyne & Wear	+44 (0)191 233 1010
Ardencote Manor Hotel, Country Club & Spa	Warwickshire	+44 (0)1926 843111
Mallory Court	Warwickshire	+44 (0)1926 330214
Nailcote Hall	Warwickshire	+44 (0)2476 466174
Wroxall Abbey Estate	Warwickshire	+44 (0)1926 484470
Bishopstrow House & The Halcyon Spa	Wiltshire	+44 (0)1985 212312
Lucknam Park Hotel & Spa	Wiltshire	+44 (0)1225 742777
The Pear Tree At Purton	Wiltshire	+44 (0)1793 772100
Whatley Manor	Wiltshire	+44 (0)1666 822888
Brockencote Hall	Worcestershire	+44 (0)1562 777876
Buckland Manor	Worcestershire	+44 (0)1386 852626
The Cottage in the Wood	Worcestershire	+44 (0)1684 588860
The Evesham Hotel	Worcestershire	+44 (0)1386 765566
Middlethorpe Hall Hotel, Restaurant & Spa	North Yorkshire	+44 (0)1904 641241
Ox Pasture Hall	North Yorkshire	+44 (0)1723 365295
Simonstone Hall	North Yorkshire	+44 (0)1969 667255

Ireland

Dromoland Castle	Clare	+353 61368144
Castlemartyr Resort	Cork	+353 214219070
Fitzpatrick Castle Hotel	Dublin	+353 1 230 5400
Ballynahinch Castle Hotel	Galway	+353 953 1006
Cashel House	Galway	+353 95 31001
Cahernane House Hotel	Kerry	+353 64 6631895
Park Hotel Kenmare & SÁMAS	Kerry	+353 64 66 41200
Ashford Castle	Mayo	+353 94 95 46003
Knockranny House Hotel & Spa	Mayo	+353 98 28600
The Horse and Jockey Hotel	Tipperary	+353 504 44192
Dunbrody Country House & Cookery School	Wexford	+353 51 389 600
Kelly's Resort Hotel & Spa	Wexford	+353 53 91 32114
Marlfield House	Wexford	+353 53 94 21124
The Ritz-Carlton, Powerscourt	Wicklow	+353 1 274 8888

N Ireland

Ten Square	Antrim	+44 (0)28 90 241 001

Scotland

Craigellachie Hotel of Speyside	Aberdeenshire	+44 (0)1340 881204
Ardanaiseig	Argyll & Bute	+44 (0)1866 833333
Stonefield Castle	Argyll & Bute	+44 (0)1880 820836
Auchen Castle	Dumfries & Galloway	+44 (0)1683 300407
Bunchrew House Hotel	Highland	+44 (0)1463 234917
Inverlochy Castle	Highland	+44 (0)1397 702177
Rocpool Reserve and Chez Roux	Highland	+44 (0)1463 240089
Royal Highland Hotel	Highland	+44 (0)1463 231926
The Torridon	Highland	+44 (0)1445 791242
Tulloch Castle Hotel	Highland	+44 (0)1349 861325
Dalhousie Castle and Aqueous Spa	Midlothian	+44 (0)1875 820153

Wales

Penrallt	Ceredigion	+44 (0)1239 810227
Bodysgallen Hall & Spa	Conwy	+44 (0)1492 584466
St Tudno Hotel & Restaurant	Conwy	+44 (0)1492 874411
Penmaenuchaf Hall	Gwynedd	+44 (0)1341 422129
Lamphey Court Hotel & Spa	Pembrokeshire	+44 (0)1646 672273
Warpool Court Hotel	Pembrokeshire	+44 (0)1437 720300
Lake Country House & Spa	Powys	+44 (0)1591 620202
Lake Vyrnwy Hotel & Spa	Powys	+44 (0)1691 870 692
Ynyshir Hall	Powys	+44 (0)1654 781209
Holm House	Vale of Glamorgan	+44 (0)2920 701572

Properties from our Recommended Small Hotels, Inns & Restaurants, Great Britain 2010 Guide

Channel Islands

The Farmhouse	Guernsey	+44 (0)1481 264 181
La Sablonnerie	Guernsey	+44 (0)1481 832061
The White House	Guernsey	+44 (0)1481 722159
Château La Chaire	Jersey	+44 (0)1534 863354

England

Cornfields Restaurant & Hotel	Bedfordshire	+44 (0)1234 378990
The Christopher Hotel Bar & Grill	Berkshire	+44 (0)1753 852359
Fox Country Inn	Buckinghamshire	+44 (0)1491 639333
The Hand & Flowers	Buckinghamshire	+44 (0)1628 482277
Shakespeare House	Buckinghamshire	+44 (0)1296 770776
The Garrack Hotel & Restaurant	Cornwall	+44 (0)1736 796199
Trevalsa Court Country House Hotel	Cornwall	+44 (0)1726 842468
Broadoaks Country House	Cumbria	+44 (0)1539 445566
Crosby Lodge Country House Hotel	Cumbria	+44 (0)1228 573618
Fayrer Garden House Hotel	Cumbria	+44 (0)15394 88195
The Pheasant	Cumbria	+44 (0)17687 76234
The Wheatsheaf, Brigsteer	Cumbria	+44 (0)15395 68254
Dannah Farm Country House	Derbyshire	+44 (0)1773 550273

Small Hotels, Great Britain

Properties listed below can be found in our Recommended Small Hotels, Inns & Restaurants, Great Britain 2010 Guide.

Donington Manor Hotel	Derbyshire	+44 (0)1332 810 253
Hassop Hall	Derbyshire	+44 (0)1629 640488
The Plough Inn	Derbyshire	+44 (0)1433 650319
The Samuel Fox Country Inn	Derbyshire	+44 (0)1433 621562
The Arundell Arms	Devon	+44 (0)1566 784666
The Cary Arms	Devon	+44 (0)1803 327110
Kingston House	Devon	+44 (0)1803 762 235
Yeoldon House Hotel	Devon	+44 (0)1237 474400
The Grange at Oborne	Dorset	+44 (0)1935 813463
Pier View	Essex	+44 (0)1702 437 900
Beaumont House	Gloucestershire	+44 (0)1242 223311
The Kings Hotel	Gloucestershire	+44 (0)1386 840256
Lower Brook House	Gloucestershire	+44 (0)1386 700286
Lypiatt House	Gloucestershire	+44 (0)1242 224994
The Redesdale Arms	Gloucestershire	+44 (0)1608 650308
The Swan Hotel	Gloucestershire	+44 (0)1285 740695
Three Choirs Vineyards Estate	Gloucestershire	+44 (0)1531 890223
The White Hart Royal Hotel	Gloucestershire	+44 (0)1608 650731
Esseborne Manor	Hampshire	+44 (0)1264 736444
The Mill At Gordleton	Hampshire	+44 (0)1590 682219
The Nurse's Cottage Restaurant with Rooms	Hampshire	+44 (0)1590 683402
Aylestone Court	Herefordshire	+44 (0)1432 341891
The Chase Hotel	Herefordshire	+44 (0)1989 763161
Glewstone Court Country House Hotel & Restaurant	Herefordshire	+44 (0)1989 770367
Wilton Court Hotel	Herefordshire	+44 (0)1989 562569
The White House and Lion & Lamb Bar & Restaurant	Hertfordshire	+44 (0)1279 870257
The Priory Bay Hotel	Isle of Wight	+44 (0)1983 613146
Rylstone Manor	Isle of Wight	+44 (0)1983 862806
Winterbourne Country House	Isle of Wight	+44 (0)1983 852 535
Little Silver Country Hotel	Kent	+44 (0)1233 850321
The Royal Harbour Hotel	Kent	+44 (0)1843 591514
Wallett's Court Hotel & Spa	Kent	+44 (0)1304 852424
The White Cliffs Hotel	Kent	+44 (0)1304 852229
Ferrari's Restaurant & Hotel	Lancashire	+44 (0)1772 783148
The Old Rectory	Norfolk	+44 (0)1603 700772
The Orchard House	Northumberland	+44 (0)1669 620 684
Waren House Hotel	Northumberland	+44 (0)1668 214581
Cockliffe Country House Hotel	Nottinghamshire	+44 (0)115 968 0179
Greenwood Lodge	Nottinghamshire	+44 (0)115 962 1206
Langar Hall	Nottinghamshire	+44 (0)1949 860559
Burford House	Oxfordshire	+44 (0)1993 823151
The Lamb Inn	Oxfordshire	+44 (0)1993 823155
The Nut Tree Restaurant	Oxfordshire	+44 (0)1865 331253
Pen-Y-Dyffryn Country Hotel	Shropshire	+44 (0)1691 653700
Soulton Hall	Shropshire	+44 (0)1939 232786
Beryl	Somerset	+44 (0)1749 678738
Compton House	Somerset	+44 (0)1934 733944
Karslake Country House and Cottage	Somerset	+44 (0)1643 851242
Dunsley Hall Hotel	Staffordshire	+44 (0)1384 877077
Moddershall Oaks Spa Restaurant Suites	Staffordshire	+44 (0)1782 399000
The Angel Hotel	Suffolk	+44 (0)1787 247388
Clarice House	Suffolk	+44 (0)1284 705550
The Cornwallis Country Hotel & Restaurant	Suffolk	+44 (0)1379 870326
The Crown Inn	Surrey	+44 (0)1428 682255
The Fish House	West Sussex	+44 (0)1243 519 444
The Old Vicarage	Warwickshire	+44 (0)1327 262626
The Castle Inn	Wiltshire	+44 (0)1249 783030
The Pear Tree Inn	Wiltshire	+44 (0)1225 709131
Stanton Manor Hotel & Gallery Restaurant	Wiltshire	+44 (0)1666 837552
Widbrook Grange	Wiltshire	+44 (0)1225 864750/8
The Cotford Hotel & L'Amuse-Bouche Restaurant	Worcestershire	+44 (0)1684 572427
Hadley Bowling Green Inn	Worcestershire	+44 (0)1905 620 294
The Old Rectory	Worcestershire	+44 (0)1527 523000
The White Lion Hotel	Worcestershire	+44 (0)1684 592551
Kilham Hall	East Riding of Yorkshire	+44 (0)1262 420466
Austwick Hall	North Yorkshire	+44 (0)15242 51794
The Austwick Traddock	North Yorkshire	+44 (0)15242 51224
Dunsley Hall	North Yorkshire	+44 (0)1947 893437
George and Dragon Inn	North Yorkshire	+44 (0)1969 663358
The Worsley Arms Hotel	North Yorkshire	+44 (0)1653 628234
Ashmount Country House	West Yorkshire	+44 (0)1535 645 726

Scotland

Loch Melfort Hotel & Restaurant	Argyll & Bute	+44 (0)1852 200 233
The Majestic Line - Argyll Coast Cruises	Argyll & Bute	+44 (0)131 623 5012
Culzean Castle – The Eisenhower Apartment	South Ayrshire	+44 (0)1655 884455
Balcary Bay Hotel	Dumfries & Galloway	+44 (0)1556 640217
Corsewall Lighthouse Hotel	Dumfries & Galloway	+44 (0)1776 853220
Craigadam	Dumfries & Galloway	+44 (0)1556 650233
The Rutland Hotel	Edinburgh	+44 (0)131 229 3402
Greshornish House	Highland	+44 (0)1470 582266
Inveran Lodge	Highland	+44 (0)1667 455 666
Kincraig Castle Hotel	Highland	+44 (0)1349 852587
Loch Ness Lodge	Highland	+44 (0)1456 459469
Royal Marine Hotel, Restaurant & Spa	Highland	+44 (0)1408 621252
Ruddyglow Park	Highland	+44 (0)1571 822216
The Steadings at The Grouse & Trout	Highland	+44 (0)1808 521314
Toravaig House	Highland	+44 (0)1471 820222

Knockomie Hotel	**Moray**	**+44 (0)1309 673146**
Castle Venlaw	Scottish Borders	+44 (0)1721 720384
The County Hotel	Scottish Borders	+44 (0)1750 721233
Fauhope Country House	Scottish Borders	+44 (0)1896 823184

Wales

Egerton Grey	Cardiff	+44 (0)1446 711666
Ty Mawr Country Hotel	Carmarthenshire	+44 (0)1267 202332
Pentre Mawr Country House	Denbighshire	+44 (0)1824 790732
Bae Abermaw	Gwynedd	+44 (0)1341 280550
Llwyndu Farmhouse	Gwynedd	+44 (0)1341 280144
Porth Tocyn Country House Hotel	Gwynedd	+44 (0)1758 713303
The Bell At Skenfrith	Monmouthshire	+44 (0)1600 750235
The Crown At Whitebrook	Monmouthshire	+44 (0)1600 860254
Penally Abbey	Pembrokeshire	+44 (0)1834 843033
Wolfscastle Country Hotel & Restaurant	Pembrokeshire	+44 (0)1437 741225

Hotels - The Americas

Recommendations in Canada

Properties listed below can be found in our Recommended Hotels, Inns, Resorts & Spas - The Americas, Atlantic, Caribbean & Pacific 2010 Guide.

CANADA - BRITISH COLUMBIA (SALT SPRING ISLAND)

Hastings House, Country House Hotel

160 Upper Ganges Road, Salt Spring Island, British Columbia V8K 2S2

Tel: +1 250 537 2362
Web: www.johansens.com/hastingshouse

CANADA - BRITISH COLUMBIA (SONORA ISLAND)

Sonora Resort

Sonora Island, British Columbia

Tel: +1 604 233 0460
Web: www.johansens.com/sonoraresort

CANADA - BRITISH COLUMBIA (SOOKE)

Sooke Harbour House

1528 Whiffen Spit Road, Sooke, British Columbia V9Z 0T4

Tel: +1 250 642 3421
Web: www.johansens.com/sookeharbour

CANADA - BRITISH COLUMBIA (TOFINO)

Clayoquot Wilderness Resort

Bedwell River Outpost, Box 130, Tofino, British Columbia V0R 2Z0

Tel: +1 250 726 8235
Web: www.johansens.com/clayoquot

CANADA - BRITISH COLUMBIA (TOFINO)

Wickaninnish Inn

Osprey Lane at Chesterman Beach, Tofino, British Columbia V0R 2Z0

Tel: +1 250 725 3100
Web: www.johansens.com/wickaninnish

CANADA - BRITISH COLUMBIA (VANCOUVER)

Pan Pacific Vancouver

300-999 Canada Place, Vancouver, British Columbia V6C 3B5

Tel: +1 604 662 8111
Web: www.johansens.com/panpacific

CANADA - BRITISH COLUMBIA (VANCOUVER)

The Sutton Place Hotel Vancouver

845 Burrard Street, Vancouver, British Columbia V6Z 2K6

Tel: +1 604 682 5511
Web: www.johansens.com/suttonplacebc

CANADA - BRITISH COLUMBIA (VANCOUVER)

Wedgewood Hotel & Spa

845 Hornby Street, Vancouver, British Columbia V6Z 1V1

Tel: +1 604 689 7777
Web: www.johansens.com/wedgewoodbc

CANADA - BRITISH COLUMBIA (VICTORIA)

Brentwood Bay Lodge & Spa

849 Verdier Avenue, Victoria, British Columbia V8M 1C5

Tel: +1 250 544 2079
Web: www.johansens.com/brentwood

CANADA - BRITISH COLUMBIA (VICTORIA)

Villa Marco Polo Inn

1524 Shasta Place, Victoria, British Columbia V8S 1X9

Tel: +1 250 370 1524
Web: www.johansens.com/villamarcopolo

CANADA - NOVA SCOTIA (EAST KEMPTVILLE)

Trout Point Lodge of Nova Scotia

189 Trout Point Road, Off the East Branch Road and Highway 203, East Kemptville, Nova Scotia B0W 1Y0

Tel: +1 902 761 2142
Web: www.johansens.com/troutpoint

CANADA - NOVA SCOTIA (WALLACE)

Fox Harb'r

1337 Fox Harbour Road, Wallace, Nova Scotia B0K 1Y0

Tel: +1 902 257 1801
Web: www.johansens.com/foxharbr

CANADA - ONTARIO (NIAGARA-ON-THE-LAKE)

The Charles Inn

209 Queen Street, Box 642, Niagara-on-the-Lake, Ontario L0S 1J0

Tel: +1 905 468 4588
Web: www.johansens.com/charlesinnca

CANADA - ONTARIO (NIAGARA-ON-THE-LAKE)

Harbour House

85 Melville Street, Box 760, Niagara-on-the-Lake, Ontario L0S 1J0

Tel: +1 905 468 4683
Web: www.johansens.com/harbourhouseca

CANADA - ONTARIO (NIAGARA-ON-THE-LAKE)

Riverbend Inn & Vineyard

16104 Niagara River Parkway, Niagara-on-the-Lake, Ontario L0S 1J0

Tel: +1 905 468 8866
Web: www.johansens.com/riverbend

CANADA - ONTARIO (NIAGARA-ON-THE-LAKE)

Shaw Club Hotel & Spa

P.O. Box 642, 92 Picton Street, Niagara-on-the-Lake, Ontario L0S 1J0

Tel: +1 905 468 5711
Web: www.johansens.com/shawclub

Hotels - The Americas

Properties listed below can be found in our Recommended Hotels, Inns, Resorts & Spas - The Americas, Atlantic, Caribbean & Pacific 2010 Guide.

CANADA - ONTARIO (TORONTO)

Windsor Arms

18 St. Thomas Street, Toronto, Ontario M5S 3E7

Tel: +1 416 971 9666
Web: www.johansens.com/windsorarms

CANADA - QUÉBEC (MONT-TREMBLANT)

Hôtel Quintessence

3004 chemin de la chapelle, Mont-Tremblant, Québec J8E 1E1

Tel: +1 819 425 3400
Web: www.johansens.com/quintessence

CANADA - QUÉBEC (MONTRÉAL)

Auberge du Vieux-Port

97 de la Commune Est, Montréal, Québec H2Y 1J1

Tel: +1 514 876 0081
Web: www.johansens.com/aubergeduvieuxport

CANADA - QUÉBEC (MONTRÉAL)

Hôtel Nelligan

106 rue Saint-Paul Ouest, Montréal, Québec H2Y 1Z3

Tel: +1 514 788 2040
Web: www.johansens.com/nelligan

CANADA - QUÉBEC (MONTRÉAL)

Le Place d'Armes Hôtel & Suites

55 rue Saint-Jacques Ouest, Montréal, Québec H2Y 3X2

Tel: +1 514 842 1887
Web: www.johansens.com/hotelplacedarmes

CANADA - QUÉBEC (NORTH HATLEY)

Manoir Hovey

575 Hovey Road, North Hatley, Québec J0B 2CO

Tel: +1 819 842 2421
Web: www.johansens.com/manoirhovey

Recommendations in México

MÉXICO - BAJA CALIFORNIA SUR (SAN JOSÉ DEL CABO)

Zoëtry Casa Del Mar Los Cabos

KM 19.5 Carretera Transpeninsular, San José del Cabo, Baja California Sur 23400

Tel: +52 624 145 7711
Web: www.johansens.com/casadelmar

MÉXICO - DISTRITO FEDERAL (MÉXICO CITY)

Hotel Boutique Casa Vieja Mexico

Eugenio Sue 45 (Colonia Polanco), México Distrito Federal 11560

Tel: +52 55 52 82 0067
Web: www.johansens.com/casavieja

MÉXICO - GUANAJUATO (GUANAJUATO)

Villa Maria Cristina

Paseo de La Presa de la Olla No. 76 Centro, Guanajuato, Guanajuato 36000

Tel: +52 473 731 2182
Web: www.johansens.com/villamariacristina

MÉXICO - GUERRERO (ACAPULCO)

Las Brisas Acapulco

Carretera Escenica 5255, Clemente Mejia, Acapulco, Guerrero 39867

Tel: +52 744 469 6900
Web: www.johansens.com/brisasacapulco

MÉXICO - GUERRERO (IXTAPA-ZIHUATANEJO)

Loma del Mar

Ixtapa-Zihuatanejo, Guerrero 40884

Tel: +52 755 555 0460
Web: www.johansens.com/lomadelmar

MÉXICO - JALISCO (COSTALEGRE - COSTA CAREYES)

El Careyes Beach Resort

Km 53.5, Carretera Barra de Navidad-Puerto Vallarta, Costa Careyes, Jalisco 48970

Tel: +52 315 351 0000
Web: www.johansens.com/elcareyes

MÉXICO - JALISCO (COSTALEGRE - PUERTO VALLARTA)

Hotelito Desconocido

Playon de Mismaloya S/N,Municipio de Tomatlán, La Cruz de Loreto, Jalisco 48460

Tel: +52 33 3611 1255
Web: www.johansens.com/hotelito

MÉXICO - JALISCO (COSTALEGRE - PUERTO VALLARTA)

Las Alamandas Resort

Carretera Barra de Navidad - Puerto Vallarta km 83.5, Col. Quemaro, Jalisco 48850

Tel: +52 322 285 5500
Web: www.johansens.com/alamandas

MÉXICO - JALISCO (PUERTO VALLARTA)

Casa Velas Hotel Boutique

Pelicanos 311, Fracc. Marina Vallarta, Puerto Vallarta, Jalisco 48354

Tel: +52 322 226 6688
Web: www.johansens.com/casavelas

Hotels - The Americas

Properties listed below can be found in our Recommended Hotels, Inns, Resorts & Spas - The Americas, Atlantic, Caribbean & Pacific 2010 Guide.

MÉXICO - MICHOACÁN (MORELIA)

Hotel Virrey de Mendoza

Avenida Madero Pte. 310, Centro Histórico, Morelia, Michoacán 58000

Tel: +52 44 33 12 06 33
Web: www.johansens.com/hvirrey

MÉXICO - MICHOACÁN (MORELIA)

Villa Montaña Hotel & Spa

Patzimba 201, Vista Bella, Morelia, Michoacán 58090

Tel: +52 443 314 02 31
Web: www.johansens.com/montana

MÉXICO - MICHOACÁN (PÁTZCUARO)

Casa de la Real Aduana Boutique Hotel

Ponce de Leon 16, Centro, Pátzcuaro, Michoacán 61600

Tel: +52 434 342 02 65
Web: www.johansens.com/realaduana

MÉXICO - MORELOS (CUERNAVACA)

Las Mañanitas Hotel, Garden Restaurant & Spa

Ricardo Linares 107, Centro 62000, Cuernavaca, Morelos

Tel: +52 777 362 00 00
Web: www.johansens.com/lasmananitas

MÉXICO - NAYARIT (NUEVO VALLARTA)

Grand Velas All Suites & Spa Resort

Av. Cocoteros 98 Sur, Nuevo Vallarta, Riviera Nayarit 63735

Tel: +52 322 226 8000
Web: www.johansens.com/grandvelas

MÉXICO - NAYARIT (PUNTA DE MITA)

Imanta Resorts Punta de Mita, México

Montenahuac Lote-L, Higuera Blanca, Nayarit CP63734

Tel: +52 329 298 4260
Web: www.johansens.com/imantaresorts

MÉXICO - OAXACA (OAXACA)

Casa Oaxaca

Calle García Vigil 407, Centro, Oaxaca, Oaxaca 68000

Tel: +52 951 514 4173
Web: www.johansens.com/oaxaca

MÉXICO - PUEBLA (CHOLULA)

La Quinta Luna

3 sur 702, San Pedro Cholula, Puebla 72760

Tel: +52 222 247 8915
Web: www.johansens.com/quintaluna

MÉXICO - QUINTANA ROO (CANCÚN - PUERTO MORELOS)

Ceiba del Mar Beach & Spa Resort

Costera Norte Lte. 1, S.M. 10, MZ. 26, Puerto Morelos, Quintana Roo 77580

Tel: +52 998 872 8060
Web: www.johansens.com/ceibadelmar

MÉXICO - QUINTANA ROO (ISLA MUJERES)

Hotel Villa Rolandi Thalasso Spa, Gourmet & Beach Club

Lotes 15 y 16-1, MZA 75 Lotes, Fracc Laguna Mar SM 7, Carretera Sac-Bajo, Isla Mujeres, Quintana Roo 77400

Tel: +52 998 999 2000
Web: www.johansens.com/villarolandi

MÉXICO - QUINTANA ROO (PLAYA DEL CARMEN)

Grand Velas All Suites & Spa Resort, Riviera Maya

Carretera Cancún-Tulum Km. 62, Playa del Carmen, Municipio del Solidaridad, Quintana Roo 77710

Tel: +52 984 877 44 40
Web: www.johansens.com/rivieramaya

MÉXICO - QUINTANA ROO (PLAYA DEL CARMEN)

Le Reve Hotel & Spa

Playa Xcalacoco Fraccion 2A, Playa del Carmen, Quintana Roo 77710

Tel: +52 984 109 5660
Web: www.johansens.com/hotellereve

MÉXICO - SONORA (ALAMOS)

Hacienda de los Santos Resort and Spa

Calle Molina 8, Alamos, Sonora 85763

Tel: +52 647 428 0222
Web: www.johansens.com/lossantos

MÉXICO - YUCATÁN (MÉRIDA)

Hacienda Xcanatún - Casa de Piedra

Calle 20 S/N, Comisaría Xcanatún, Km. 12 Carretera Mérida - Progreso, Mérida, Yucatán 97302

Tel: +52 999 941 0273
Web: www.johansens.com/xcanatun

Recommendations in USA

U.S.A. - ARIZONA (GREER)

Hidden Meadow Ranch

620 County Road 1325, Greer, Arizona 85927

Tel: +1 928 333 1000
Web: www.johansens.com/hiddenmeadow

Hotels - The Americas

Properties listed below can be found in our Recommended Hotels, Inns, Resorts & Spas - The Americas, Atlantic, Caribbean & Pacific 2010 Guide.

U.S.A. - ARIZONA (PARADISE VALLEY)

The Hermosa Inn

5532 North Palo Cristi Road, Paradise Valley, Arizona 85253

Tel: +1 602 955 8614
Web: www.johansens.com/hermosa

U.S.A. - CALIFORNIA (CARMEL VALLEY)

Bernardus Lodge

415 Carmel Valley Road, Carmel Valley, California 93924

Tel: +1 831 658 3400
Web: www.johansens.com/bernardus

U.S.A. - ARIZONA (TUBAC)

Tubac Golf Resort & Spa

One Otero Road, Tubac, Arizona 85646

Tel: +1 520 398 2211
Web: www.johansens.com/tubac

U.S.A. - CALIFORNIA (CARMEL-BY-THE-SEA)

L'Auberge Carmel

Monte Verde at Seventh, Carmel-by-the-Sea, California 93921

Tel: +1 831 624 8578
Web: www.johansens.com/laubergecarmel

U.S.A. - ARIZONA (TUCSON)

Tanque Verde Ranch

14301 East Speedway Boulevard, Tucson, Arizona 85748

Tel: +1 520 296 6275
Web: www.johansens.com/tanqueverde

U.S.A. - CALIFORNIA (CARMEL-BY-THE-SEA)

Tradewinds Carmel

Mission Street at Third Avenue, Carmel-by-the-Sea, California 93921

Tel: +1 831 624 2776
Web: www.johansens.com/tradewinds

U.S.A. - CALIFORNIA (BIG SUR)

Post Ranch Inn

Highway 1, P.O. Box 219, Big Sur, California 93920

Tel: +1 831 667 2200
Web: www.johansens.com/postranchinn

U.S.A. - CALIFORNIA (HEALDSBURG)

Hotel Healdsburg

25 Matheson Street, Healdsburg, California 95448

Tel: +1 707 431 2800
Web: www.johansens.com/healdsburg

U.S.A. - CALIFORNIA (BIG SUR)

Ventana Inn and Spa

48123 Highway One, Big Sur, California 93920

Tel: +1 831 667 2331
Web: www.johansens.com/ventanainn

U.S.A. - CALIFORNIA (HEALDSBURG)

Les Mars

27 North Street, Healdsburg, California 95448

Tel: +1 707 433 4211
Web: www.johansens.com/lesmarshotel

U.S.A. - CALIFORNIA (CALISTOGA)

Calistoga Ranch

580 Lommel Road, Calistoga, California 94515

Tel: +1 707 254 2800
Web: www.johansens.com/calistogaranch

U.S.A. - CALIFORNIA (LA JOLLA)

Hotel Parisi

1111 Prospect Street, La Jolla, California 92037

Tel: +1 858 454 1511
Web: www.johansens.com/hotelparisi

U.S.A. - CALIFORNIA (CALISTOGA)

The Chanric Inn

1805 Foothill Boulevard, Calistoga, California 94515

Tel: +1 707 942 4535
Web: www.johansens.com/chanricinn

U.S.A. - CALIFORNIA (MENDOCINO)

The Stanford Inn By The Sea

Coast Highway One & Comptche-Ukiah Road, Mendocino, California 95460

Tel: +1 707 937 5615
Web: www.johansens.com/stanfordinn

U.S.A. - CALIFORNIA (CALISTOGA)

Cottage Grove Inn

1711 Lincoln Avenue, Calistoga, California 94515

Tel: +1 707 942 8400
Web: www.johansens.com/cottagegrove

U.S.A. - CALIFORNIA (MONTEREY)

Old Monterey Inn

500 Martin Street, Monterey, California 93940

Tel: +1 831 375 8284
Web: www.johansens.com/oldmontereyinn

Hotels - The Americas

Properties listed below can be found in our Recommended Hotels, Inns, Resorts & Spas - The Americas, Atlantic, Caribbean & Pacific 2010 Guide.

U.S.A. - CALIFORNIA (NAPA)

1801 First Inn

1801 First Street, Napa, California 94559

Tel: +1 707 224 3739
Web: www.johansens.com/1801first

U.S.A. - CALIFORNIA (SAUSALITO)

CAVALLO POINT - the Lodge at the Golden Gate

601 Murray Circle, Sausalito, California 94965

Tel: +1 415 339 4700
Web: www.johansens.com/cavallopoint

U.S.A. - CALIFORNIA (NAPA)

White House Inn & Spa

443 Brown Street, Napa, California 94559

Tel: +1 707 254 9301
Web: www.johansens.com/whitehousenapa

U.S.A. - CALIFORNIA (SHELL BEACH)

Dolphin Bay Resort & Spa

2727 Shell Beach Road, Shell Beach, California 93449

Tel: +1 805 773 4300
Web: www.johansens.com/thedolphinbay

U.S.A. - CALIFORNIA (NEWPORT BEACH)

Balboa Bay Club & Resort

1221 West Coast Highway, Newport Beach, California 92663

Tel: +1 949 645 5000
Web: www.johansens.com/balboabayclub

U.S.A. - CALIFORNIA (ST. HELENA)

The Inn at Southbridge

1020 Main Street, St. Helena, California 94574

Tel: +1 707 967 9400
Web: www.johansens.com/southbridge

U.S.A. - CALIFORNIA (PALM SPRINGS)

Korakia Pensione

257 South Patencio Road, Palm Springs, California 92262

Tel: +1 760 864 6411
Web: www.johansens.com/korakia

U.S.A. - CALIFORNIA (ST. HELENA)

Meadowood Napa Valley

900 Meadowood Lane, St. Helena, California 94574

Tel: +1 707 963 3646
Web: www.johansens.com/meadowood

U.S.A. - CALIFORNIA (RANCHO SANTA FE)

The Inn at Rancho Santa Fe

5951 Linea del Cielo, Rancho Santa Fe, California 92067

Tel: +1 858 756 1131
Web: www.johansens.com/ranchosantafe

U.S.A. - COLORADO (DENVER)

Castle Marne Bed & Breakfast Inn

1572 Race Street, Denver, Colorado 80206

Tel: +1 303 331 0621
Web: www.johansens.com/castlemarne

U.S.A. - CALIFORNIA (SAN DIEGO)

Tower23 Hotel

4551 Ocean Blvd., San Diego, California 92109

Tel: +1 858 270 2323
Web: www.johansens.com/tower23

U.S.A. - COLORADO (ESTES PARK)

Taharaa Mountain Lodge

P.O. Box 2586, 3110 So. St. Vrain, Estes Park, Colorado 80517

Tel: +1 970 577 0098
Web: www.johansens.com/taharaa

U.S.A. - CALIFORNIA (SAN FRANCISCO)

Campton Place, A Taj Hotel

340 Stockton Street, San Francisco, California 94108

Tel: +1 415 781 5555
Web: www.johansens.com/camptonplace

U.S.A. - COLORADO (MANITOU SPRINGS)

The Cliff House at Pikes Peak

306 Cañon Avenue, Manitou Springs, Colorado 80829

Tel: +1 719 685 3000
Web: www.johansens.com/thecliffhouse

U.S.A. - CALIFORNIA (SAN FRANCISCO BAY AREA)

Inn Above Tide

30 El Portal, Sausalito, California 94965

Tel: +1 415 332 9535
Web: www.johansens.com/innabovetide

U.S.A. - COLORADO (STEAMBOAT SPRINGS)

Vista Verde Guest Ranch

P.O. Box 770465, Steamboat Springs, Colorado 80477

Tel: +1 970 879 3858
Web: www.johansens.com/vistaverderanch

Hotels - The Americas

Properties listed below can be found in our Recommended Hotels, Inns, Resorts & Spas - The Americas, Atlantic, Caribbean & Pacific 2010 Guide.

U.S.A. - COLORADO (TELLURIDE)

The Hotel Telluride

199 North Cornet Street, P.O. Box 1740, Telluride, Colorado 81435

Tel: +1 970 369 1188
Web: www.johansens.com/telluride

U.S.A. - COLORADO (VAIL)

Manor Vail Lodge

595 East Vail Drive, Vail, Colorado 81657

Tel: +1 970 476 5000
Web: www.johansens.com/manorvail

U.S.A. - COLORADO (VAIL)

Vail Mountain Lodge & Spa

352 East Meadow Drive, Vail, Colorado 81657

Tel: +1 970 476 0700
Web: www.johansens.com/vailmountain

U.S.A. - CONNECTICUT (GREENWICH)

Delamar Greenwich Harbor

500 Steamboat Road, Greenwich, Connecticut 06830

Tel: +1 203 661 9800
Web: www.johansens.com/delamar

U.S.A. - DELAWARE (REHOBOTH BEACH)

Boardwalk Plaza Hotel

Olive Avenue & The Boardwalk, Rehoboth Beach, Delaware 19971

Tel: +1 302 227 7169
Web: www.johansens.com/boardwalkplaza

U.S.A. - DELAWARE (REHOBOTH BEACH)

Hotel Rehoboth

247 Rehoboth Avenue, Rehoboth Beach, Delaware 19971

Tel: +1 302 227 4300
Web: www.johansens.com/hotelrehoboth

U.S.A. - DELAWARE (WILMINGTON)

Inn at Montchanin Village & Spa

528 Montchanin Road and Kirk Road, Montchanin, Wilmington, Delaware 19710

Tel: +1 302 888 2133
Web: www.johansens.com/montchanin

U.S.A. - DISTRICT OF COLUMBIA (WASHINGTON)

The Hay-Adams

Sixteenth & H. Streets N.W., Washington D.C., District of Columbia 20006

Tel: +1 202 638 6600
Web: www.johansens.com/hayadams

U.S.A. - FLORIDA (FISHER ISLAND)

Fisher Island Hotel & Resort

One Fisher Island Drive, Fisher Island, Florida 33109

Tel: +1 305 535 6000
Web: www.johansens.com/fisherisland

U.S.A. - FLORIDA (MIAMI BEACH)

Casa Casuarina

1116 Ocean Drive, Miami Beach, Florida 33139

Tel: +1 305 672 6604
Web: www.johansens.com/casacasuarina

U.S.A. - FLORIDA (MIAMI BEACH)

Hotel Victor

1144 Ocean Drive, Miami Beach, Florida 33139

Tel: +1 305 428 1234
Web: www.johansens.com/hotelvictor

U.S.A. - FLORIDA (MIAMI BEACH)

The Setai

2001 Collins Avenue, Miami Beach, Florida 33139

Tel: +1 305 520 6000
Web: www.johansens.com/setai

U.S.A. - FLORIDA (SANTA ROSA BEACH)

WaterColor Inn & Resort

34 Goldenrod Circle, Santa Rosa Beach, Florida 32459

Tel: +1 850 534 5000
Web: www.johansens.com/watercolor

U.S.A. - FLORIDA (ST. AUGUSTINE)

Casa Monica Hotel

95 Cordova Street, St. Augustine, Florida 32084

Tel: +1 904 827 1888
Web: www.johansens.com/casamonica

U.S.A. - GEORGIA (ADAIRSVILLE)

Barnsley Gardens Resort

597 Barnsley Gardens Road, Adairsville, Georgia 30103

Tel: +1 770 773 7480
Web: www.johansens.com/barnsleygardens

U.S.A. - GEORGIA (CUMBERLAND ISLAND)

Greyfield Inn

Cumberland Island, Georgia

Tel: +1 904 261 6408
Web: www.johansens.com/greyfieldinn

Hotels - The Americas

Properties listed below can be found in our Recommended Hotels, Inns, Resorts & Spas - The Americas, Atlantic, Caribbean & Pacific 2010 Guide.

U.S.A. - GEORGIA (SAVANNAH)

The Presidents' Quarters Inn

225 East President Street, Savannah, Georgia 31401-3806

Tel: +1 912 233 1600
Web: www.johansens.com/presidentsquarters

U.S.A. - IDAHO (KETCHUM)

Knob Hill Inn

960 North Main Street, P.O. Box 800, Ketchum, Idaho 83340

Tel: +1 208 726 8010
Web: www.johansens.com/knobhillinn

U.S.A. - ILLINOIS (CHICAGO)

The Talbott Hotel

20 E. Delaware Place, Chicago, Illinois 60611

Tel: +1 312 944 4970
Web: www.johansens.com/talbotthotel

U.S.A. - KANSAS (LAWRENCE)

The Eldridge Hotel

701 Massachusetts, Lawrence, Kansas 66044

Tel: +1 785 749 5011
Web: www.johansens.com/eldridge

U.S.A. - MAINE (GREENVILLE)

The Lodge At Moosehead Lake

368 Lily Bay Road, P.O. Box 1167, Greenville, Maine 04441

Tel: +1 207 695 4400
Web: www.johansens.com/lodgeatmooseheadlake

U.S.A. - MAINE (KENNEBUNK BEACH)

The White Barn Inn & Spa

37 Beach Avenue, Kennebunk Beach, Maine 04043

Tel: +1 207 967 2321
Web: www.johansens.com/whitebarninn

U.S.A. - MAINE (PORTLAND)

Portland Harbor Hotel

468 Fore Street, Portland, Maine 04101

Tel: +1 207 775 9090
Web: www.johansens.com/portlandharbor

U.S.A. - MARYLAND (ANNAPOLIS)

The Annapolis Inn

144 Prince George Street, Annapolis, Maryland 21401-1723

Tel: +1 410 295 5200
Web: www.johansens.com/annapolisinn

U.S.A. - MARYLAND (FROSTBURG)

Savage River Lodge

1600 Mt. Aetna Road, Frostburg, Maryland 21532

Tel: +1 301 689 3200
Web: www.johansens.com/savageriver

U.S.A. - MASSACHUSETTS (BOSTON)

Boston Harbor Hotel

70 Rowes Wharf, Boston, Massachusetts 02110

Tel: +1 617 439 7000
Web: www.johansens.com/bhh

U.S.A. - MASSACHUSETTS (BOSTON)

Fifteen Beacon

15 Beacon Street, Boston, Massachusetts 02108

Tel: +1 617 670 1500
Web: www.johansens.com/xvbeacon

U.S.A. - MASSACHUSETTS (BOSTON)

The Liberty Hotel

215 Charles Street, Boston, Massachusetts 02114

Tel: +1 617 224 4000
Web: www.johansens.com/liberty

U.S.A. - MASSACHUSETTS (CAPE COD)

Wequassett Resort and Golf Club

On Pleasant Bay, Chatham, Massachusetts 02633

Tel: +1 508 432 5400
Web: www.johansens.com/wequassett

U.S.A. - MASSACHUSETTS (IPSWICH)

The Inn at Castle Hill

280 Argilla Road, Ipswich, Massachusetts 01938

Tel: +1 978 412 2555
Web: www.johansens.com/castlehill

U.S.A. - MASSACHUSETTS (LENOX)

Blantyre

16 Blantyre Road, P.O. Box 995, Lenox, Massachusetts 01240

Tel: +1 413 637 3556
Web: www.johansens.com/blantyre

U.S.A. - MASSACHUSETTS (MARTHA'S VINEYARD)

The Charlotte Inn

27 South Summer Street, Edgartown, Massachusetts 02539

Tel: +1 508 627 4151
Web: www.johansens.com/charlotte

Hotels - The Americas

Properties listed below can be found in our Recommended Hotels, Inns, Resorts & Spas - The Americas, Atlantic, Caribbean & Pacific 2010 Guide.

U.S.A. - MICHIGAN (ROCHESTER)

Royal Park Hotel

600 E. University Drive, Rochester, Michigan 48307

Tel: +1 248 652 2600
Web: www.johansens.com/royalparkmi

U.S.A. - MISSISSIPPI (JACKSON)

Fairview Inn

734 Fairview Street, Jackson, Mississippi 39202

Tel: +1 601 948 3429
Web: www.johansens.com/fairviewinn

U.S.A. - MISSISSIPPI (NATCHEZ)

Monmouth Plantation

36 Melrose Avenue, Natchez, Mississippi 39120

Tel: +1 601 442 5852
Web: www.johansens.com/monmouthplantation

U.S.A. - MISSOURI (KANSAS CITY)

The Raphael Hotel

325 Ward Parkway, Kansas City, Missouri 64112

Tel: +1 816 756 3800
Web: www.johansens.com/raphael

U.S.A. - MONTANA (DARBY)

Triple Creek Ranch

5551 West Fork Road, Darby, Montana 59829

Tel: +1 406 821 4600
Web: www.johansens.com/triplecreek

U.S.A. - NEVADA (LAS VEGAS)

SKYLOFTS at MGM Grand

3977 Las Vegas Boulevard South, Las Vegas, Nevada 89101

Tel: +1 702 891 3832
Web: www.johansens.com/skylofts

U.S.A. - NEW MEXICO (ESPAÑOLA)

Rancho de San Juan

P.O. Box 4140, Highway 285, Española, New Mexico 87533

Tel: +1 505 753 6818
Web: www.johansens.com/ranchosanjuan

U.S.A. - NEW MEXICO (SANTA FE)

Encantado, an Auberge Resort

198 State Road 592, Santa Fe, New Mexico 87506

Tel: +1 505 946 5700
Web: www.johansens.com/encantado

U.S.A. - NEW MEXICO (SANTA FE)

Hacienda del Cerezo

100 Camino del Cerezo, Santa Fe, New Mexico 87506

Tel: +1 505 982 8000
Web: www.johansens.com/haciendadelcerezo

U.S.A. - NEW YORK (NEW YORK CITY)

The Greenwich Hotel

377 Greenwich Street, New York City, New York 10013

Tel: +1 212 941 8900
Web: www.johansens.com/thegreenwichhotel

U.S.A. - NEW YORK (NEW YORK CITY)

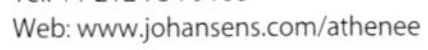

Hôtel Plaza Athénée

37 East 64th Street, New York City, New York 10065

Tel: +1 212 734 9100
Web: www.johansens.com/athenee

U.S.A. - NEW YORK (NEW YORK CITY)

The Inn at Irving Place

56 Irving Place, New York, New York City 10003

Tel: +1 212 533 4600
Web: www.johansens.com/irving

U.S.A. - NEW YORK (NEW YORK CITY)

Trump International Hotel & Tower

One Central Park West, New York City, New York 10023

Tel: +1 212 299 1000
Web: www.johansens.com/trumpnewyork

U.S.A. - NEW YORK (TARRYTOWN)

Castle On The Hudson

400 Benedict Avenue, Tarrytown, New York 10591

Tel: +1 914 631 1980
Web: www.johansens.com/hudson

U.S.A. - NEW YORK (VERONA)

The Lodge at Turning Stone

5218 Patrick Road, Verona, New York 13478

Tel: +1 315 361 8525
Web: www.johansens.com/turningstone

U.S.A. - NEW YORK/LONG ISLAND (EAST HAMPTON)

The Baker House 1650

181 Main Street, East Hampton, New York 11937

Tel: +1 631 324 4081
Web: www.johansens.com/bakerhouse

Hotels - The Americas

Properties listed below can be found in our Recommended Hotels, Inns, Resorts & Spas - The Americas, Atlantic, Caribbean & Pacific 2010 Guide.

U.S.A. - NEW YORK/LONG ISLAND (EAST HAMPTON)

The Mill House Inn

31 North Main Street, East Hampton, New York 11937

Tel: +1 631 324 9766
Web: www.johansens.com/millhouse

U.S.A. - NEW YORK/LONG ISLAND (SOUTHAMPTON)

1708 House

126 Main Street, Southampton, New York 11968

Tel: +1 631 287 1708
Web: www.johansens.com/1708house

U.S.A. - NORTH CAROLINA (CHAPEL HILL)

The Franklin Hotel

311 West Franklin Street, Chapel Hill, North Carolina 27516

Tel: +1 919 442 9000
Web: www.johansens.com/franklinhotelnc

U.S.A. - NORTH CAROLINA (HIGHLANDS)

Inn at Half Mile Farm

P.O. Box 2769, 214 Half Mile Drive, Highlands, North Carolina 28741

Tel: +1 828 526 8170
Web: www.johansens.com/halfmilefarm

U.S.A. - OKLAHOMA (OKLAHOMA CITY)

Colcord Hotel

15 North Robinson, Oklahoma City, Oklahoma 73102

Tel: +1 405 601 4300
Web: www.johansens.com/colcord

U.S.A. - OKLAHOMA (TULSA)

Hotel Ambassador

1324 South Main Street, Tulsa, Oklahoma 74119

Tel: +1 918 587 8200
Web: www.johansens.com/ambassador

U.S.A. - PENNSYLVANIA (LEOLA)

The Inn at Leola Village

38 Deborah Drive, Route 23 Leola, Pennsylvania 17540

Tel: +1 717 656 7002
Web: www.johansens.com/leolavillage

U.S.A. - PENNSYLVANIA (NEW HOPE)

The Inn at Bowman's Hill

518 Lurgan Road, New Hope, Pennsylvania 18938

Tel: +1 215 862 8090
Web: www.johansens.com/bowmanshill

U.S.A. - PENNSYLVANIA (PHILADELPHIA)

Rittenhouse 1715, A Boutique Hotel

1715 Rittenhouse Square, Philadelphia, Pennsylvania 19103

Tel: +1 215 546 6500
Web: www.johansens.com/rittenhouse

U.S.A. - PENNSYLVANIA (SKYTOP)

Skytop Lodge

One Skytop, Skytop, Pennsylvania 18357

Tel: +1 570 595 7401
Web: www.johansens.com/skytop

U.S.A. - RHODE ISLAND (NEWPORT)

Castle Hill Inn & Resort

590 Ocean Drive, Newport, Rhode Island 02840

Tel: +1 401 849 3800
Web: www.johansens.com/castlehillinn

U.S.A. - RHODE ISLAND (NEWPORT)

Chanler at Cliff Walk

117 Memorial Boulevard, Newport, Rhode Island 02840

Tel: +1 401 847 1300
Web: www.johansens.com/chanler

U.S.A. - SOUTH CAROLINA (CHARLESTON)

Charleston Harbor Resort & Marina

20 Patriots Point Road, Charleston, South Carolina 29464

Tel: +1 843 856 0028
Web: www.johansens.com/charlestonharbor

U.S.A. - SOUTH CAROLINA (KIAWAH ISLAND)

The Sanctuary at Kiawah Island Golf Resort

One Sanctuary Beach Drive, Kiawah Island, South Carolina 29455

Tel: +1 843 768 6000
Web: www.johansens.com/sanctuary

U.S.A. - TEXAS (HOUSTON)

Hotel Granduca

1080 Uptown Park Boulevard, Houston, Texas 77056

Tel: +1 713 418 1000
Web: www.johansens.com/granduca

U.S.A. - TEXAS (SAN ANTONIO)

Emily Morgan Hotel

705 East Houston Street, San Antonio, Texas 78205

Tel: +1 210 225 5100
Web: www.johansens.com/emilymorgan

Hotels - The Americas

Properties listed below can be found in our Recommended Hotels, Inns, Resorts & Spas - The Americas, Atlantic, Caribbean & Pacific 2010 Guide.

U.S.A. - TEXAS (SAN ANTONIO)

Hotel Valencia Riverwalk San Antonio

150 East Houston Street, San Antonio, Texas 78205

Tel: +1 210 227 9700
Web: www.johansens.com/valenciariverwalk

U.S.A. - UTAH (MOAB)

Sorrel River Ranch Resort & Spa

Mile 17 Scenic Highway 128, H.C. 64 BOX 4002, Moab, Utah 84532

Tel: +1 435 259 4642
Web: www.johansens.com/sorrelriver

U.S.A. - VERMONT (MANCHESTER VILLAGE)

Equinox Resort & Spa

3567 Main Street Route 7A, Manchester Village, Vermont 05254

Tel: +1 802 362 4700
Web: www.johansens.com/equinoxresort

U.S.A. - VIRGINIA (IRVINGTON)

Hope and Glory Inn

65 Tavern Road, Irvington, Virginia 22480

Tel: +1 804 438 6053
Web: www.johansens.com/hopeandglory

U.S.A. - VIRGINIA (MIDDLEBURG)

The Goodstone Inn & Estate

36205 Snake Hill Road, Middleburg, Virginia 20117

Tel: +1 540 687 4645
Web: www.johansens.com/goodstoneinn

U.S.A. - VIRGINIA (RICHMOND)

The Jefferson

101 West Franklin Street, Richmond, Virginia 23220

Tel: +1 804 788 8000
Web: www.johansens.com/jeffersonva

U.S.A. - VIRGINIA (STAUNTON)

Frederick House

28 North New Street, Staunton, Virginia 24401

Tel: +1 540 885 4220
Web: www.johansens.com/frederickhouse

U.S.A. - VIRGINIA (WILLIAMSBURG)

Wedmore Place

5810 Wessex Hundred, Williamsburg, Virginia 23185

Tel: +1 757 941 0310
Web: www.johansens.com/wedmoreplace

U.S.A. - WASHINGTON (BELLEVUE)

The Bellevue Club Hotel

11200 S.E. 6th Street, Bellevue, Washington 98004

Tel: +1 425 455 1616
Web: www.johansens.com/bellevue

U.S.A. - WASHINGTON (SEATTLE)

Hotel Ändra

2000 Fourth Avenue, Seattle, Washington 98121

Tel: +1 206 448 8600
Web: www.johansens.com/hotelandra

U.S.A. - WASHINGTON (SEATTLE)

Inn at the Market

86 Pine Street, Seattle, Washington 98101

Tel: +1 206 443 3600
Web: www.johansens.com/innatthemarket

U.S.A. - WASHINGTON (SPOKANE)

The Davenport Hotel and Tower

10 South Post Street, Spokane, Washington 99201

Tel: +1 509 455 8888
Web: www.johansens.com/davenport

U.S.A. - WASHINGTON (SPOKANE)

Hotel Lusso

808 West Sprague Avenue, Spokane, Washington 99201

Tel: +1 509 747 9750
Web: www.johansens.com/hotellusso

U.S.A. - WASHINGTON (WINTHROP)

Sun Mountain Lodge

P.O. Box 1,000, Winthrop, Washington 98862

Tel: +1 509 996 2211
Web: www.johansens.com/sunmountain

U.S.A. - WASHINGTON (WOODINVILLE)

The Herbfarm

14590 North East 145th Street, Woodinville, Washington 98072

Tel: +1 425 485 5300
Web: www.johansens.com/herbfarm

U.S.A. - WYOMING (JACKSON HOLE)

Amangani

1535 North East Butte Road, P.O. Box 15030, Jackson Hole, Wyoming 83002

Tel: +1 307 734 7333
Web: www.johansens.com/amangani

Hotels - The Americas

Properties listed below can be found in our Recommended Hotels, Inns, Resorts & Spas - The Americas, Atlantic, Caribbean & Pacific 2010 Guide.

Recommendations in Central America

COSTA RICA - ALAJUELA (BAJOS DEL TORO)

El Silencio Lodge & Spa

Bajos del Toro, Alajuela

Tel: +506 2761 0301
Web: www.johansens.com/elsilencio

BELIZE - AMBERGRIS CAYE

Matachica Beach Resort

5 miles North of San Pedro, Ambergris Caye

Tel: +501 220 5010
Web: www.johansens.com/matachica

BELIZE - AMBERGRIS CAYE (SAN PEDRO)

Victoria House

P.O. Box 22, San Pedro, Ambergris Caye

Tel: +501 226 2067
Web: www.johansens.com/victoriahouse

BELIZE - CAYO DISTRICT (MOUNTAIN PINE RIDGE)

Hidden Valley Inn

P.O. Box 170, Belmopan

Tel: +501 822 3320
Web: www.johansens.com/hiddenvalleyinn

BELIZE - CAYO DISTRICT (SAN IGNACIO)

Ka'ana Boutique Resort

Mile 69 1/4, Benque Viejo Road, San Ignacio, Cayo District

Tel: +501 824 3350
Web: www.johansens.com/kaanabelize

BELIZE - CAYO DISTRICT (SAN IGNACIO)

The Lodge at Chaa Creek

P.O. Box 53, San Ignacio, Cayo District

Tel: +501 824 2037
Web: www.johansens.com/chaacreek

BELIZE - ORANGE WALK DISTRICT (GALLON JUG)

Chan Chich Lodge

Gallon Jug, Orange Walk District

Tel: +501 223 4419
Web: www.johansens.com/chanchich

COSTA RICA - ALAJUELA (ALAJUELA)

Xandari Resort & Spa

APDO 1485-4050, Central Valley, Alajuela, Alajuela

Tel: +506 2443 2020
Web: www.johansens.com/xandari

COSTA RICA - ALAJUELA (LA FORTUNA DE SAN CARLOS)

Tabacón Grand Spa Thermal Resort

La Fortuna de San Carlos, Arenal

Tel: +506 2519 1999
Web: www.johansens.com/tabacon

COSTA RICA - GUANACASTE (NICOYA)

Hotel Punta Islita

Islita, Nicoya, Guanacaste

Tel: +506 2231 6122
Web: www.johansens.com/hotelpuntaislita

COSTA RICA - GUANACASTE (PLAYA CONCHAL)

Reserva Conchal

Playa Conchal, Cabo Velas, Guanacaste

Tel: +506 2654 6000
Web: www.johansens.com/reservaconchal

COSTA RICA - PUNTARENAS (MANUEL ANTONIO)

Gaia Hotel & Reserve

Km 2.7 Carretera Quepos, Manuel Antonio, Puntarenas

Tel: +506 2777 9797
Web: www.johansens.com/gaiahr

COSTA RICA - PUNTARENAS (PLAYA ESTERILLOS ESTE)

Xandari by the Pacific Resort & Spa

Playa Esterillos Este, Puntarenas

Tel: +506 2778 7070
Web: www.johansens.com/xandaripacific

COSTA RICA - PUNTARENAS (UVITA DE OSA)

Rancho Pacifico

1 Rancho Pacifico Road, Uvita de Osa, Puntarenas

Tel: +506 8851 6346
Web: www.johansens.com/ranchopacifico

COSTA RICA - SAN JOSÉ (SAN JOSÉ)

Beacon Escazú

150 mts oeste del Parque, Central de Escazu, San José, San José

Tel: +506 2228 3110
Web: www.johansens.com/beaconescazu

Hotels - The Americas

Properties listed below can be found in our Recommended Hotels, Inns, Resorts & Spas - The Americas, Atlantic, Caribbean & Pacific 2010 Guide.

GUATEMALA - SACATEPÉQUEZ (LA ANTIGUA GUATEMALA)

Un Paseo por La Antigua

Calle de Los Duelos, Las Gravileas 7 & 8, La Antigua Guatemala

Tel: +502 7832 3354
Web: www.johansens.com/unpaseo

GUATEMALA - SACATEPÉQUEZ (SAN JUAN ALOTENANGO - LA ANTIGUA GUATEMALA)

La Reunión Antigua Golf Resort

Km. 91.5 Ruta Nacional 14, San Juan Alotenango, Sacatepéquez

Tel: +502 7873 1400
Web: www.johansens.com/lareunion

GUATEMALA - SOLOLÁ (SANTA CRUZ LA LAGUNA - LAKE ATITLÁN)

Laguna Lodge Eco-Resort & Nature Reserve

No. 1 Tzantizotz, Santa Cruz La Laguna, Lake Atitlán, Sololá

Tel: +502 7823 2529
Web: www.johansens.com/lagunalodge

HONDURAS - ATLÁNTIDA (LA CEIBA)

The Lodge at Pico Bonito

A. P. 710, La Ceiba, Atlántida, C. P. 31101

Tel: +504 440 0388
Web: www.johansens.com/picobonito

HONDURAS - BAY ISLANDS (ROATAN)

Mayoka Lodge

Sandy Bay, Roatan, Bay Islands

Tel: +504 445 3043
Web: www.johansens.com/mayokalodge

Recommendations in South America

ARGENTINA - BUENOS AIRES (CIUDAD DE BUENOS AIRES)

The Belgrano

11 de Septiembre 1300, Ciudad de Buenos Aires, Buenos Aires

Tel: +54 11 4780 3955
Web: www.johansens.com/thebelgrano

ARGENTINA - BUENOS AIRES (CIUDAD DE BUENOS AIRES)

Legado Mitico

Gurruchaga 1848, C1414DIL Ciudad de Buenos Aires, Buenos Aires

Tel: +54 11 4833 1300
Web: www.johansens.com/legadomitico

ARGENTINA - BUENOS AIRES (CIUDAD DE BUENOS AIRES)

Mansión Vitraux Boutique Hotel - Wine Lounge & Spa

Carlos Calvo 369, C1102AAG Ciudad de Buenos Aires, San Telmo, Buenos Aires

Tel: +54 11 4300 6886
Web: www.johansens.com/mansionvitraux

ARGENTINA - BUENOS AIRES (CIUDAD DE BUENOS AIRES)

Mine Hotel Boutique

Gorriti 4770, Palermo Soho, C1414BJL Ciudad de Buenos Aires, Buenos Aires

Tel: +54 11 4832 1100
Web: www.johansens.com/minehotel

ARGENTINA - BUENOS AIRES (CIUDAD DE BUENOS AIRES)

Moreno Hotel Buenos Aires

Moreno 376, C1091AAH Ciudad de Buenos Aires, San Telmo, Buenos Aires

Tel: +54 11 6091 2000
Web: www.johansens.com/moreno

ARGENTINA - BUENOS AIRES (CIUDAD DE BUENOS AIRES)

Nuss Buenos Aires Soho

El Salvador 4916, Palermo Soho, Ciudad de Buenos Aires, Buenos Aires

Tel: +54 11 4833 6222
Web: www.johansens.com/nusshotel

ARGENTINA - BUENOS AIRES (CIUDAD DE BUENOS AIRES)

Ultra Hotel Buenos Aires

Gorriti 4929, Palermo Soho, C1414BJO Ciudad de Buenos Aires, Buenos Aires

Tel: +54 11 4833 9200
Web: www.johansens.com/hotelultra

ARGENTINA - BUENOS AIRES (CIUDAD DE BUENOS AIRES)

Vitrum Hotel

Gorriti 5641, Palermo Hollywood, Cuidad de Buenos Aires, Buenos Aires

Tel: +54 11 4776 5030
Web: www.johansens.com/vitrumhotel

ARGENTINA - NEUQUÉN (PATAGONIA - VILLA LA ANGOSTURA)

Hotel Las Balsas

Bahía Las Balsas s/n, 8407 Villa La Angostura, Neuquén

Tel: +54 2944 494308
Web: www.johansens.com/lasbalsas

ARGENTINA - RÍO NEGRO (PATAGONIA - SAN CARLOS BARILOCHE)

Isla Victoria Lodge

Isla Victoria, Parque Nacional Nahuel Huapi, C.C. 26 (R8401AKU)

Tel: +54 43 94 96 05
Web: www.johansens.com/islavictoria

Hotels - The Americas

Properties listed below can be found in our Recommended Hotels, Inns, Resorts & Spas - The Americas, Atlantic, Caribbean & Pacific 2010 Guide.

ARGENTINA - SALTA (CIUDAD DE SALTA)

Legado Mitico Salta

Mitre 647, A4400EHM Ciudad de Salta, Salta

Tel: +54 0387 4228786/4214650
Web: www.johansens.com/legadomitico

BRAZIL - MINAS GERAIS (TIRADENTES)

Pousada dos Inconfidentes

Rua João Rodrigues Sobrinho 91, Tiradentes 36325-000, Minas Gerais

Tel: +55 32 3355 2135
Web: www.johansens.com/inconfidentes

ARGENTINA - TIERRA DEL FUEGO (PATAGONIA - USHUAIA)

Los Cauquenes Resort and Spa

De la Ermita 3462, Barrio Bahía Cauquén, 9410 Ushuaia, Tierra del Fuego, Patagonia

Tel: +54 11 4735 2648
Web: www.johansens.com/loscauquenes

BRAZIL - PERNAMBUCO (FERNANDO DE NORONHA)

Pousada Maravilha

Rodovia BR-363, s/n, Sueste, Ilha de Fernando de Noronha, Pernambuco 53990-000

Tel: +55 81 3619 0028
Web: www.johansens.com/maravilha

BRAZIL - ALAGOAS (SÃO MIGUEL DOS MILAGRES)

Pousada do Toque

Rua Felisberto de Ataide, Povoado do Toque, São Miguel dos Milagres, Alagoas 57940-000

Tel: +55 82 3295 1127
Web: www.johansens.com/pousadadotoque

BRAZIL - PERNAMBUCO (PORTO DE GALINHAS)

Nannai Beach Resort

Rodovia PE-09, acesso à Muro Alto, Km 3, Ipojuca, Pernambuco 55590-000

Tel: +55 81 3552 0100
Web: www.johansens.com/nannaibeach

BRAZIL - BAHIA (ARRAIAL D'AJUDA)

Maitei Hotel

Estrada do Mucugê 475, Arraial D'Ajuda, Porto Seguro, Bahia 45816-000

Tel: +55 73 3575 3877
Web: www.johansens.com/maitei

BRAZIL - RIO DE JANEIRO (ARMAÇÃO DOS BÚZIOS)

Villa Rasa Marina

Av. José Bento Ribeiro Dantas 299, Armação dos Búzios, Rio de Janeiro 28950-000

Tel: +55 21 2172 1001
Web: www.johansens.com/villarasamarina

BRAZIL - BAHIA (CORUMBAU)

Vila Naiá - Paralelo 17°

Ponta do Corumbau, Bahia

Tel: +55 11 3061 1872
Web: www.johansens.com/vilanaia

BRAZIL - RIO DE JANEIRO (BÚZIOS)

Casas Brancas Boutique-Hotel & Spa

Alto do Humaitá 10, Armação dos Búzios, Rio de Janeiro 28950-000

Tel: +55 22 2623 1458
Web: www.johansens.com/casasbrancas

BRAZIL - BAHIA (PENÍNSULA DE MARAÚ - MARAÚ)

Kiaroa Eco-Luxury Resort

Loteamento da Costa, área SD6, Distrito de Barra Grande, Municipio de Maraú, Bahia, CEP 45 520-000

Tel: +55 71 3272 1320
Web: www.johansens.com/kiaroa

BRAZIL - RIO DE JANEIRO (BÚZIOS)

Hotel Le Relais La Borie

1374 Rua dos Gravatás, Praia de Geribá, Armação dos Búzios, Rio de Janeiro 28950-000

Tel: +55 22 2620 8504
Web: www.johansens.com/laborie

BRAZIL - BAHIA (PRAIA DO FORTE)

Tivoli Ecoresort Praia do Forte

Avenida do Farol, Praia do Forte - Mata de São João, Bahia

Tel: +55 71 36 76 40 00
Web: www.johansens.com/praiadoforte

BRAZIL - RIO DE JANEIRO (BÚZIOS)

Insólito Boutique Hotel

Rua E1 - Lot 3 e 4 , Condomínio Atlático, Armação de Búzios, Rio de Janeiro 28,950-000

Tel: +55 22 2623 2172
Web: www.johansens.com/insolitohotel

BRAZIL - BAHIA (TRANCOSO)

Etnia Pousada and Boutique

Trancoso, Bahia 45818-000

Tel: +55 73 3668 1137
Web: www.johansens.com/etnia

BRAZIL - RIO DE JANEIRO (PARATY)

Casa Turquesa

50 rua Doutor Pereira, Centro Histórico Paraty, Rio de Janeiro

Tel: +55 24 3371 1037
Web: www.johansens.com/casaturquesa

Hotels - The Americas

Properties listed below can be found in our Recommended Hotels, Inns, Resorts & Spas - The Americas, Atlantic, Caribbean & Pacific 2010 Guide.

BRAZIL - RIO DE JANEIRO (PETRÓPOLIS)

Parador Santarém Marina

Estrada Correia da Veiga, 96 Santa Mônica, Itaipava, Petrópolis, Rio de Janeiro 25745-260

Tel: +55 24 2222 9933
Web: www.johansens.com/paradorsantarem

BRAZIL - RIO DE JANEIRO (PETRÓPOLIS)

Solar do Império

Koeler Avenue, 376 Centro, Petrópolis, Rio de Janeiro

Tel: +55 24 2103 3000
Web: www.johansens.com/solardoimperio

BRAZIL - RIO DE JANEIRO (PETRÓPOLIS)

Tankamana EcoResort

Estrada Júlio Cápua, S/N Vale Do Cuiabá, Itaipava - Petrópolis, Rio De Janeiro 25745-050

Tel: +55 24 2232 2900
Web: www.johansens.com/tankamana

BRAZIL - RIO DE JANEIRO (RIO DE JANEIRO)

Hotel Marina All Suites

Av. Delfim Moreira, 696, Praia do Leblon, Rio de Janeiro 22441-000

Tel: +55 21 2172 1001
Web: www.johansens.com/marinaallsuites

BRAZIL - RIO GRANDE DO NORTE (PRAIA DA PIPA)

Toca da Coruja

Avenida Baia dos Golfinhos, 464, Praia da Pipa, Tibau do Sul, Rio Grande do Norte 59178-000

Tel: +55 84 3246 2226
Web: www.johansens.com/tocadacoruja

BRAZIL - RIO GRANDE DO SUL (GRAMADO)

Estalagem St. Hubertus

Rua Carrieri, 974, Gramado, Rio Grande do Sul 95670-000

Tel: +55 54 3286 1273
Web: www.johansens.com/sthubertus

BRAZIL - RIO GRANDE DO SUL (GRAMADO)

Kurotel - Longevity Center and Spa

Rua Nacões Unidas 533, P.O. Box 65, Gramado, Rio Grande do Sul 95670-000

Tel: +55 54 3295 9393
Web: www.johansens.com/kurotel

BRAZIL - RIO GRANDE DO SUL (SÃO FRANCISCO DE PAULA)

Pousada do Engenho

Rua Odon Cavalcante, 330, São Francisco de Paula 95400-000, Rio Grande do Sul

Tel: +55 54 3244 1270
Web: www.johansens.com/pousadadoengenho

BRAZIL - SANTA CATARINA (GOVERNADOR CELSO RAMOS)

Ponta dos Ganchos

Rua Eupídio Alves do Nascimento, 104, Governador Celso Ramos, Santa Catarina 88190-000

Tel: +55 48 3953 7000
Web: www.johansens.com/pontadosganchos

BRAZIL - SANTA CATARINA (PALHOÇA)

Ilha do Papagaio

Ilha do Papagaio, Palhoça, Santa Catarina 88131-970

Tel: +55 48 3286 1242
Web: www.johansens.com/ilhadopapagaio

BRAZIL - SANTA CATARINA (PRAIA DO ROSA)

Pousada Solar Mirador

Estrada Geral do Rosa s/n, Praia do Rosa, Imbituba, Santa Catarina 88780-000

Tel: +55 48 3355 6144
Web: www.johansens.com/solarmirador

BRAZIL - SÃO PAULO (CAMPOS DO JORDÃO)

Hotel Frontenac

Av. Dr. Paulo Ribas, 295 Capivari, Campos do Jordão - São Paulo 12460-000

Tel: +55 12 3669 1000
Web: www.johansens.com/frontenac

BRAZIL - SÃO PAULO (CAMPOS DO JORDÃO)

Villa Casato Residenza Ristorante & Antiquario

Rua Andre Kotchkoff 297, Capavari, Campos do Jordão, São Paulo 12460-000

Tel: +55 12 3663 7341
Web: www.johansens.com/villacasato

BRAZIL - SÃO PAULO (ILHABELA)

DPNY Beach Hotel

Av. José Pacheco do Nascimento, 7668, Praia do Curral, Ilhabela, São Paulo 11630-000

Tel: +55 12 3894 2121
Web: www.johansens.com/dpnybeach

BRAZIL - SÃO PAULO (SÃO PAULO)

Hotel Unique

Avenida Brigadeiro Luis Antonio, 4.700, São Paulo, São Paulo 01402-002

Tel: +55 11 3055 4710
Web: www.johansens.com/hotelunique

BRAZIL - SÃO PAULO (SERRA DA CANTAREIRA)

Spa Unique Garden

Estrada Laramara, 3500, Serra da Cantareira, São Paulo 07600-970

Tel: +55 11 4486 8700
Web: www.johansens.com/uniquegarden

Hotels - The Americas

Properties listed below can be found in our Recommended Hotels, Inns, Resorts & Spas - The Americas, Atlantic, Caribbean & Pacific 2010 Guide.

COLOMBIA - BOLÍVAR (CARTAGENA DE INDIAS)

Casa Pestagua

Calle Santo Domingo No. 33-63, Cartagena de Indias, Bolívar

Tel: +57 5 664 9510
Web: www.johansens.com/casapestagua

COLOMBIA - BOLÍVAR (CARTAGENA DE INDIAS)

Casa Quero

Calle Quero No. 9-53, Cartagena de Indias, Bolívar

Tel: +57 5 664 4493
Web: www.johansens.com/hotelcasaquero

COLOMBIA - BOLÍVAR (CARTAGENA DE INDIAS)

Hotel Bovedas de Santa Clara

Calle del Torno No. 39-29, Barrio San Diego, Cartagena de Indias, Bolívar

Tel: +57 5 664 60 70 ext. 2069-4008
Web: www.johansens.com/bovedasdesantaclara

COLOMBIA - BOLÍVAR (CARTAGENA DE INDIAS)

Hotel Charleston Santa Teresa Cartagena

Cra. 3ª, N° 31–23, Centro Plaza de Santa Teresa, Cartagena de Indias, Bolívar

Tel: +57 5 664 9494
Web: www.johansens.com/charlestonsantateresa

COLOMBIA - BOLÍVAR (CARTAGENA DE INDIAS)

Hotel LM

Centro Calle de la Mantilla No. 3-56, Cartagena de Indias, Bolívar

Tel: +57 5 664 9100/9564
Web: www.johansens.com/hotellm

COLOMBIA - BOLÍVAR (CARTAGENA DE INDIAS)

Hotel Quadrifolio

Calle del Cuartel No.36-118, Cartagena de Indias, Bolívar

Tel: +57 5 664 6053
Web: www.johansens.com/hotelquadrifolio

COLOMBIA - BOLÍVAR (CARTAGENA DE INDIAS)

Hotel San Pedro de Majagua

Isla Grande, Islas del Rosario, Cartagena de Indias, Bolívar

Tel: +57 5 664 60 70 ext. 2069-4008
Web: www.johansens.com/hotelmajagu

CHILE - II REGIÓN DE ANTOFAGASTA (SAN PEDRO DE ATACAMA)

Kunza Hotel & Spa

Ayllu de Yaye, San Pedro de Atacama, II Región de Antofagasta

Tel: +56 2 246 8635/6
Web: www.johansens.com/hotelkunza

CHILE - IX REGIÓN DE ARAUCANÍA (VILLARRICA)

Villarrica Park Lake Hotel

Camino Villarrica Pucón Km 13, Villarrica, IX Región de Araucanía

Tel: +56 2 207 7070
Web: www.johansens.com/villarrica

CHILE - XI REGIÓN DE AYSÉN (PATAGONIA - PUERTO GUADAL)

Hacienda Tres Lagos

Carretera Austral Sur Km 274, Localidad Lago Negro, Puerto Guadal, XI Región de Aysén, Patagonia

Tel: +56 2 333 4122
Web: www.johansens.com/treslagos

CHILE - X REGIÓN DE LOS LAGOS (PATAGONIA - PUERTO MONTT)

Nomads of the Seas

Puerto Montt, X Región de los Lagos

Tel: +562 414 4600
Web: www.johansens.com/nomadsoftheseas

CHILE - X REGIÓN DE LOS LAGOS (PATAGONIA - PUERTO VARAS)

The Cliffs Preserve

Decher 450, Of. 4, Puerto Varas, X Región de Los Lagos

Tel: +56 6543 9512
Web: www.johansens.com/cliffspreserve

CHILE - XII REGIÓN DE MAGALLANES (PATAGONIA - PUERTO NATALES)

Indigo Patagonia Hotel & Spa

Ladrilleros 105, Puerto Natales, XII Región de Magallanes

Tel: +56 6 141 3609
Web: www.johansens.com/indigopatagonia

CHILE - XII REGIÓN DE MAGALLANES (PATAGONIA - PUERTO NATALES)

Remota

Ruta 9 Norte, Km 1.5, Huerto 279, XII Región de Magallanes

Tel: +56 2 387 1500
Web: www.johansens.com/remota

ECUADOR - AZUAY (CUENCA)

Mansión Alcázar Boutique Hotel

Calle Bolívar 12-55 Y Tarqui, Cuenca, Azuay

Tel: +593 72823 918
Web: www.johansens.com/mansionalcazar

ECUADOR - COTOPAXI (LASSO)

Hacienda San Agustin de Callo

77km south of Quito on the Panamerican Highway, Lasso, Cotopaxi

Tel: o Office: +593 2 2906157/8
Web: www.johansens.com/haciendasanagustin

Hotels - The Americas & Atlantic

Properties listed below can be found in our Recommended Hotels, Inns, Resorts & Spas - The Americas, Atlantic, Caribbean & Pacific 2010 Guide.

ECUADOR - GALÁPAGOS ISLANDS (GALÁPAGOS ISLANDS)

Integrity - Luxury Yacht

Galápagos Islands

Tel: +1 510 420 1550
Web: www.johansens.com/integrity

ECUADOR - GALÁPAGOS ISLANDS (SANTA CRUZ ISLAND)

Royal Palm Hotel - Galápagos

Km. 18 Via Baltra, Santa Cruz Island, Galápagos

Tel: +593 5 252 7408
Web: www.johansens.com/royalpalmgalapagos

ECUADOR - IMBABURA (ANGOCHAGUA)

Hacienda Zuleta

Angochagua, Imbabura

Tel: +593 6 266 2182
Web: www.johansens.com/zuleta

ECUADOR - IMBABURA (COTACACHI)

La Mirage Garden Hotel and Spa

Cotacachi, Imbabura

Tel: +593 6 291 5237
Web: www.johansens.com/mirage

ECUADOR - PICHINCHA (QUITO)

Hacienda Rumiloma

Obispo Diaz de la Madrid, s/n al final de la calle, Pichincha, Quito

Tel: +593 2 254 8206
Web: www.johansens.com/rumiloma

ECUADOR - PICHINCHA (QUITO)

Le Parc Hotel

Avenida Republica de El Salvador N34-349 e Irlanda, Quito, Pichincha

Tel: +593 2 227 6800
Web: www.johansens.com/leparc

ECUADOR - PICHINCHA (QUITO)

Villa Colonna Bed & Breakfast

Benalcazar 1128 y Esmeraldas (Centro Histórico), Pichincha, Quito

Tel: +593 2 295 5805
Web: www.johansens.com/villacolonna

ECUADOR - TUNGURAHUA (BAÑOS)

Samari Spa Resort

Avenida de las Amazonas, Vía a Puyo Km. 1, Baños, Tungurahua

Tel: +593 3 274 1855
Web: www.johansens.com/samarispa

PERÚ - CUSCO (MACHU PICCHU)

Sumaq Machu Picchu Hotel

Av. Hermanos Ayar MZ 1 Lote 3, Machu Picchu, Cusco

Tel: +511 4470579
Web: www.johansens.com/sumaqhotelperu

PERÚ - LIMA (YAUYOS)

Refugios Del Perú - Viñak Reichraming

Santiago de Viñak, Yauyos, Lima

Tel: +511 421 7777
Web: www.johansens.com/refugiosdelperu

URUGUAY - MALDONADO (JOSÉ IGNACIO)

Casa Suaya

Ruta 10 Km 186,5, José Ignacio

Tel: +1 323 468 0200
Web: www.johansens.com/casasuaya

URUGUAY - MALDONADO (PUNTA DEL ESTE)

Hotel-Art & Spa Las Cumbres

Ruta Nacional Nº12 Km 3.9, Laguna del Sauce, Punta del Este

Tel: +598 42 578689
Web: www.johansens.com/cumbres

URUGUAY - MALDONADO (PUNTA DEL ESTE)

L'Auberge

Carnoustie y Av. del Agua, Barrio Parque del Golf, Punta del Este CP20100

Tel: +598 42 48 8888
Web: www.johansens.com/laubergeuruguay

Recommendations in the Atlantic

ATLANTIC - THE BAHAMAS (GRAND BAHAMA ISLAND)

Old Bahama Bay

West End, Grand Bahama Island

Tel: +1 242 350 6500
Web: www.johansens.com/oldbahamabay

ATLANTIC - BERMUDA (HAMILTON)

Rosedon Hotel

P.O. Box Hm 290, Hamilton Hmax

Tel: +1 441 295 1640
Web: www.johansens.com/rosedonhotel

Hotels - Atlantic & Caribbean

Properties listed below can be found in our Recommended Hotels, Inns, Resorts & Spas - The Americas, Atlantic, Caribbean & Pacific 2010 Guide.

ATLANTIC - BERMUDA (SOMERSET)

Cambridge Beaches Resort & Spa

Sandys, Somerset

Tel: +1 441 234 0331
Web: www.johansens.com/cambeaches

CARIBBEAN - ANTIGUA (ST. JOHN'S)

Galley Bay Resort & Spa

Five Islands, St. John's

Tel: +1 954 481 8787
Web: www.johansens.com/galleybay

Recommendations in the Caribbean

CARIBBEAN - ANTIGUA (ST. JOHN'S)

The Inn at English Harbour

P.O. Box 187, St. John's

Tel: +1 268 460 1014
Web: www.johansens.com/innatenglishharbour

CARIBBEAN - ANGUILLA (BARNES BAY)

Cerulean Villa

Barnes Bay, West End

Tel: +1 264 497 8840
Web: www.johansens.com/ceruleanvilla

CARIBBEAN - ANTIGUA (ST. JOHN'S)

The Verandah Resort & Spa

Indian Town Road, St. John's

Tel: +1 954 481 8787
Web: www.johansens.com/verandah

CARIBBEAN - ANGUILLA (MAUNDAYS BAY)

Cap Juluca

Maundays Bay, AI-2640

Tel: +1 264 497 6666
Web: www.johansens.com/capjuluca

CARIBBEAN - ANTIGUA (ST. MARY'S)

Carlisle Bay

Old Road, St. Mary's

Tel: +1 268 484 0000
Web: www.johansens.com/carlislebay

CARIBBEAN - ANGUILLA (RENDEZVOUS BAY)

CuisinArt Resort & Spa

P.O. Box 2000, Rendezvous Bay

Tel: +1 264 498 2000
Web: www.johansens.com/cuisinartresort

CARIBBEAN - BARBADOS (CHRIST CHURCH)

Little Arches

Enterprise Beach Road, Christ Church

Tel: +1 246 420 4689
Web: www.johansens.com/littlearches

CARIBBEAN - ANGUILLA (WEST END)

Sheriva Villa Hotel

Maundays Bay Road, West End AI-2640

Tel: +1 264 498 9898
Web: www.johansens.com/sheriva

CARIBBEAN - BRITISH VIRGIN ISLANDS (PETER ISLAND)

Peter Island Resort

Peter Island

Tel: +616 458 6767
Web: www.johansens.com/peterislandresort

CARIBBEAN - ANTIGUA (ST. JOHN'S)

Blue Waters

P.O. Box 257, St. John's

Tel: +44 870 360 1245
Web: www.johansens.com/bluewaters

CARIBBEAN - BRITISH VIRGIN ISLANDS (PETER ISLAND)

The Villas at Peter Island

Peter Island

Tel: +616 458 6767
Web: www.johansens.com/villaspeterisland

CARIBBEAN - ANTIGUA (ST. JOHN'S)

Curtain Bluff

P.O. Box 288, St. John's

Tel: +1 268 462 8400
Web: www.johansens.com/curtainbluff

CARIBBEAN - BRITISH VIRGIN ISLANDS (SCRUB ISLAND)

Scrub Island

Scrub Island

Tel: +1 813 849 4100
Web: www.johansens.com/scrubisland

Hotels - Caribbean

Properties listed below can be found in our Recommended Hotels, Inns, Resorts & Spas - The Americas, Atlantic, Caribbean & Pacific 2010 Guide.

CARIBBEAN - BRITISH VIRGIN ISLANDS (VIRGIN GORDA)

Biras Creek Resort

North Sound, Virgin Gorda

Tel: +1 248 364 2421
Web: www.johansens.com/birascreek

CARIBBEAN - CAYMAN ISLANDS (GRAND CAYMAN)

Cotton Tree

375 Conch Point Road, P.O. Box 31324, Grand Cayman KY1-1206

Tel: +1 345 943 0700
Web: www.johansens.com/caymancottontree

CARIBBEAN - DOMINICAN REPUBLIC (PUERTO PLATA)

Casa Colonial Beach & Spa

P.O. Box 22, Puerto Plata

Tel: +1 809 320 3232
Web: www.johansens.com/casacolonial

CARIBBEAN - DOMINICAN REPUBLIC (PUNTA CANA)

Sivory Punta Cana

Playa Sivory, Uvero Alto/Punta Cana

Tel: +1 809 333 0500
Web: www.johansens.com/sivory

CARIBBEAN - DOMINICAN REPUBLIC (PUNTA CANA)

Tortuga Bay, Puntacana Resort & Club

Punta Cana

Tel: +1 809 959 2262
Web: www.johansens.com/puntacana

CARIBBEAN - GRENADA (ST. GEORGE'S)

Spice Island Beach Resort

Grand Anse Beach, St. George's

Tel: +1 473 444 4423/4258
Web: www.johansens.com/spiceisland

CARIBBEAN - JAMAICA (MONTEGO BAY)

Half Moon

Rose Hall

Tel: +1 876 953 2211
Web: www.johansens.com/halfmoon

CARIBBEAN - JAMAICA (MONTEGO BAY)

The Tryall Club

P.O. Box 1206, Montego Bay

Tel: +1 876 956 5660
Web: www.johansens.com/tryallclub

CARIBBEAN - JAMAICA (OCHO RIOS)

Royal Plantation, Ocho Rios

Main Street , P.O. Box 2, Ocho Rios

Tel: 0800 0223 773
Web: www.johansens.com/royalplantation

CARIBBEAN - PUERTO RICO (RINCÓN)

Horned Dorset Primavera

Apartado 1132, Rincón 00677

Tel: +1 787 823 4030
Web: www.johansens.com/horneddorset

CARIBBEAN - SAINT-BARTHÉLEMY (ANSE DE TOINY)

Hôtel Le Toiny

Anse de Toiny

Tel: +590 590 27 88 88
Web: www.johansens.com/letoiny

CARIBBEAN - SAINT-BARTHÉLEMY (GRAND CUL DE SAC)

Hotel Guanahani & Spa

Grand Cul de Sac

Tel: +590 590 27 66 60
Web: www.johansens.com/guanahani

CARIBBEAN - ST. KITTS & NEVIS (NEVIS)

Montpelier Plantation

P.O. Box 474, Nevis

Tel: +1 869 469 3462
Web: www.johansens.com/montpelierplantation

CARIBBEAN - ST. LUCIA (CAP ESTATE)

Cap Maison Resort & Spa

Smugglers Cove Drive, Cap Estate, Gros Islet

Tel: +1 758 457 8670
Web: www.johansens.com/capmaison

CARIBBEAN - ST. LUCIA (CASTRIES)

The Landings St. Lucia

Rodney Bay, Castries

Tel: +1 758 458 7300
Web: www.johansens.com/landingsstlucia

CARIBBEAN - ST. LUCIA (CASTRIES)

Windjammer Landing Villa Beach Resort & Spa

P.O. Box 1504, Castries

Tel: +1 758 456 9000
Web: www.johansens.com/windjammerlanding

Hotels - Caribbean & Pacific

Properties listed below can be found in our Recommended Hotels, Inns, Resorts & Spas - The Americas, Atlantic, Caribbean & Pacific 2010 Guide.

CARIBBEAN - ST. LUCIA (SOUFRIÈRE)

Anse Chastanet

Soufrière

Tel: +1 758 459 7000
Web: www.johansens.com/ansechastanet

CARIBBEAN - ST. LUCIA (SOUFRIÈRE)

Jade Mountain at Anse Chastanet

Soufrière

Tel: +1 758 459 4000
Web: www.johansens.com/jademountain

CARIBBEAN - ST. LUCIA (SOUFRIÈRE)

Ladera Resort

Soufrière

Tel: Toll Free: 1 800 290 0978
Web: www.johansens.com/ladera

CARIBBEAN - THE GRENADINES (BEQUIA)

Firefly Plantation

Bequia

Tel: +1 784 458 3414
Web: www.johansens.com/fireflybequia

CARIBBEAN - THE GRENADINES (MUSTIQUE)

Firefly

Mustique Island

Tel: +1 784 488 8414
Web: www.johansens.com/firefly

CARIBBEAN - THE GRENADINES (PALM ISLAND)

Palm Island

Palm Island

Tel: +1 954 481 8787
Web: www.johansens.com/palmisland

CARIBBEAN - TURKS & CAICOS ISLANDS (GRACE BAY BEACH)

The Estate at Grace Bay Club

Grace Bay Beach, P.O. Box 128, Providenciales

Tel: +649 946 5050
Web: www.johansens.com/estateatgracebay

CARIBBEAN - TURKS & CAICOS ISLANDS (GRACE BAY BEACH)

Gansevoort Turks & Caicos, A Wymara Resort

Lower Bight Road, Grace Bay Beach, Providenciales

Tel: +1 649 941 7555
Web: www.johansens.com/gansevoorttc

CARIBBEAN - TURKS & CAICOS ISLANDS (GRACE BAY BEACH)

Grace Bay Club

Grace Bay Beach, P.O. Box 128, Providenciales

Tel: +1 649 946 5050
Web: www.johansens.com/gracebayclub

CARIBBEAN - TURKS & CAICOS ISLANDS (GRACE BAY BEACH)

Point Grace

Grace Bay Beach, P.O. Box 700, Providenciales

Tel: +1 649 946 5096
Web: www.johansens.com/pointgrace

CARIBBEAN - TURKS & CAICOS ISLANDS (GRACE BAY BEACH)

The Regent Palms, Turks & Caicos

Grace Bay Beach, P.O. Box 681, Providenciales

Tel: +649 946 8666
Web: www.johansens.com/regentpalms

CARIBBEAN - TURKS & CAICOS ISLANDS (GRACE BAY BEACH)

The Somerset on Grace Bay

Grace Bay Beach, Princess Drive, Providenciales

Tel: +1 649 946 5900
Web: www.johansens.com/somersetgracebay

CARIBBEAN - TURKS & CAICOS ISLANDS (PARROT CAY)

Parrot Cay & COMO Shambhala Retreat

P.O. Box 164, Providenciales

Tel: +1 649 946 7788
Web: www.johansens.com/parrotcay

CARIBBEAN - TURKS & CAICOS ISLANDS (WEST GRACE BAY BEACH)

Turks & Caicos Club

West Grace Bay Beach, P.O. Box 687, Providenciales

Tel: +1 649 946 5800
Web: www.johansens.com/turksandcaicos

Recommendations in the Pacific

PACIFIC - FIJI ISLANDS (LABASA)

Nukubati Island, Great Sea Reef, Fiji

P.O. Box 1928, Labasa

Tel: +679 603 0919
Web: www.johansens.com/nukubati

Hotels - Pacific

Properties listed below can be found in our Recommended Hotels, Inns, Resorts & Spas - The Americas, Atlantic, Caribbean & Pacific 2010 Guide.

PACIFIC - FIJI ISLANDS (PACIFIC HARBOUR)

Taunovo Bay Resort & Spa

Queens Highway, Pacific Harbour

Tel: +679 999 2227
Web: www.johansens.com/taunovobay

PACIFIC - FIJI ISLANDS (YAQETA ISLAND)

Navutu Stars Resort

P.O. Box 1838, Lautoka

Tel: +679 664 0553/4
Web: www.johansens.com/navutustars

PACIFIC - FIJI ISLANDS (QAMEA ISLAND)

Qamea Resort & Spa

P.A. Matei, Taveuni

Tel: +649 360 0858
Web: www.johansens.com/qamea

PACIFIC - FIJI ISLANDS (YASAWA ISLANDS)

Turtle Island, Fiji

Nadi, Yasawa Islands

Tel: +1 360 256 4347
Web: www.johansens.com/turtleisland

PACIFIC - FIJI ISLANDS (UGAGA ISLAND)

Royal Davui Island Resort - Fiji

P.O. Box 3171, Lami

Tel: +679 336 1624
Web: www.johansens.com/royaldavui

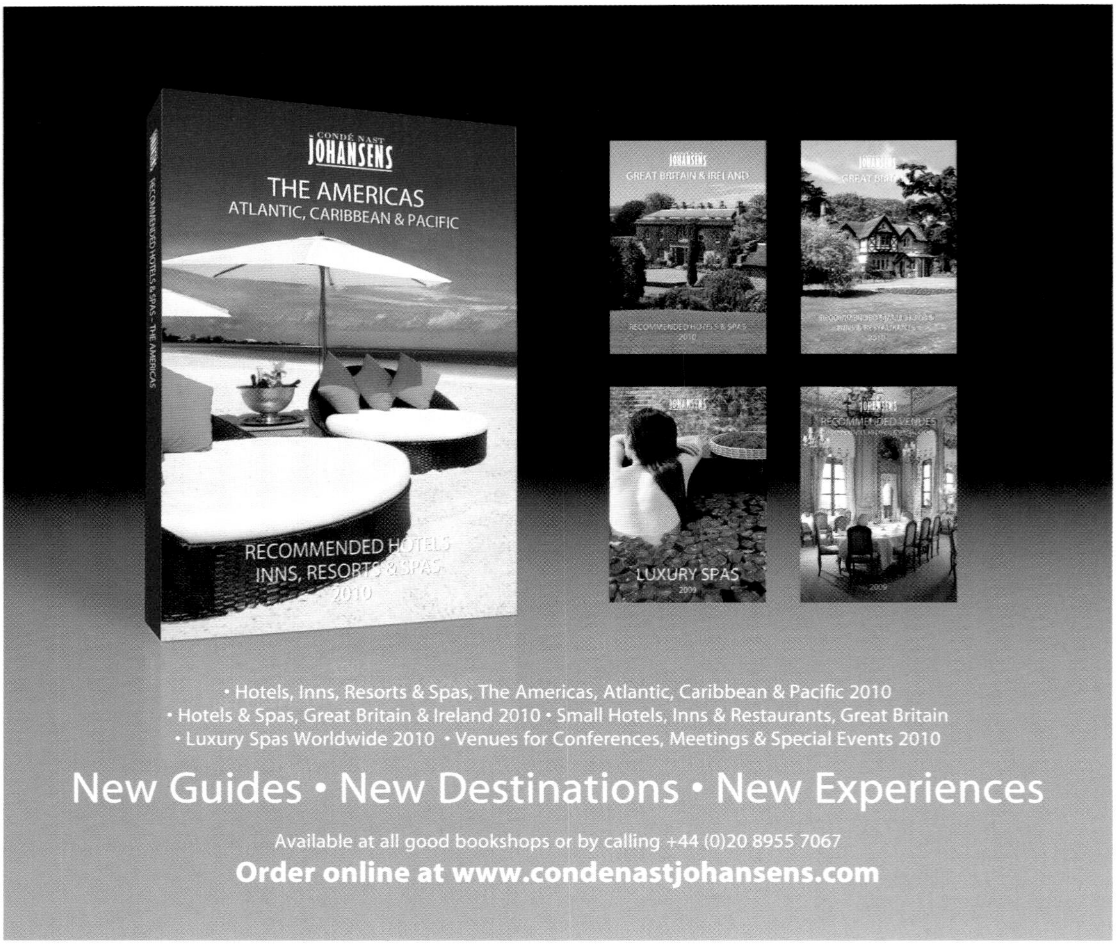

Index by Property

Andorra

Austria

Belgium

Channel Islands

Czech Republic

France

Great Britain

Greece

Index by Property

Hungary

Italy

Index by Property

Luxembourg

Malta

Morocco

The Netherlands

Portugal

Russia

Slovenia

Spain

Index by Property

Sweden

Switzerland

Turkey

Index by Hotel Organisation

Hotel Organisations

Abitare la Storia

Authentic Hotels

Charme & Relax

CHÂTEAUX & HÔTELS COLLECTION

Châteaux & Hôtels Collection

Design Hotels

GREAT HOTELS OF THE WORLD

Great Hotels of the World

Index by Hotel Organisation

Leading Hotels of the World

Luxury Lifestyles Hotels & Resorts

Relais & Châteaux

Relais du Silence

Romantik Hotels

RUSTICAE

Rusticae

Index by Hotel Organisation / Group

Small Luxury Hotels of the World

Symboles de France

Hotel Groups

Corinthia Hotels & Resorts

Derby Hotels Collection

Heritage Hotels Lisboa

HOSPES - Hotels & Moments

Tivoli Hotels & Resorts

Tell us about your stay

Following your stay in a Condé Nast Johansens Recommendation, please spare a moment to complete this short questionnaire. This is an important source of information for Condé Nast Johansens in order to maintain the highest standards for our Recommendations and to support our team of Inspectors. It is also the prime source of nominations for Condé Nast Johansens Awards for Excellence, which are held annually and include properties from all over the world that represent the finest standards and best value for money in luxury, independent travel.

1. Your details

Your name: ....

....

Your address: ....

....

....

Postcode: ....

Country: ....

E-Mail: ....

Telephone: ....

Please tick if you would like to receive information or offers from The Condé Nast Publications Ltd by telephone ☐ or SMS ☐ or E-mail ☐. Please tick if you would like to receive information or offers from other selected companies by telephone ☐ or SMS ☐ or E-mail ☐. Please tick this box if you prefer not to receive direct mail from The Condé Nast Publications Ltd ☐ and other reputable companies ☐.

2. Hotel details

Name of hotel: ....

Country: ....

Date of visit: .... Room no: ....

3. How did you book?

❍ Telephone ❍ E-Mail ❍ Hotel's Website

❍ Internet ❍ Travel Agent

Are you: ❍ a Guide User ❍ Web User ❍ or Both

Would you like to receive our monthly e-club newsletter with hotel offers and competitions? ☐ Yes.

4. Any other comments

....

....

If you wish to make additional comments, please write separately to the Publisher, Condé Nast Johansens Ltd, 6-8 Old Bond Street, London W1S 4PH, Great Britain

5. Your rating of the hotel

Please tick one box in each category below (as applicable)

	EXCELLENT	GOOD	DISAPPOINTING	POOR
Bedrooms				
Comfort	❍	❍	❍	❍
Amenities	❍	❍	❍	❍
Bathroom	❍	❍	❍	❍
Public Areas				
Inside	❍	❍	❍	❍
Outside	❍	❍	❍	❍
Housekeeping				
Cleanliness	❍	❍	❍	❍
Maintenance	❍	❍	❍	❍
Service				
Check in/out	❍	❍	❍	❍
Professionalism	❍	❍	❍	❍
Friendliness	❍	❍	❍	❍
Dining	❍	❍	❍	❍
Internet Facilities				
Bedrooms	❍	❍	❍	❍
Public Areas	❍	❍	❍	❍
Ambience	❍	❍	❍	❍
Value For Money	❍	❍	❍	❍
Food And Drink				
Breakfast	❍	❍	❍	❍
Lunch	❍	❍	❍	❍
Dinner	❍	❍	❍	❍
Choice of dishes	❍	❍	❍	❍
Wine list	❍	❍	❍	❍
Did The Hotel Meet Your Expectations?	❍	❍	❍	❍

I most liked: ....

I least liked: ....

My favourite member of staff: ....

Please fax your completed survey to +44 (0)207 152 3566 or go to www.condenastjohansens.com where you can complete the survey online

Racontez-nous votre séjour

Merci de bien vouloir prendre quelques minutes pour renseigner ce questionnaire. Vos observations nous aident à garantir les standards de qualité attendus par les hôtes des hôtels recommandés par Condé Nast Johansens. De même, vos commentaires sont importants pour la sélection des hôtels nommés pour notre remise de prix annuel.

1. Vos renseignements

Nom: ....

Adresse: ....

Ville: ....

Code Postal: ....

Pays: ....

Téléphone: ....

E-mail: ....

Merci de cocher si vous souhaitez recevoir d'informations de The Condé Nast Publications Ltd par téléphone ❍ ou SMS ❍ ou E-mail ❍. Merci de cocher si vous souhaitez recevoir d'informations ou d'offres de sociétés sélectionnées par téléphone ❍ ou SMS ❍ ou E-mail ❍. Merci de cocher si vous ne souhaitez pas recevoir d'informations ou d'offres de The Condé Nast Publications Ltd ❍ ou d'autres sociétés sélectionnées ❍

2. L'Hôtel

Nom: ....

Pays: ....

Date du séjour: .... Numéro de Chambres: ....

3. Comment avez-vous réservé?

❍ Téléphone ❍ E-Mail ❍ Site Internet de l'hôtel
❍ Internet ❍ Agent de Voyage

Utilisez-vous: ❍ les guides ❍ l'internet ❍ ou les deux

Souhaitez-vous recevoir la newsletter mensuelle de notre e-club sur laquelle figurent les promotions d'hôtels et des jeux concours? ❍

4. Autres commentaires

....

....

....

....

Si vous souhaitez faire de plus amples commentaires merci décrire à Publishing Director
Condé Nast Johansens Ltd, 6-8 Old Bond Street, London W1S 4PH, Great Britain

5. Votre Expérience

Cochez une case par catégorie.

	Excellent	Bien	Décevant	Mauvais
Les Chambres				
Confort	❍	❍	❍	❍
Equipements	❍	❍	❍	❍
Salle de bain	❍	❍	❍	❍
Lieux Publiques				
Intérieur	❍	❍	❍	❍
Extérieur	❍	❍	❍	❍
Entretien				
Propreté	❍	❍	❍	❍
Maintenance	❍	❍	❍	❍
Service				
Check in/out	❍	❍	❍	❍
Professionnalisme	❍	❍	❍	❍
Cordialité	❍	❍	❍	❍
Restauration	❍	❍	❍	❍
L'Equipement Internet				
Dans les Chambres	❍	❍	❍	❍
Dans les Lieux Publiques	❍	❍	❍	❍
L'Ambiance	❍	❍	❍	❍
Rapport Qualité - Prix	❍	❍	❍	❍
La Cuisine				
Le Petit-Déjeuner	❍	❍	❍	❍
Le Déjeuner	❍	❍	❍	❍
Le Dîner	❍	❍	❍	❍
Variété du Menu	❍	❍	❍	❍
La Carte des Vins	❍	❍	❍	❍
Est ce que l'hôtel à satisfait vos attentes?	❍	❍	❍	❍

Ce que j'ai aimé le plus: ....

Ce que j'ai aimé le moins: ....

Mon membre du personnel préféré: ....

Merci de faxer ce questionnaire au +44 (0) 207 152 3566 ou connectez-vous sur www.condenastjohansens.com et vous pourrez compléter ce questionnaire en ligne

Comentarios sobre su estancia

Le agradecería dedicase unos minutos para completar este breve cuestionario pues sus comentarios nos ayudan a mantener el nivel de excelencia que se espera en hoteles recomendados por Condé Nast Johansens. Sus observaciones también nos sirven para seleccionar los hoteles nominados para recibir nuestros premios anuales.

1. Datos personales

Nombre: ....

Dirección: ....

Ciudad: ....

Código Postal: ....

País: ....

Teléfono: ....

E-mail: ....

Por favor, indique si desea recibir información u ofertas de Condé Nast Publications Ltd por teléfono ❍ o SMS ❍ o E-mail ❍. Por favor, indique si desea recibir información u ofertas de otras compañías selectas por teléfono ❍ o SMS ❍ o E-mail ❍. Por favor, indique si no quiere recibir información de Condé Nast Publications Ltd ❍ o de otras compañías selectas ❍

2. El hotel

Nombre del hotel: ....

País: ....

Fecha de su estancia: .... Número de habitación: ....

3. ¿Como ha hecho su reserva?

❍ Teléfono ❍ E-Mail ❍ Página web del hotel
❍ Internet ❍ Agencia de Viajes

Suele utilizar: ❍ Guías ❍ Internet ❍ Las dos cosas

¿Le gustaria recibir nuestro boletin mensual que incluye ofertas de hoteles y competiciones? ❍ Si

4. Otros comentarios

....

....

....

....

....

Por favor, envié cualquier comentario adicional al Director de Publicación, Condé Nast Johansens Ltd, 6-8 Old Bond Street, London W1S 4PH, Great Britain

5. Su evaluación del hotel

Marque una casilla en cada categoría, por favor.

	EXCELENTE	BUENA	DECEPCIONANTE	MALA
Habitaciones				
Confort	❍	❍	❍	❍
Instalaciones	❍	❍	❍	❍
Baño	❍	❍	❍	❍
Zonas Comunes				
Interior	❍	❍	❍	❍
Exterior	❍	❍	❍	❍
Mantenimiento				
Limpieza	❍	❍	❍	❍
General	❍	❍	❍	❍
Servicio				
Check in/out	❍	❍	❍	❍
Profesionalismo	❍	❍	❍	❍
Amabilidad	❍	❍	❍	❍
Restauración	❍	❍	❍	❍
Servicios de Internet				
En habitaciones	❍	❍	❍	❍
En zonas comunes	❍	❍	❍	❍
Ambiente	❍	❍	❍	❍
Relación precio-calidad	❍	❍	❍	❍
La Cocina				
Desayuno	❍	❍	❍	❍
Almuerzo	❍	❍	❍	❍
Cena	❍	❍	❍	❍
Variedad de platos	❍	❍	❍	❍
Carta de Vinos	❍	❍	❍	❍
¿El hotel ha alcanzado sus expectativas?	❍	❍	❍	❍

Lo que más me ha gustado: ....

Lo que menos me ha gustado: ....

Mi miembro del personal preferido: ....

Por favor, envie por fax a +44 (0) 207 152 3566 o vaya a nuestro sitio web www.condenastjohansens.com donde se puede también completar el cuestionario